Seaworthiness

The Forgotten Factor

Revised Edition

C A Marchaj

ADLARD COLES NAUTICAL
London

Tiller
St Michaels, MD, USA

To Jana
Who contributed so much

Revised edition published 1996 by Adlard Coles Nautical
an imprint of A & C Black (Publishers) Ltd
35 Bedford Row, London WC1R 4JH

Copyright © C A Marchaj 1986, 1996

First published in Great Britain by Adlard Coles 1986
Reprinted 1987
Revised edition published by Adlard Coles Nautical 1996

ISBN 0–7136–4347–1

Revised edition published 1996 by Tiller Publishing
605 Talbot St, PO Box 447
St Michaels, MD 21663, USA
First published in the USA by International Marine 1986

ISBN 1–888671–09–2

A CIP catalogue record for this book is available from the
British Library.

Printed in Great Britain by
Butler & Tanner Ltd, Frome and London

Contents

*'Every age is fed on illusion, lest men should
renounce life early and the human race come to
an end'*

Joseph Conrad *Victory*

Preface

In the light of accumulated evidence it appears that recent trends in sailing yacht design (largely encouraged by rating rules such as the International Offshore Rule, IOR) must take some blame for the increased rate of casualties amongst contemporary yachts. Incidentally, for similar reasons, casualties amongst modern fishing vessels have worsened over the last decades too.*

Sailing people have an uncomfortable feeling that the IOR type of ocean-going boat, aggressively invading the whole boat building industry, is unfit for seagoing. Admittedly, sensible, sober and prudent cruising owners have been alerted that this fashion may contaminate yacht design in general; as a result, many boat buyers nowadays '... cannot properly distinguish an honest sturdy and long-lasting cruising boat from a flimsy, unseaworthy and short-lived racer'.

Are IOR boats and other boats built to similar rules and designed with singlemindedness of purpose really fit for *offshore* racing? Fitness of sailing craft is measured by their behaviour and ultimate effects – their statistical propensity to survive in adverse weather. This appears to be lamentable.

The sailing hull has evolved from the seaworthy fishing vessels of the 19th century. Gradually, the influence of various racing rules has changed the shape, not always for the better. The advent of new materials and design technology

---

* The evaluated losses of ships of length 61 m (200 ft) and below registered by Lloyd's Register since the beginning of this century indicate a similar trend. That is, the number of small vessels reported abandoned, foundered and missing is progressively increasing. Thus, ships lost in the period 1899 to 1913 amounted to 36 per cent of casualties; this percentage increased to 48 from 1919 to 1938 and further to 66 per cent from 1946 to 1955. (No statistical data since 1955 is available.) Apparently those vessels have been overwhelmed by forces, the effect of which they were built to withstand. (*Fishing Boats of the World*, Vol. 2.)

since World War II caused this slow change to speed up radically; the availability of better rescue facilities has meant that the penalty for poor design is not always fatal these days. A sort of amnesia concerning previous developments, discoveries and achievements in the field of sailing craft design is partly responsible for our current predicament. The time is ripe for a detailed analysis of the situation and a look at the future.

This book sets out to consider objectively the design features which contribute to seaworthiness and analyse logically – as distinct from emotionally conditioned views – what has gone wrong with the contemporary concept of the ocean-going racer or would-be cruiser, and why. The author's arguments are based on a number of immutable natural laws – the laws of physics; these laws follow a logic which does not necessarily always conform to ideas of logic instigated by wishful thinking, illusions or fertile imagination. A boat disaster or her dangerous misbehaviour in rough sea is proof of the existence of these relentless natural laws.

Although the subject of seaworthiness and associated dynamic behaviour of a boat in heavy seas appears to be extremely complex and difficult, the nature of the problem can be grasped without much mathematics. Consequently, the author has made an effort to present the subject of seaworthiness using simple mathematics and relying rather on graphics and reader's intuition. He believes that much of the so-called *applied mathematics*, or mechanics for that matter, expounded today is, to quote the prominent expert M.A. Biot: '. . . almost diametrically opposite to its function. It is permeated with legalistic hair-splitting, and shrouded in pretentious language, as if the purpose were to obscure, and surround with an air of mystery and profundity what is very often a simple and even trivial subject'.

Good physical insight combined with theoretical simplicity may provide the shortcuts leading immediately to the core of even extremely complex problems and to straightforward solutions.

In one way or another many people and a number of scientific establishments contributed to this book and I gratefully acknowledge my debt to all authors whose names are given in the list of references. I should also like to record my thanks for kind permission to use cartoons and photographs made by or belonging to M. Pocock, Payton S. Salter, J. Taylor, A. Claughton, Beken, *Practical Boat Owner*, *Yachts and Yachting*, *Yachting World*, National Maritime Institute and Press Association. Finally, I am greatly indebted to Jeremy Howard-Williams and Peter Coles, my editors, for their efforts in correcting my foreign English and advising me about the manuscript.

C.A. Marchaj

Author's Note

Because of the recent (rather slow) change being made from the Imperial to the SI metric measurement system, one may expect some criticism at the retention of the time-honoured and familiar terms such as knots, displacement/length ratios etc. when presenting the results of experiments or calculations. The only excuse for the author's attitude in this respect is that there will unavoidably be a period when both systems are in use. Since this book is addressed to the general reader rather than the scientist, the author believes that an indiscriminate or dogmatic introduction of the metric system would only cause unnecessary confusion. Those who might be interested in conversion of the Imperial unit into the metric equivalent can do so with the help of the Conversion Factors given on page xi.

List of symbols

A	area of the hull superstructure, also keel area (ft^2)
A_n	area of negative stability (lb/ft)
A_p	area under the stability curve (positive) (lb/ft)
A_x	area of the hull section below WL (ft^2)
AR	aspect ratio
a	acceleration (centrifugal) (ft/sec^2)
B	beam of the hull, also centre of buoyancy (ft)
b_A	aerodynamic damping coefficient
b_H	hydrodynamic damping coefficient
b_R	resulting damping coefficient
C_D	drag coefficient
C_L	lift coefficient
C_n	nondimensional coefficient of the normal force on keel
C_x	section coefficient (hull)
CGF	centre of gravity factor

non-dimensional

c	wave velocity (celerity) (ft/sec or knots)
D	depth of the hull (ft)
D_r	draft of the hull below WL (ft)
d	girth difference ($G_s - G_c$) (ft)
E	energy
E_i	wave impact energy
E_k	kinetic energy
E_p	potential energy
E_r	rolling energy
E_{tot}	total energy

(lb/ft)

F	freeboard, also force (ft or lb respectively)
F_D	damping force on keel
F_{ef}	effective rudder force
F_H	heeling force
F_R	aerodynamic driving force
F_{rud}	rudder force
F_T	total aerodynamic force

(lb)

G_c	chain girth (ft)
G_s	skin girth (ft)

GM	metacentric height (ft)
GZ	righting lever (ft)
g	acceleration due to gravity (32.2 ft/sec^2)
H_w	wave height (ft)
I_a	added moment of inertia of entrained water
I_r	roll moment of inertia
I_t	transverse moment of inertia
I_{tot}	total roll moment of inertia of the boat

(lb/ft^2)

k	gyradius (ft^2)
L	length of the hull, also lift (ft or lb respectively)
L_a	actual momentary lift in unsteady flow conditions (lb)
L_s	lift in steady flow conditions (lb)
L_w	wave length
LOA	length over all
LWL	waterline length
l	length in general
M	metacentre

(ft)

M_d	damping moment
M_i	impact moment
M_R	righting moment
M_r	rolling moment

(lb/ft)

m	mass (lb)
R	orbit of water particles at the wave surface (ft)
Re	Reynolds Number (non-dimensional)
S	
S_A	sail area (ft^2)
T	wave period
T_e	period of wave encounter
T_n	natural period of rolling
T_p	pitching period

(sec)

T_R	tenderness ratio
t	time (sec)
U	orbital current (ft/sec)
U_o	orbital current at the wave surface (ft/sec)
$\triangledown$	volume of water displaced by the hull (ft^3)
V_A	apparent wind speed
V_S	boat speed
V_T	true wind speed
v	resultant flow velocity (at the keel)
v_1	local velocity within breaking wave
v_r	local velocity due to roll (at the keel)

(ft/sec or knots)

W	weight of the boat (displacement), also work done (ton = 2240 lb or lb/ft respectively)

α (alpha)	steepness of wave, also incidence angle of the keel or sail (degrees)
$α_w$	wave slope (degrees)
β (beta)	course sailed relative to the apparent wind, also angle of encounter with waves (degrees)
Δ (delta)	buoyancy force (displacement) usually in long tons (1 ton = 2240 lb)*
$+Δ_p$	differential water pressure (positive)
$-Δ_p$	differential water pressure (negative)
δ (delta)	decrement coefficient
$δ_m$	trim angle of the mainsail
Θ (theta)	heel or rolling angle
Φ (phi)	angle of pitching
φ (phi)	phase angle

(degrees)

ω (omega)	angular velocity (radians/sec)

≈	approximately equal to
>	greater than
<	less than
∝	is proportional to
÷( )	is proportional or is a function of the factors given between brackets

* According to Archimedes' principle, the buoyant force acting on an immersed part of the hull is equal to the weight of the water it displaces. For this reason the weight of a boat is called her displacement.

Conversion Factors

	Multiply	by	to obtain
A. *Length*	inches	2.54	centimetres
	feet	0.3048	metres
	miles	5280	feet
	miles	1.609	kilometers
	miles	0.8684	nautical miles
	nautical miles	6080	feet
B. *Area*	sq. inches	6.45	sq. centimetres
	sq. feet	0.0093	sq. metres
	sq. feet	144	sq. inches
C. *Volume*	cubic feet	0.0283	cubic metres
	cubic feet	1728	cubic inches
D. *Velocity (speed)*	ft./sec.	0.592	knots
	ft./sec.	0.682	miles/hour
	ft./sec.	1.097	kilometres/hour
	knot	1.69	ft./sec.
	metre/sec.	3.28	ft./sec.
	metre/sec.	3.6	kilometres/hour
	kilometre/hour	0.915	feet/sec.
	kilometre/hour	0.539	knots
	kilometre/hour	0.278	metres/sec.
E. *Weight*	tons (short)	2000	pounds
	tons (short)	907.18	kilogrammes
	tons (metric)	1000	kilogrammes
	tons (metric)	2205	pounds
	kilogramme	2.205	pounds
	pounds	0.454	kilogrammes
F. *Pressure*	Atmospheres	76.0	centimetres of mercury
	Atmospheres	29.92	inches of mercury
	Atmospheres	1.033	kilogrammes/sq. centimetre
	Atmospheres	14.7	pounds/sq. inch
	Atmospheres	2116.2	pounds/sq. foot
	inches of water	5.198	pounds/sq. foot
	inches of water	25.38	kilogrammes/sq. metre
	kilogramme/sq. metre	0.2048	pounds/sq. foot
G. *Force*	lbf	4.45	newton*
	lbf	0.454	kilogramme

* Newton (N), unit of force. That force which, applied to a mass of 1 kilogramme, gives an acceleration of 1 metre per second per second (m/sec^2).

Velocity Equivalents

Metres per sec	Metres per min	Km per hr	Ft per sec	Ft per min	Knots
1	60	3.6	3.281	196.85	1.943
0.01667	1	0.06	0.05468	3.281	0.03238
0.2778	16.67	1	0.9113	54.68	0.53960
0.3048	18.29	1.097	1	60	0.59209
0.005080	0.3048	0.01829	0.01667	1	0.00987
0.51479	30.887	1.8532	1.68894	101.337	1

'I say unto you, that every idle word that men shall speak, they shall give account thereof in the day of judgement. For by thy words thou shalt be justified, and by thy words thou shalt be condemned.'

Matthew 12: 36–37

1 The Nature of the Problem

Sailing yachts can be considered from two different aspects associated with two profoundly different approaches and expectations. To some people the primary function of a sailing boat is to provide, let us call it, a romantic recreation. Byron's 'Quiet sail as a noiseless wing to waft me from distraction' is a means of escape from civilisation and from an everyday life full of exhausting competition. A visual image of such an approach to sailing might well be represented in Fig. 1, which shows the interior of a cup painted about 2500 years ago by Exekias of Greece. It has been labelled by learned archaeologists 'A lonely voyage of Dionysus'.

Whoever the helmsman is, a God or an ordinary mortal, one thing seems to be apparent: he is relaxed and leisurely enjoying the elementary forces of nature. His craft is a delight to the eye and appears perfectly fitted to its environment.

For successors to this ancient sailor, and perhaps to most cruising people, the boat was and still is 'an object of art and as such a joy forever' – as Francis Herreshoff once said – 'for the principal function of a yacht is to give pleasure'.[1]*

Although the word *cruising* appears to be so subjective as to be almost impossible to define, we might agree that it is a way of living rather than a sport. As Phillips-Birt pertinently noted, 'cruising people claim that they only sail in order to get to places. They do not mean quite that of course. One knows, however, that much though they like the sail, they are suggesting that their particular wish is to find somewhere at the other end of it not too similar

* *See References and Notes at the end of the book.*

Fig. 1. *The relaxed, romantic approach to sailing: a sailor of Ancient Greece.*

to the home port which they left behind. They want to carry their house with them but not their own country too.'

However rough the passage, the boat should not arrive in the destination harbour full of wet sails, wet clothes or wet people. If you are trying to get somewhere, you want to reach it in a civilized state, ready to go ashore or have visitors on board. H.G. Hasler remarked on one occasion: 'It may even be worth remembering – for such things still happen in the Welfare State – that there may be on board a gentleman and a lady who regard each other with something warmer than mere tolerance, and would like to have an opportunity of proving it.' A cruising boat should be designed to be sailed by a small crew and, as far as possible, to be worked without exceptional skill or endurance.

Fig. 2. *The extreme approach to sailing: a hydrofoil-assisted sailing craft. Habitability, seaworthiness and other characteristics valued by cruising men and women have been sacrificed for the sake of speed at all costs.* Yachting World.

Fig. 3. *A competitive approach to sailing: above all, speed. Relatively small, overcanvassed and over-powered boats, suffering notorious lack of stability, dominate the contemporary racing scene. The trapeze is an effective way of balancing large heeling forces, and offers a cheap alternative to beam. These spectacularly fast, open Australian eighteen footers, can average 14 knots sailed by a large crew. Being driven hard, their hulls suffer enormous fatigue, and they seldom survive more than two or three sailing seasons.*

Fig. 4. *Fortunately or otherwise, the method of acquiring power to carry sail as shown by this One-Tonner, has not yet been accepted. The demand for high performance apparently clashes with good seaman-like manners.* Beken.

Fig. 5. *Live ballast in operation. Provided the torso is still inboard, dangling the legs over the topsides is accepted as a legitimate means of acquiring unrated stability. This sort of contribution to boat stability could not possibly have been recognised as seaworthy by the older generation of sailors. And one may rightly argue that this fashionable ploy of manning the rail like a row of sparrows on a telephone wire is bad seamanship.*

Fig. 6. *A boat built to the IOR (1980), with a bulge deliberately made of foam and fibreglass or micro-balloons (indicated by the arrow). The only purpose of such a distortion at the waterline beam measurement station is to obtain a reduction in rating. Although such a bump may increase hull resistance (and thus decrease speed), it may also make the boat 'faster' for her rating.* This kind of tinkering and trickery with an existing hull may prolong the life of an obsolescent racing machine for one more season.*

   An entirely different, and extreme, approach to sailing, common in the middle of our supersonic century, is illustrated by Figs 2–6. People who sail these boats seem to like action, speed and achievement that can be measured in simple physical units such as knots, with time measured in seconds rather than hours. To them, sailing and boats mean just another form of competition which they admire and accept on their day out – and they like winning. Such people are constantly changing boats – always chasing a mirage of an illusive ultimate. Nowadays, serious offshore racing appears to be a semi-professional sport with

* A boat with bumps is lighter for her rated displacement.

hardly any room left for amateurs. Consequently the best offshore racer is the one that provides the maximum amount of hard work and exposure for the maximum number of men. That is what they came for. They want offshore racing to be difficult, to call for every ounce of skill and endurance they can muster. With, possibly, one reward – publicity. As Mark Twain once remarked: 'One of the commonest form of madness is the desire to be noticed, the pleasure derived from being noticed.'

These two attitudes to sailing are conflicting. To quote Francis Herreshoff again: 'I must say I detest those men who call themselves sailors and who only use boats or yachts to gain notoriety. As a class they will cheat or do anything to win races; the yacht to them is but a means to an end, and that end is vainglory'.

Nothing has changed since these words were written many years ago. Even worse, the Machiavellian ethic of 'winning is the only thing – it is not how you play the game, it is whether you win or lose' has definitely taken over in racing. Blatant cheating or something bordering on cheating has become so ingrained in our society that the only solution is either to police the sport or to change the rules radically.

Extreme approaches towards sailing, sketched above in rather sharp black and white contours, do not always manifest themselves in pure form. In fact the attitudes of individuals, as well as of generations, are composed of combinations of these two opposing concepts, and they change with time and age. There were periods in yachting history when the former recreational or romantic aspect predominated; others when the latter competitive spirit held sway.

Referring to the present time, the following problem appears to bother many yachtsmen: is it possible to reconcile these contrasting attitudes to sailing in such a way that, say, offshore cruiser-racers could be developed which might satisfy the majority of sea enthusiasts? So far, the International Offshore Rule (IOR) has failed to meet the needs of the dual-purpose sailor. As a matter of fact, the yachting cult in America is increasingly cruiser orientated. The word *racing* is fun, but *racing boat* is becoming a dirty word. And there is little hope that this rather rapidly increasing gap between the people who, after all, sail a common sea and share the same natural power, could be bridged without radical change in the rules of the game.

The cruising man chooses his boat using a different set of priorities from that of the man with a thirst for racing. This being so, there is probably no better way to start a violent argument than to ask what constitutes a modern cruiser-racer. We might, however, agree that the following requirements are of primary importance from the viewpoint of the cruising man:

Seaworthiness – strong durable and watertight construction, structurally sound rig, good survival characteristics in extreme weather conditions,*
Seakindliness – easy motion – freedom from jerky, breakneck rolling motion. In broad terms, that quality in a boat which enables her to receive the forces of a violent sea and to render them kindly to animate beings and inanimate

---

* My very good American friend Robin Lageman, shortly before his tragic encounter with the relentless sea in 1990, offered the following definition of seaworthiness (being worthy of the sea): 'Designing, building, using and maintaining watercraft with appreciation and respect for the sea.'

objects. To phrase it differently: seakindliness is that property in a boat which produces a comparatively slow, small and easy motion in spite of rough sea and weather,

Habitability – space for living quarters with good headroom and comfort. It is concerned with providing the crew with an environment that permits them to function effectively without degrading their mental and physical performance because of the boat's interaction with the sea producing excessive motion (rolling, pitching) and accelerations.

When these objectives have been achieved, the cruising man may compromise and consider some other features which contribute to speed performance, being aware that comfort does not necessarily mean slow but merely less fast. A tenth of a knot improvement to windward is an earth-shaking breakthrough for the racing man. But it is irrelevant for the cruiser if achieved, say, by weight savings coming from a hull and deck which are built with lighter, more complex and much more costly construction methods.

On the other hand, bearing in mind the nature, purpose and spirit of competition, the racing man is not prepared to accept any trade-off for speed performance, because speed is the single virtue of the boat that matters most. It wins races. However, even inside the camp of dedicated, world-ranging racing people there is a growing concern for the current evolution towards light displacement. Let's quote again – 'I don't know how to do it, but the Rule should have some way of stopping some of these *frightening* trends towards weight saving. If we keep on doing this kind of thing, we're going to lose a lot of people and not very long in the future. I find myself going to sea in the modern yacht and not enjoying the thing, possibly because of *plain, flat-out fear*.'[2] Risks have to be somewhat balanced by reward. Apparently, publicity by itself is failing as a reward.

Thus, it appears that there is at least one non-controversial issue which may reconcile both the cruising and racing people. The *proper boat* must be safe at sea, i.e. she should be seaworthy. Of course, the safety at sea aspect covers much more than just the strength of the hull and rig. Official policy of the Offshore Racing Council (ORC), a body responsible for the foundation upon which the IOR has been erected, is formulated as follows: '*IOR exists to provide ratings for a diverse group of yachts. The Council will manage the Rule, changing it as necessary to permit the development of seaworthy offshore racing yachts . . . The Council will act to discourage developments which lead to excessive costs, or to reduced safety or the suitability of yachts for cruising.*'[3]*

Laudable claim! The problem is that the true meaning of the term *seaworthy* can be found only by observing what a man does with it, not by what he says about it. The strange thing about ORC policy is that, so far, there is no single measurement factor incorporated into the rule which could safeguard seaworthiness. Could it be because the word seaworthy is a vague term?

To start sensible discussion about seaworthiness, those taking part must first agree upon the precise meaning attributed to the term. And here the trouble begins! What follows illustrates the point.

* Although frequent references are made to the International Offshore Rule in this book, the discussion of factors which contribute to seaworthiness and the conclusions reached are applicable to all sorts of boats designed to different rules or to no rating rules at all.

A well-known designer of one of the best-selling boats in England was asked after the 1979 Fastnet disaster whether the International Offshore Rule produces safe and seaworthy boats. He replied: *'Seaworthiness and seakindliness are based on balance and the matching of sail area, length and beam. The worst type of boat you could be in in those conditions would be a Colin Archer which just sits in the water and waits for the wave to hit it. A modern boat gives you far more control to pick a path through the waves downwind and it goes upwind as well.'*[4A]

Figure 7 shows these two types of boat in question. To many readers this opinion – by no means isolated amongst present day designers – will appear at least an embarrassment. After all, the Fastnet race was a harsh lesson – '48% of the fleet, 112 boats, reported that on one or more occasions the yacht was knocked-down to the horizontal during the storm.' Fifteen lives were lost and 136 had to be rescued by outside agencies.[4B]

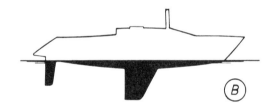

Fig. 7. *Hull planforms of two boats of similar length (about 12 m LOA) designed in different centuries to different rules.*
(A) A Colin Archer boat (end of 19th century).
(B) A Ron Holland One-Ton Cup boat built to the International Offshore Rule (1981).

In addition to earlier retirements from the race, 24 yachts were abandoned (of these 5 were lost and 19 recovered later). This suggests that poor seaworthiness and poor seakindliness of boats – their erratic, aggravated or excessive motion at sea – may cause rapid degradation of crew morale and task performance.*

One more excerpt from a contemporary report may serve to refresh the memory: 'The wind was very square so, naturally, the yachts began to roll . . . Suddenly the broaches were no longer hilarious; they were damnable – a damning of a rule that produces boats which, though *handled by the best in the*

---

* Six years later approximately half the Fastnet and Channel race fleets retired in conditions that were by no means exceptional. In the 1984 Sydney–Hobart débâcle 106 out of 152 starters retired due to rig failure, hull, steering and sail damage. Such events prompt the questions, 'Were those boats designed to conform to the forces of wind and sea?' 'Who benefits from the IOR constraints?'

world, run amok in sheltered waters, off-wind. *Something is seriously wrong with the state of the art.*'

What is wrong with modern yachts? Why does it happen and what can we do to prevent its recurrence?

Even a partial solution to these questions would, undoubtedly, represent a desirable advance. Until explanation has been found the controversy will persist, proper design requirements will remain elusive and unseaworthy boats will be built and sailed at unnecessary risk. If we could establish which are the primary design factors that determine boats' behaviour in heavy weather, and thus contribute to safety, seaworthy yachts might be developed. These factors, if known, would serve as a kind of guidance for the designer enabling him to set about deliberately reducing the probability of capsize.

According to earlier quoted opinion, expressed by a professional designer, these factors are: sail area, length and beam. Unfortunately, it will soon become apparent that no matter how these geometry parameters are 'matched' or 'balanced', a seaworthy boat cannot be produced on this principle. And the singular reason is that these are not the primary parameters which really matter in dangerous sea conditions – except that smaller vessels are more liable to loss.

The trouble with many, if not most, professional designers is that they are not professional enough and not designers enough. If they are to become useful and respected as designers, then they must do so by the refinement of their professional discipline and not by its dilution. Although they have little to learn about publicity there is a great deal to learn about proper design.

*'There is no expedient to which man will not
resort to avoid real labour of thinking'*

Sir Joshua Reynolds

2 Seaworthiness and Safety at Sea

It is known, from at least the time of the adventurous journey of Odysseus, that one can go to sea on a raft, or any other bizarre craft, and survive if the gods are merciful and willing.[5] Figure 8A illustrates an artist's impression of Odysseus's sailing vessel, in which he luckily managed to go through the dreaded Straits of Messina where Scylla, the six-headed monster which barked like a dog from its vantage point of a dangerous rock, and Charybdis which swallowed the waters and spewed them up again three times daily, thus causing a hazardous whirlpool opposite Scylla, were powerless in the face of the time-honoured faith of humans in a special Providence. Although all of Odysseus's fellow-travellers perished in the course of a long and tortuous journey, he survived because he was a favourite of Zeus – the father of all Gods of the Greek antiquity.

Since not every mortal is equally favoured by the gods, the profession of naval architect had to be invented in order to foster design of seaworthy vessels which, hopefully, would be capable of protecting the lives of seafarers and their estate against the incursion and danger of the sea.

We have come a long way from Odysseus's sailing craft, but in principle the dominating attitude in contemporary yachting is much the same. Strangely enough, and apparently preferable to rationality, is sheer faith in Providence – operating nowadays in the welfare society in the guise of lifeboats and helicopters called out to rescue those who are often foolishly trapped in a yachting disaster.

The prerequisite of the sensible approach would be the determination of trends in seaworthiness and seakeeping variables with changes in hull design features to allow for reasonable choices to be made by designers and builders so as to produce seaworthy boats.

Fig. 8. *(A) An artist's impression of* Argo, *Ulysses's sailing vessel.*
(B) A modern version of Ulysses's sailing vessel. An example of many attempts to design a boat that will sail faster than the IOR thinks she will. The anticipated displacement of Mach 1 *was about 1,170 lbs without crew, and some 2,500 lbs with crew and stores. Her stability comes almost entirely from the crew, exploited as live ballast, using enormous wings to give extra sitting out power. Her LWL of 29 feet is 11 feet above her rated length; the long bow is utilised as a rating dodge. A commentator defending the concept has suggested that this is '. . . a unique idea in its own right – a concept that is very new in the history of the offshore yacht'. The only forgotten factor is seaworthiness.*

A

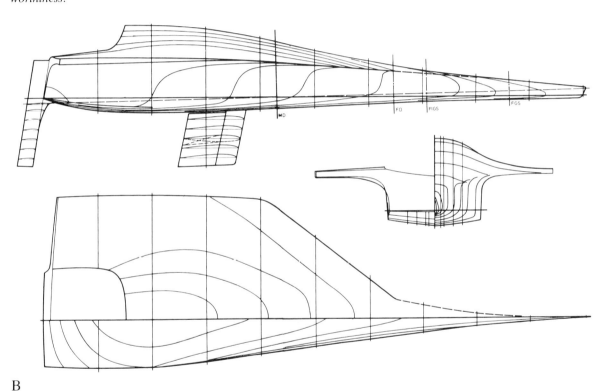

B

A. Definition of seaworthiness

To a certain extent, we must compromise in the definition of seaworthiness; although the concept is an ancient one and is utilised in shipping law to attach liability, it unfortunately lacks clarity. 'To the seeker after precision in law, seaworthiness is a disconcerting doctrine because by its very nature, it is not reducible to exactitude. It is relative and a nebulous term; it does not lend itself to easy application or absolute definition.' This quotation, taken from the *Survey Of Marine Doctrine of Seaworthiness*[6], adequately reflects the confusion associated with seaworthiness. There is however, a discernible agreement among people who have ventured upon the task of defining this elusive term. For example: a seaworthy vessel is one 'prepared to resist and if possible to overcome the perils of the sea'; or a vessel 'in a fit state as to equipment, crew and in all other respects, to encounter the ordinary perils of the sea'; or a vessel 'that is fit to withstand wind and waves in heavy weather, and to ride out of storm and claw off the lee-shore'; or a vessel which has 'that degree of fitness which an ordinary careful and prudent owner would require his vessel to have.' The common thread which goes through all these definitions is: *to be seaworthy, the vessel must be able to defend herself against the incursion and perils of the sea.*

That is what the lawyers have said about seaworthiness. But it does not help us to distinguish which vessel is capable of defending herself against heavy seas, and which is not; the proper design requirements remain elusive and our boat at risk, although the lawyers admit that 'liability for unseaworthiness evident in both the civil and criminal branches of the law could be wide and far-reaching.'

But surely, our intuition whispers, there must be something in the hull lines or shape which makes one boat more seaworthy than another. Could it really be true that a heavy displacement boat with long hull underbody of wine-glass section and deeply immersed rudder of the Colin Archer type shown in Fig. 7A, is indeed not seaworthy – as our quoted designer maintained? And is a contemporary light-displacement, dinghy-like boat with separate keel/rudder configuration, as shown in Fig. 7B, really just the type of wholesome, seaworthy craft sailing people have been waiting for?

It could be remarked in defence of the Colin Archer type of boat, that they were deliberately built as rescue craft 'to contend wind and sea in any weather . . . and to be able to carry out safely any manoeuvre necessary . . . rendering assistance to those in distress.' For instance, 'the *Oskar Tybring*, designed and built in 1895 by Colin Archer, was credited with assisting 102 craft and saving 329 men's lives.' These vessels 'when properly canvased and handled, have shown themselves capable of beating off a lee shore in the strongest blow. One of their remarkable features was the ability to tow four or five smaller fishing boats off a lee shore under sail in bad weather.'[7]

Historical evidence appears to indicate that Colin Archer's boats were in fact exceptionally seaworthy. However, one may argue that this view does not disprove another view, namely that contemporary boats built to the IOR requirement may not be even better in this respect. Some yachting journalist has written: 'Old wives' tales are still told and misconceptions persist. Unfortunately, one of these misconceptions is the negative attitude held by a large percentage of otherwise knowledgeable deep-sea sailors toward the fin keel.'

One thing is certain, the whole issue of seaworthiness is unlikely to be resolved through opinion polls. The only promising path to follow is through sensible, logical analysis of the dynamic aspects of boat behaviour in heavy seas. The ultimate object of such an exercise supported, when necessary, by experimental evidence, would be to find a clean-cut answer to two questions:

(1) what are the forces and mechanisms which capsize the boat?
(2) what are the resistive design characteristics that the boat *must* possess in order to increase the probability of survival in extreme conditions?

If we succeed in this effort then we shall advance our understanding of seagoing qualities in a major way. Subsequently, the designer's as well as the rule-maker's objective would be to minimise the content of luck and maximise the effect of intelligent design.

B. The boat as a system

Before we attempt to find an answer to these questions in some detail, we shall first try to establish whether it is possible to draw a clear demarcation line between what is seaworthy and what is not. To proceed in an orderly and logical fashion, open to rational criticism, we must therefore look at boat behaviour in rough seas as the response of a *physical system* to wind and wave forces. A sailing boat, like any other machine designed by humans, can be regarded as a system. One thing physical systems have in common is that they are all assemblies of certain components closely interconnected with each other; and as we shall see, the system performance cannot be determined from the performance of any individual part alone.

In other words, the whole is more than the sum of its parts. Thus, the character and consequences of boat motion in a seaway largely depend on her three fundamental components, namely: the amount and disposition of *weight* (displacement, mass inertia), *damping* and *stability*. Taken together, the relative magnitudes of these components and the way they are blended into a unified whole, determine what might be called the *dynamical personality* of the boat, so that different boats have different dynamical personalities and, as such, they respond different to the same wave and wind forces.

It is impossible to design a waterborne craft which would be totally immune from all perils of the weather and so be fit and safe at sea in all statistically probable conditions. A watertight barrel with a good bung might be regarded as a seaworthy vessel – unless, of course, the crew were inside; anything less than this might be considered unseaworthy. Incidently, the RNLI appears to follow this dictum closely because their latest lifeboats are designed with a 100% watertight superstructure, and are self-righting; in other words, their stability is positive at any angle of heel. Notwithstanding, the hard fact remains that anything which floats on the air/water interface, including the latest breed of lifeboat, may be destroyed by sea forces. However, we may all agree that, by enlightened choice of the three fundamental components listed above, the probability of disaster can be reduced. Thus, other things being the same, some boats may have a better chance of survival in heavy weather conditions than others.

C. The weather and human factors

The second contributory factor to safety at sea is the weather. Wind and sea forces may dominate the boat behaviour or even overwhelm her physically. Although a well designed, strongly built boat has a good chance of surviving the worst ravages of the open sea, crew competence, i.e. how the boat is handled, is another matter.

This is the third contributory factor to safety. A helmsmen's error in applying proper defensive tactics may result in a failure of equal consequence to that of bad design. An incompetent or sick crew can easily make a fine, seagoing boat unseaworthy, but even the most experienced, prudent and vigilant crew cannot turn a badly designed, unseaworthy craft into a safe one. Man can be looked upon as a part of the total system and, as with any other physical system, a human being may suffer weaknesses or fail altogether. This is of great importance when man controls other systems in combination: for example, helmsman/boat, or pilot/aircraft systems. Among these weaknesses are overloading, fatigue, inability to perform as precisely as required, or inability to respond in a manner compatible with the situation. The boat and the man have something in common.

Overloading may occur when the demands on the helmsman, or on the boat, are greater than can be borne either mentally or physically. In an emergency situation, such as that experienced in the 1979 Fastnet race, some helmsmen as well as boats might – depending on their personalities – be totally incapable of responding adequately to all demands placed upon them. Overloading may occur in most systems, including ourselves, by which time we may, however, through fatigue or fear, be unaware of this possibility until disaster strikes.

The overlap between these basic factors contributing to safety in a seaway is schematically shown in Fig. 9. These are the factors which are amenable to rational inquiry. There is also included an extra irrational factor, luck; bad or good it can be traced in every human activity. Not infrequently salvation is linked directly to luck.

All the factors shown in Fig. 9 are closely related and in certain combinations may cause the boat to founder. Thus, safety at sea may be considered in terms of high or low *probability of survival*. In the UK and the USA, as well as in many other countries, the casualty rate is about 35 times higher for people working at sea than for people working in industry ashore[8]. The only consoling fact is that there was a time when sailing upon the high seas was far less safe than it is today. In ancient Greece the human population was aptly divided into three categories – 'those who are alive, those who are dead and those who are at sea' (as testified by a seafarer Anacharsis).

Following the logic of Fig. 9 the problems of seaworthiness are discussed from three different aspects:

(1) fundamental design features which determine a boat's behaviour in extreme conditions and her seaworthiness in terms of probability of capsize. Although there seem to be a large number of different capsize

Fig. 9. *Overlap between factors contributing to safety at sea. The strength of a chain is determined by its weakest link, and so is safety at sea.*
(1) Basic Hull Factors.
  Displacement and inertia.
  Damping.
  Stability.
(2) Weather Factor.
  Seaway forces (waves and wind).
(3) Human Factors.
  Seamanship.
  Crew competence and prudence.
  Defensive tactics.
  Errors . . .
(4) Luck.
  A boat may or may not be in the wrong place at the wrong time. The omnipresence of luck and its power to drown good seamen and save mediocre ones has been well documented. Usually, however, luck favours the prudent crew.

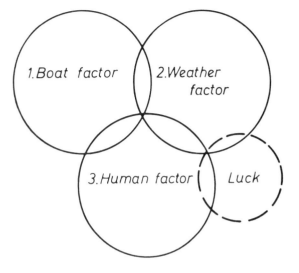

situations with different mechanisms involved, their number can be reduced to a few basic modes.
(2) the dynamic aspects of wind and wave forces particularly relevant to survival situation.
(3) some survival tactics. Good seamanship in heavy weather is not a quality which can be learned from reading books alone. It is, however, reasonable to expect that a man who learns much from his own experience can also gain a little from the experience of others, or from knowledge acquired through scientific experiments. These may help him to make rational decisions regarding survival strategy in particular sea conditions.

The last factor contributing to the safety at sea – luck or chance – is not discussed here. This can be regarded as a term expressive of human inability to grasp the ultimate cause. It belongs, perhaps, to the province of poets and story tellers. An Arab proverb says: 'Throw a lucky man into the sea and he will come up with a fish in his mouth.'

*'To think up new and better methods of arguing
in any field is to make a major advance, not
just in logic, but in the substantive field itself'*

Stephen Toulmin

3 The Effect of Rating Rules on Yacht Design

No better way could be found to start this chapter than by recalling two expert opinions on the subject of yacht design. Here is the late Douglas Phillips-Birt's view: 'systems of measurement have a more profound effect on the shape of yachts than the sea in all its moods . . . The story of racing yachts is about competition against the rules rather than the sea. The rules make the mould in which the shape of a yacht hull is cast . . . they became the forcing house of design; and the progress of sailing yacht architecture has been for part of its time the wayward and often eccentric changes in design produced by unforseen mathematical quirks in the measurement rule in force.'[9,10]

More recently Rob Humphreys in his comment on the International Offshore Rule wrote: 'it is somewhat fallacious to assume that the character and constitution of the offshore racing yacht is bred directly and unswervingly by the racing rule influence . . . In short, a rating rule has precious little bearing on the basic geometry of offshore boats.'[11]

Where the pundits contradict each other so flagrantly, the field is open to inquiry. As a matter of fact, the yachting magazines tell us that 'we have witnessed in the past dozen years revolutionary changes in hull shape', or similarly, 'the last ten years have brought about more changes in basic hull design than did the long years before them.' Thus the current fashion for light displacement boats with separate keel/rudder configuration on an almost dinghy-like hull, became the epitome of that revolutionary progress and superseded the traditional long continuous keel/rudder planform.

Questions arise: has the modern yacht evolved despite the Rating Rule or as a result of it? Have we really witnessed any genuinely new, outstanding developments in hull form (quite apart from the glittering effects of modern technology) and if so, should those and other 'revolutionary changes' – or as we shall see, rediscoveries – be classified as a regression from or a progression towards a better cruiser-racer? What does a rating rule really do?

A. Origins of seaworthy boats

'Those things are better which are perfected by Nature than those which are finished by art'

> Marcus Cicero
> (Roman philosopher, 106-43BC)

'Nature never deceives us; it is always we who deceive ourselves'

> J.J. Rousseau
> (French philosopher, XVIII century)

In order to answer all these questions and assess the effect of rating rules on boat design, particularly on seaworthiness, it seems reasonable to step back, for a while, into the past. Such a trip may be rewarding in the sense that it allows us to view the hot problem of immediate concern in a wider perspective, and so to gain some insight necessary to resolve the difficulties that still lie ahead.

Evolution of the sailing yacht began when, in the XIX century, yachtsmen turned for inspiration to fast pilot and revenue boats or to fishing craft. Sailing people of this period keenly admired those sturdy, seaworthy working boats, capable of standing up to the severe gales such as those which rage along the western approaches to Britain. Figures 10-13 show some of these vessels which were sailed by men without any relieving hope that hovering helicopters or lifeboats might pick them from the sea if anything went wrong. Their builders had to satisfy a number of requirements. Just to mention a few: the vessels were expected to *keep the sea all year round and in all weathers*; and to have an easy motion which provided a stable working deck in rough water over a range of speeds when fishing or carrying pilots. These boats were not, till the end of the 19th century, designed in the modern sense of the word, i.e. on the drawing board. Plans were rarely or never used, but hulls were built by eye from a half model which had previously been approved by the owner and his advisers. Half-models were sufficient for the well trained eye, possibly aided by the shipwright's intuitive experience, so that the finished boat was not always in exact conformity with the model. These boats evolved, like sea animals, through a long but reliable process of trial, error and memory to create more advanced forms and mercilessly eliminate the unsuited, in a sort of Darwinian natural selection, or survival of the fittest.

If one can be permitted by a stretch of imagination, to liken working boats to

Fig. 10. The Bristol Channel Pilot Cutter. *Note the large lateral area of the hull underbody – an essential feature of the boat's seaworthiness. One might argue that a cut in the fore-foot would reduce any tendency to broach in following and quartering seas. However, a long curved fore-foot introduced by some shipyards around the turn of the 20th century was not accepted, and 'many pilots refused to adopt them' on the ground that 'the wonderful seakeeping qualities of a long straight keel were lost to a great extent'. Few indeed were the cutters lost at sea over the years (some were run down by steamers); a mast going by the board was almost unknown. Quite apart from the better damping characteristic of a long keel as compared with a short one, the long keel was in all probability necessary to allow these pilot cutters to lie-to comfortably for long periods in rough weather.*

It might be added that the shores of the Bristol Channel run in eastward for about 100 miles, gradually converging until they meet the river Severn. This funnel, combined with the swift tidal movements meeting the fierce current from inland, can kick up vicious seas. The Channel is also noted for its great tidal range (48 feet in places at Springs, among the highest in the world). These conditions demanded a particularly fine type of pilot boat, one easily handled in crowded waters yet able to face the full force of an Atlantic gale, and above all having an easy motion when hove-to on station.

Fig. 11. The Brixham Trawler. *The salient features of fishing boats of that time were the long straight keel, short or no overhangs, heavy displacement, relatively small sail area for the size of hull, and low freeboard (though this feature was disguised by high bulwarks). There was about two-and-a-half times the depth of hull under water than there was above; this served as a convenient platform to handle the nets. With little area of keel surface, these boats lacked weatherliness as compared with the Quay Punt shown in Fig. 13. Not without reason, fishermen of the north-east coast swore that the fore-foot took their craft to windward.*

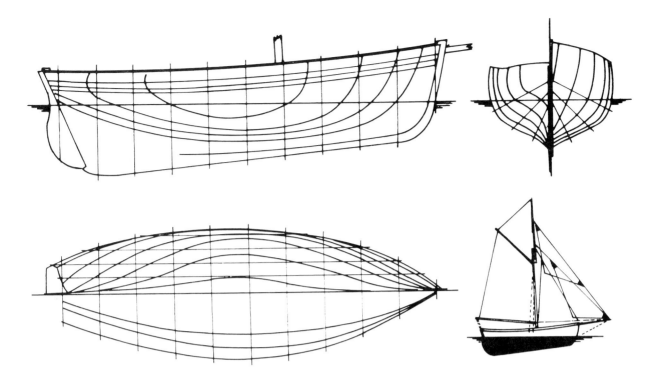

DYARCHY

LOA   41.6 ft.
LWL   38.0 ft.
Draft   7.0 ft.
Beam 12.9 ft.
Displ. 24.0 tons TM

Fig. 12. The Pilot Cutter Dyarchy. *The most successful pilot boats had more of the qualities demanded of a yacht, than had trawlers or other fishing craft. They had higher freeboard, more reserve buoyancy, and so more power to lift to the sea. A small area of salient keel appeared sufficient to improve the weatherliness of pilot boats as compared with that of trawlers (c.f. Fig. 11).*

sea animals, then one might agree that their adaptation or fitness for their task in a hostile environment might be measured by their actual success in survival – in a word, seaworthiness. *Survive or perish was the rule*. Unfit species and inappropriate mutations were ruthlessly eliminated by severe environmental pressure.

There are various mechanisms by which not only variations, but the whole hereditary material is controlled by elimination. Some allow only small mutations to spread; big changes, i.e. 'hopeful monsters' (Fig. 14) are, as a rule, eliminated – although they may temporarily survive in artifically favourable conditions rather like zoos. These evolutionary changes can be looked upon as a creative response to the challenges of the sea. Instead of senseless repetition, Nature appears to prefer something not only *novel but also better*.

Frequently, as a result of ill-conceived ambitions or wrongly identified aims, humans create unnatural, favourable conditions which are in conflict with some fundamental laws of Nature. In biology, miscreation means – in the long term – extinction. Similar to paleontology, boat archeology frequently shows that extinction is the usual end of unsuited, badly shaped specimens – '. . . an

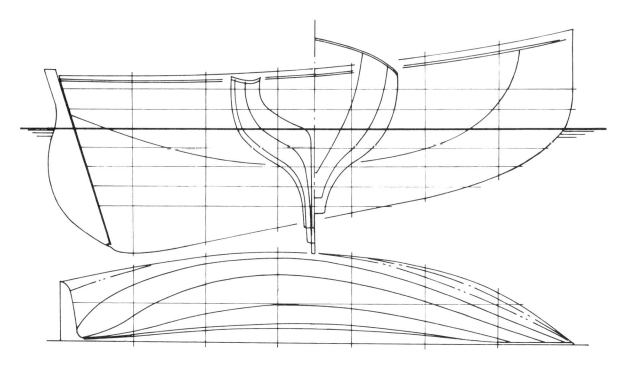

CURLEW

Falmouth Quay Punt

Fig. 14. *A 'hopeful monster' such as this – an evolutionary blunder – could not develop under natural environmental pressure. But in favourable, man-made conditions, various cripples, failures, cranks and mutations (the results of misdirected ambitions) may occur, prosper and even temporarily dominate the stage of civilisation.* Yachting World.

Fig. 13. The Falmouth Quay Punt Curlew. *A typical representative of her type, her immersed depth of hull of wineglass section gave a better sailing performance than that of a trawler or pilot cutter (cf. Figs. 11 and 12). The Quay Punt was the model for many yachts, and their influence can be recognised in many of Laurent Giles' cruisers. The disadvantage of low freeboard – an essential requirement for fishing boats – was not shared by the Quay Punts, which were high sided boats. The fore-foot was reduced and the keel ran in a gentle curve from stem head to the heel of the very deep, powerful rudder. The hulls, from 20 to 35 feet long, were built with great strength to withstand the south-westerly gales of the Western Approaches.*

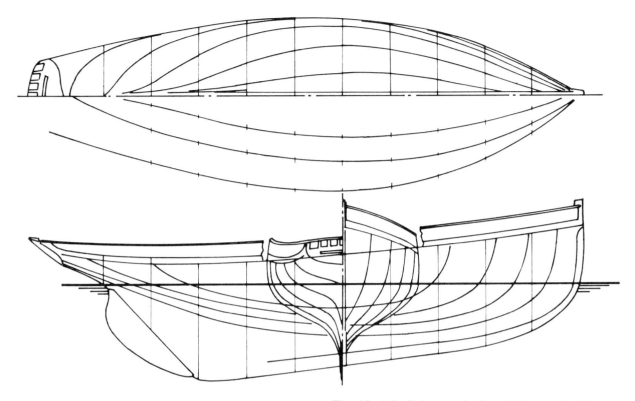

JOLIE BRISE

L O A	56.0 ft.
L W L	48.0 ft.
Draft	10.2 ft.
Beam	15.75 ft.
Sail Area	2400 sq.ft.

Fig. 15. Jolie Brise *was built in 1913 as a Le Havre pilot cutter; she is now owned by Dauntsey's school and run in conjunction with the Exeter Maritime Museum. E.G. Martin, at one time her owner, was one of the most experienced deep water sailors of small craft (and a founder of the Royal Ocean Racing Club); he held the general belief of the period that reasonably heavy displacement and great depth of fore-foot were essential in an ocean-going yacht. 'The basic quality in a yacht designed for deep water sailing is ability, not speed,' he said. 'Provided she is weatherly, and absolutely dependable in all conditions of wind and sea, it seems to me to be far more important that she should be steady and comfortable in rough water, than that she should sail very fast.'*

avalanche of obsolescence hurling itself into the sea of non-existence' – to borrow from a biologist.

Shape and structure of the hull, including appendages, must correspond to the efficient function of the boat if she is destined to survive the environmental pressure. Considering the emerging shape of working boats through the centuries, one must admit that at least in some creations of simple man living close to the elements, there is evidence that he was capable of developing an admirable instinctive understanding of the sea requirements. It can be said

* *Jolie Brise* is still being sailed, occasionally transporting wine from France. The name the Dauntsey's school comes from the founder and sponsor's name.

without exaggeration that his naturally acquired wisdom surpassed, in some respects, our current knowledge. Thus, it is not unreasonable to attempt to resurrect the evolutionary processes which past generations experienced and later sailors have perhaps yet to discover.

Viewed from the seaworthiness angle, the gradually evolving hull forms of the pilot and fishing boats of the past can be regarded as genuinely progressive forms – rugged but efficient and reliable. It should perhaps be added that *Jolie Brise* (Fig. 15), originally a pilot boat converted to a cruising yacht, became one of the most successful ocean racers of her day. According to contemporary reports, *Jolie Brise*, with the characteristic ghosting ability of yachts of her kind, and carrying light winds with her almost the whole way to Fastnet in 1925, gained and held the lead . . . by her record in winning the Fastnets of 1925, 1929 and 1930 she remains today the most famous. The model of her, standing in the Fastnet room at 20 St James's Place, London, is a reminder of the important place that she holds in the history of yacht architecture.[12]

Lacking any written knowledge to guide them, yacht designers turned for inspiration to tradition, i.e. the pilot, smugglers and revenue cutters which had been bred from long years of painfully slow trial-and-error experience. The time honoured procedure of copying and refining the design of boats of good performance, to obtain a succeeding design which would produce a boat of equally good or superior performance, is reflected in hull shapes B,C,D,E, shown in Fig. 16. They are products of gradual evolution from the common ancestor A, before speed fever descended upon sailing people, and speed for speed's sake became the only desired and rewarding feature of boats built according to man-made rules, and not those of the sea.

Changes in hull form, which became fashionable in the second half of the 20th century, such as shown in Fig. 16 F,G,H, together with redistribution of weight and other features, whose effects were previously considered unimportant or even undesirable, have produced a new type of boat which although marginally faster, does not under many circumstances behave as well as the old ones at sea. From the viewpoint of seaworthiness they have, in fact, undergone a regressive evolution. The rating rules have played an important part in this process.

The art of sailing yacht design has been influenced to various degrees of importance by several factors:

(1) Tradition or custom
(2) Genuine or semi-scientific developments, based on improved knowledge of hydrodynamics and aerodynamics
(3) Prevailing rating rules
(4) Economic, or commercial motives.

Tradition

By tradition or custom we understood the ideas or knowledge incorporated into

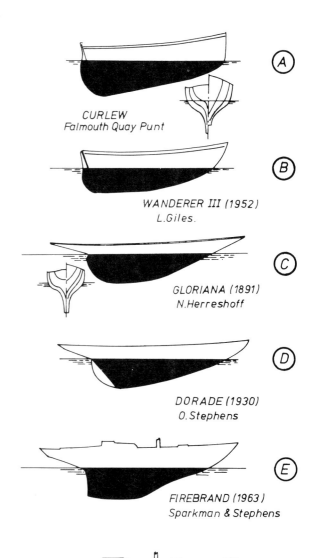

A

CURLEW
Falmouth Quay Punt

B

WANDERER III (1952)
L.Giles.

C

GLORIANA (1891)
N.Herreshoff

D

DORADE (1930)
O. Stephens

E

FIREBRAND (1963)
Sparkman & Stephens

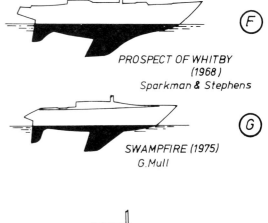

F

PROSPECT OF WHITBY
(1968)
Sparkman & Stephens

G

SWAMPFIRE (1975)
G.Mull

H

GRIMALKIN

Fig. 16. *Hull evolution of the sailing yacht over the last hundred years. The time-honoured procedure of copying and refining designs of proven performance, to obtain a succeeding design which would produce a boat of equally good or superior performance, is reflected in hull shapes B, C, D and E. They are products of gradual evolution from the common ancestor A, before speed-fever descended upon sailing people so that speed for the sake of speed, became the only desired feature of boats built according to rules made by man and not by the sea.*

Changes in hull form, such as shown in sketches F, G and H, plus other features whose effects were considered unimportant or were not known or appreciated, have produced a new type of boat which, although marginally faster, often does not behave as well as the old ones at sea. From the viewpoint of seaworthiness they have, in fact, undergone a regressive evolution.

the shape of boats which survived the test of time. The renowned English designer Laurent Giles once said that yachts 'really are very like horses – there is a strong hereditary influence, and if the line of descent is straight and of the best blood, the young entry stands a good chance of continuing the strain . . . The most careful selection must be made of ancestral qualities – remembering at the same time that "quite unknown parents may produce winners".'[13]

One may argue that sailing boats are examples of the persistence of a tradition which can hardly be rivalled in any other human creation. Take, for example, Colin Archer double-ender shown in Fig. 17 and designed late in the 19th century. The canoe-stern hull has the basic characteristics of the Viking ship (Fig. 19) and other sailing boats, as recorded by F. Chapman (Fig. 18) more than 200 years before Archer embarked upon improving the seaworthiness of Norwegian working boats. These were generally undecked and possessed only crude accommodation; fatalities were frequent. Archer retained the pointed stern which as a custom descended from the Stone Age. When he applied it to yachts this design feature, known since as the Colin Archer stern, soon became the epitome of seaworthiness.

Notwithstanding, it has been argued that we cannot be sure that such a stern is, in fact, more seaworthy than any other. Phillips-Birt said: 'Seaworthiness was needed in the trawlers of Brixham . . . and the Bristol Channel pilot cutters, as well as in boats doing the same work off the Scandinavian coastline. Yet, the pointed stern was not adopted; nor was it in local types round the English coast that had not felt the Scandinavian influence'.[9] Technically, that is true, we have no evidence which could assure us of the merits of the double-ender. No one tested it scientifically in the towing tank. Nevertheless, it was tried by natural selection – the mechanism by which new ideas and variations introduced by designers are controlled through elimination. So far the pointed stern custom has survived this natural test.

B. Impact of science

*'If instead of sending the observations of able seamen to able
mathematicians on land, the land would send able
mathematicians to sea, it would signify much more to the
improvement . . . of the safety of men's lives on that
element'*

Sir Isaac Newton

Scientific knowledge grows through gradually developing theories, in the sense that tentative hypotheses are tried out to see whether they work in the real world. All experimental corroborations are simply the result of tests deliberately undertaken in an attempt to find out whether our theories err. Not infrequently, it takes many years of inquiry before a positive answer can be given.

The practical question every boat designer must answer is how to shape the

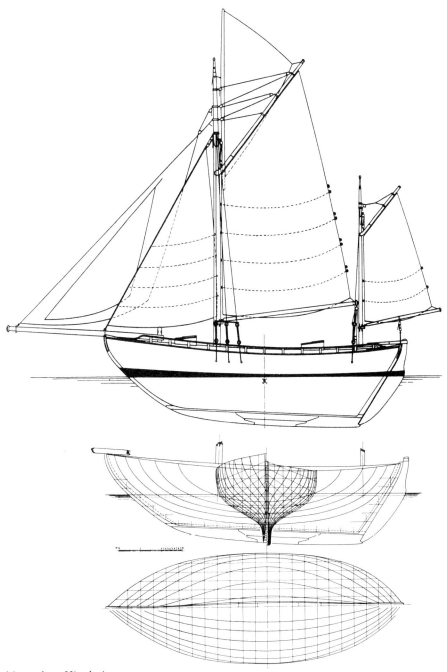

Fig. 17. The Colin Archer Double-ender. *His designs have the reputation of being able to keep the sea comfortably for long periods. By contemporary standards, their handling often seems slow, but they have a sureness and seaworthiness – virtues which modern light displacement hulls often lack. Once the cruising value of Archer's boats became known, interest in traditional design seems to have flourished strongly. The exploits and voyages of these vessels have been well documented in such cruising classics as* The Voyage of the Dream Ship *by R. Stock and* The Cruise of the Teddy *by Erling Tambs, not to mention reports of Nansen's discoveries in the* Fram. *The figure shows the Colin Archer Club project:*

LOA 12.0 m (39 ft); Disp. 14 tons; sail area 120–140 m^2 (depending on rig).

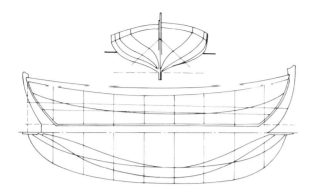

Fig. 18. *The lines of a sailing boat of the east coast of Norway, recorded by F. Chapman (1768). This pointed-stern hull, which had the basic characteristics of the Viking ship (see Fig. 19), was a model for Colin Archer from which he developed his famous pilot, fishing and rescue boats. Many yachts from his drawing board, inspired by the thousand year old tradition, initiated what is known today as the Colin Archer type (see Fig. 17).*

Fig. 19. *The Osberg Viking boat, excavated during the summer of 1904 (Bygdøy-Oslo Museum, Viking Ship Hall). With a crew of 95 men and all the necessary equipment, displacement has been calculated to be about 11 tons. Total length was 21.6 m (71 ft), with a beam of 5.1 m (16.7 ft) at the broadest part of the hull; the depth from gunwale to keel was about 1.6 m (5.2 ft). The boat was buried in the middle of the 9th century, when it was about 50 years old, and the* pointed stern as a design custom can be traced to the Stone Age. What strikes one most forcibly on seeing this vessel, is the extreme lightness of her scantlings, and the absence of longitudinal stringers, or similar contrivances for promoting the strength and rigidity needed in a sea-going vessel. Even the designation 'ship' is apt to convey a false idea; she is in fact a gigantic sailing-rowing canoe.

hull in order to minimise its drag in the water. In the early days of naval architecture designers turned to fish for inspiration. The hypothesis to be tried was that, what is good for fish should be good for a ship. The earliest documented example of relating the underwater hull of a ship to the shape of a fish, is shown in Fig. 20A. A common feature of most fish is that the afterbody curves to a finer taper than the forebody. For some reason it was assumed and widely accepted in those days that the ideal shape was a combination of the cod's head and mackerel's tail. Today, our understanding of the principles of water resistance indicates that the lessons that may be learnt from fish or marine mammals is of some value for submarines and other fully submerged bodies such as aircraft, but not for surface ships. Simply, the resistance law applicable to fully submerged bodies does not apply to water-surface skimmers generating a peculiar wave system which contributes to drag.

A

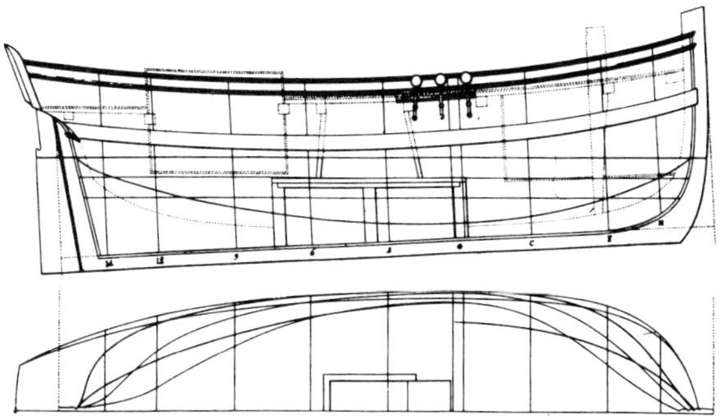

Fig. 20. *(A) An Elizabethan galleon in side view. A false analogy of the fish form tended to govern hull design until the first half of the 19th century; the above example, attributed to Matthew Baker, the famous master shipwright of the 16th century, occurs in a manuscript in the Pepysian Library (Ref. 14).*
(B) Lines of a typical fishing cutter designed some 200 years ago, taken from Chapman's Architecture Navalis Mercatoria *(Ref. 15). Ship design in those times had largely to be guessed at, and the fish analogy ('a cod's head and a mackerel's tail make the shape of a ship to sail') dominated European and British design till the second half of the century.*

B

Hundreds of years passed before the false analogy of the fish form was rejected, to be replaced by other hydrodynamically invalid theories. About the middle of the 19th century John Scott Russell propounded that the bow should be longer than the afterbody of the hull, and this began to be accepted as nearer to the truth than the prevailing theory of the cod's head. This concept refers, in a way, to an earlier idea suggested in the latter half of the 1700s by F.H. Chapman: namely that the rate of increase or decrease of immersed volume (displacement distribution) of the hull with its length is what really matters. Scott Russell argued that the resulting flow pattern over the underwater hull – including local velocities and pressures (which in turn determine the energy expended in creating waves) – is tied in with the longitudinal distribution of displacement as reflected by the water lines curvature. To deflect or push transversely the incident water at the bow with a small acceleration, i.e. with the minimum lateral accelerating force, appeared to be advantageous. Consequently, he devised such a waterline in the form called 'curve of versed sines', so making the waterline of the hull's run a sort of complement to the wave profile. This was done in order to use – in his words: 'the lateral displacement of wavy water to correct the effects of its undulating surface'.[16,17] In other words, if the wave-making resistance were to be reduced, the shape of the bow waterlines as well as the aft-end waterlines should correspond with the form of bow and stern waves respectively.

J. Scott Russell designed and built a 60 ft boat called the *Wave* with an entrance shaped on this principle. The *Wave* had, indeed, much less resistance at given speeds than other craft of her size and vintage. Soon after in 1848, a remarkable boat made of steel was built on the Thames as an exponent of Scott Russell's theory. This was the *Mosquito* cutter of 59 ft waterline, shown in Fig. 21. Her bow was long with the entrance angle only 17 degrees. According to the contemporary records, 'she excelled in all the good qualities claimed for the bluff-bowed craft; she was faster than any other yacht of her length on any point of sailing and in a strong wind to windward was a marvel compared with other yachts.'

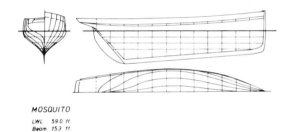

MOSQUITO
LWL   59.0 ft.
Beam 15.3 ft.

Fig. 21. Mosquito, *a cutter built in 1848 according to Scott Russell's wave-line theory; her midship section was placed 4.5 ft abaft the middle of the waterline length. The new trend in design was towards a long, knife-like forebody.*

Although Scott Russell's wave-line theory was ingenious, the hull shape arrangement suggested appears to have no foundation in hydrodynamics, certainly not as a cause rather than an effect; and the theory has since been discredited by many naval architects.

Colin Archer made an effort to modify this wave-line theory, as follows: 'it is evident that the rate at which water is thrown off (at the entrance) is best determined not by the shape given to any set of lines whatever, but by the *rate of increase* in area of the transverse sections.'[18] This theory has also been discredited although, let us quote Colin Archer, 'I have built nearly a dozen boats of various sizes on the system we have adopted, and I have every reason to believe that it is far superior to any I have used before . . . No very marked improvement on the best existing boats is, however, to be expected, since . . . builders have intuitively found out the best form without the aid of science.'

Indeed, as a matter of fact, the merits of a slimmer bow than the cod's head were intuitively discovered well before Scott Russell published his ideas. Thus, for instance, the cutter *Menai* designed by T. Assheton-Smith, a famous sportsman of those days, and built about 1829; she is memorable for being the first vessel in which hollow lines were adopted. Not for the first time in the history of human achievements the inventors, although wrong (sometimes utterly wrong) in their theories, were right in their intuition. Indeed, not infrequently science must be content to generalise the teaching of practical experience.

Referring again to the cutter *Mosquito* (Fig. 21) so strong was prejudice against the 'long, lean bow' that prediction were made that some day she would 'take a dive and never come up again'. The prophecy was not fulfilled and *Mosquito*, after as long and brilliant a career as has fallen to any yacht, finished her working life as a pilot boat off Barrow-in-Furness. Apparently, she was not destined to have an important influence on British yacht building. Ironically perhaps, it was the *America*, shown in Fig. 22, which was effective in spreading the hollow bow feature embodied first in the *Mosquito* hull. The old round bow was utterly condemned and 'every one went more or less crazy on the long hollow bow'. In spite of the fact that her success at Cowes in 1851 over the

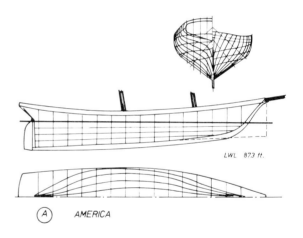

Fig. 22. *(A) Lines of the* America *(launched 1st May 1851); designed by George Steers and built by W.H. Brown. The Marquis of Anglesey, who was 80 years of age and whose memory extended back to Nelson's time, is reported to have exclaimed when he saw her for the first time 'If she is right, we must be wrong'. Although the schooner's success helped to popularise the hollow bow, she was not in fact the first to have such a slim entrance (see Fig. 21).*

(B) The schooner America, *from the* Illustrated London News *of 30th August 1851. The visitor's sails were flat and made of close woven machine-spun cotton, as compared with the baggy flaxen canvas common in Britain at that time. The consensus of opinion among contemporary experts was that 'these flat sails certainly suited the easy form of the* America *... and it is undoubtedly a fact that, for some years after (her) victory, sails were got too flat, at least for many of the full-bodied boats that they were put over. The want of flow of the older-fashioned loose-footed sails was sadly missed when there came to be any work off the wind'.*

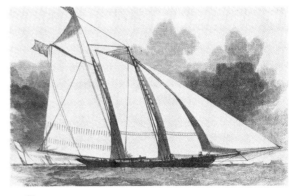

British schooners was not a result of her hull qualities but was due to the unusual flatness and close weave of her sails (contributing greatly to her fine weatherliness) and, mainly, the lack of any handicap system in this particular race which initiated the *America*'s cup challenges[19], her hull shape has acquired an almost mystical reputation.

The progress in the science of naval architecture goes on, and each successor profits from the experience and failures of his predecessors. In place of the Scott Russell and Colin Archer theories many others have been proposed. The final answer has not yet arrived and in all probability it never will. The reason is that in the meantime it became evident that several considerations must influence the designer in selecting hull shape. In addition to the consideration of the wave drag requirement, a certain amount of waterline area placed outward from the centreline is needed to give the boat adequate transverse metacentric stability to carry sails effectively; to say nothing about useful internal space within the hull. The degree of hull fullness must therefore be a compromise between the advantage of obtaining useful waterplane area on the one hand, and the disadvantage of increased drag on the other.

Balance in hull shape

In smooth water at relative speeds below that at which wave-making is small (say, a relative speed/length ratio $V_s/\sqrt{L}$ = about 0.5), even blunt entrance lines do not develop unduly large pressure drag. However, once wave-making starts in earnest (and the pressure drag due to wave-making varies from the second or third up to the sixth power of the speed), fine waterline entrance may become sufficiently effective to justify some sacrifice in other design features. The ultimate aim is to enclose the required volume within the hull for the desired stability and internal arrangement in a *seaworthy form of minimum resistance*. To achieve this to full satisfaction is the most elusive goal. And there is yet one more difficulty in reaching a best compromise in the hull shape. This is balance.

Of what, then, is balance composed?

J. Laurent Giles, a prominent British designer, answered this question in its broadest sense as follows: good balance is 'freedom from objectionable tendencies to gripe or fall off the wind regardless of angle of heel, speed or direction of wind . . . an easy motion in a seaway, which may be understood as an easy passing over the waves, neither tending to plunge the bow deeply into the next wave ahead, nor to throw the nose high in the air as a wave passes the fore-body, nor to fail to lift the stern to an oncoming following sea.

'One requires of the balanced yacht that she should retain the utmost docility and sureness of movement in manoeuvering at sea, in good or bad weather, she must maintain a steady course when left to herself, but must be instantly responsive to her helm so that the heavier seas may be dodged if circumstances permit. She must be capable of being left to her own devices, sailing, hove-to, or under bare poles.'

In a narrower sense this means that an inherently balanced hull does not substantially alter its longitudinal trim and does not alter its course during the process of heeling and rolling. The term 'well balanced yacht' usually implies that small rudder moments are necessary to maintain a straight course at possibly all realistic heel angles. If the boat is poorly balanced then the force required on the tiller to maintain a straight course may increase with increasing wind strength, to the point where more than one man is required on the tiller.

Speed may be achieved without balance – although good balance is likely to assist speed – but, almost by definition, *seaworthiness cannot be achieved if the boat is badly balanced*. A hull which is unbalanced will tend to yaw violently when heeled or when rolling so that broaching, eventually leading to capsize, may easily happen.

In the 1930s Rear Admiral A. Turner developed a theory of the whys and therefores of balance, using the experience gained through the numerous model racing yachts he designed. He also critically analysed the lines of many yachts – successful and unsuccessful.[20] In his theory which, as usual, had evoked controversy, he attempted to answer the following questions: What are the causes of imbalance? Why do so many boats pull hard on their helm when heeled? How can these effects be eliminated?

We shall return to the problem of balance in the chapter dealing with directional stability. At the moment suffice it to say that Turner's idea, which became widely known as the 'metacentric shelf theory', had a similar effect on hull shape to that developed earlier by the English designer and writer Dixon Kemp (1839-99). In principle, it is a geometric system based on hydrostatic considerations and the outcome is that, to be well balanced, a hull should immerse an approximately similar volume of topsides forward and aft on heeling, i.e. a certain compatible relationship must exist between the fore-and-aft distribution of displacement; as the hull is heeled, pressure distribution over its immersed and asymmetrical surface shall not vary greatly. This implies a certain uniformity of the hull lines. If carried to ultimate perfection the hull becomes a metacentroid, that is a shape such that the positions of the centre of buoyancy (B) and metacentre (M) are independent of heel angle (see Fig. 47 for definition of B and M). Simple examples are uniform spheres, circular cylinders and ellipsoids.

Older theories, amongst them that of Scott Russell – as incorporated in the hulls of *Mosquito* (Fig. 21) and *America* (Fig. 22) – insisted that hollow entries are better than straight ones, yet, Turner argued, 'straight or even convex lines are general in sailing yacht to-day . . . and why straight lines are better than hollow-ones is a question of balance and seaworthiness.'

Typical old-fashion metre-boats and boats like those in Fig. 16C and D, would have satisfactory balance. On the other hand, designs that have gone to extreme hull shapes to gain in sail-carrying ability – notably those built to the current offshore rule (IOR) – are, as a rule, unbalanced; usually when they heel the stern is lifted and the bow falls. Consequently, these boats are difficult to control by rudder and are unseaworthy.

The main criticism directed against Turner's concept of the metacentric shelf as the sole criterion of balance is that, for convenience, it involves only hydrostatics. It assumes the yacht to be heeled in smooth water and without bow and quarter waves which, it is argued, must upset the areas of heeled sections. Evidently, the forces acting on the hull in motion are different from those in static conditions; there are different wave patterns on each side depending on speed. Aerodynamic forces on the rig also vary. For these reasons a yacht will change course unless an equilibrium of the water and air forces is maintained by use of the rudder.

Nevertheless, to quote K.C. Barnaby's comment expressed during a discussion of Turner's paper, 'we may doubt the accuracy of some of his reasoning, but the fact remains that boats balanced on his metacentric shelf principle do turn out to be uncannily steady on their course.' In practice, Turner's theory has proved remarkably reliable in predicting yacht behaviour from the lines plan, so the error introduced by ignoring the wave system cannot be serious.

No better closing remark to end this section on the origins of the seaworthy boat can be found than that expressed some years ago by Laurent Giles: 'Taking the prototype as the contemporary fishing and pilot vessel, the early yachts were essentially balanced hulls, for the evil influences later to be introduced (rating rules) had not then appeared. They represented the culmination of development untrammelled by requirements leading away from the natural and rational trend. A balanced type was therefore to be expected since with no other distractions the seaman's demand for good manners becomes paramount.'

C. Rating rules

'Rule-makers, do something to stop us enthusiasts from
drowning ourselves'

> From a letter to the editor of *Sail*
> magazine by Ch. Bouzaid,
> President, Hood Sailmakers, USA
> – March 1980.*

'It seems very pretty (said Alice), but it's rather hard to
understand! Somehow it seems to fill my head with ideas –
only I don't exactly know what they are!'

> Lewis Carroll
> *Through the Looking Glass*

Historically, measurement rules have originated from the necessity of eliminating the element of mere size from competition in order to provide, as far as may be, that a boat shall win by virtue of her superior speed and not by virtue of her superior size. It became patently obvious, at least from the time when *America* (Fig. 22) won the race sailed round the Isle of Wight in 1851,

---

* Ch. Bouzaid is an experienced ocean racing sailor who participated in the 1979 Fastnet race as a helmsman on *Police Car*.

that in the same racing conditions, a larger boat is faster than a smaller one. According to available evidence the British 57 ft waterline *Aurora* finished the race about eight minutes after the 87.3 ft waterline *America*. *Aurora*'s tonnage was only 47 while *America*'s was 170.[1] Thus *Aurora* would have beaten *America* easily in this race if there had been time allowance based on tonnage or any other measure of size for that matter. It has been said that 'by modern ideas *Aurora* would get at least 35 minutes time allowance, but she got none . . . luck, muddle and misadventure gave *America* the cup and a reputation on a plate.'[19]

As a matter of fact, well before the 1851 *America* race, yachtsmen had been sporadically trying to arrive at a method of calculating the time allowance related to size of the boat. In those days, the size of a vessel was given by her tonnage calculated according to the formula:

$$\frac{\text{Length} \times \text{Beam} \times \text{Depth of hold}}{100} = \text{Tonnage} \qquad (1)$$

In 1843 an elaborate time allowance system was worked out by G.H. Ackers, a member of the Royal Yacht squadron. Thus, for example, the allowance was 45 seconds per ton per mile for sloops, with an increase in time for the increase of tonnage. The present time allowance table of the North American Yacht Racing Union (NAYRU) given in the author's *Sailing Theory and Practice*, page 16, is a direct descendant of this early method of handicapping.

As yacht racing evolved as a summer pastime a rating, enabling boats of different size to compete on the time allowance principle, became a compelling requirement. And the size measure adopted was simply the registered tonnage of the day, ready at hand and known as the Builder's Old Measurement (BOM), the formula being:

$$\frac{(\text{L} - 3/5\,\text{B}) \times \text{B} \times 1/2\,\text{B}}{94} = \text{tons} \qquad (2)^*$$

This measurement system based on the length (L) and beam (B) of the hull served well in the case of merchant vessels, when the object was to establish mere size of the hull and nothing else.

These were built according to the universally accepted view that the best sailing ship, speeds being equal, is the one which will carry the most cargo with the smallest sail area, thus requiring the lowest cost of crew wages and sustenance.[21] Such a point of view could readily be accepted by most yachtsmen of that period to whom the best yacht, speeds being equal, was the one which gave the best accommodation below and could be handled by the

---

* In order to calculate the *tonnage* of a boat to this or any other formula given in this book, the old Imperial units of measurement should be used. Assume, for example, that the length (L) of the hull (measured along the rabbet of the keel, from the forward perpendicular to the afterside of the sternpost) is 57 ft, and the beam (B) taken outside of the planking is 14 ft, then the tonnage of the boat would be:

$$\frac{(57 - \frac{3}{5} \times 14) \times 14 \times 7}{94} = 50.67 \text{ tons.}$$

America's tonnage was measured according to this rule.

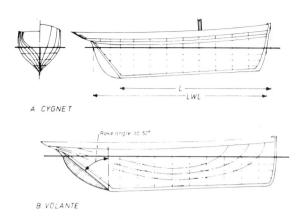

A CYGNET

B VOLANTE

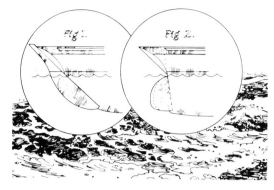

C. WANDERER V *(Rudder modification)*

Fig. 23. *(A)* Cygnet *cutter (35 tons), built by Wanhill of Poole in 1846. Rake of the sternpost was deliberately used to reduce the tonnage measurement, i.e. the racing 'size' of the boat.**
(B) Volante *of 48 tons BOM (Builders' Old Measurement) designed and built by J. Harvey in 1851. Note the extreme rake of the sternpost (so-called dog-legged), about 50 degrees; desire to cheat the rule was the only reason for this development.* Volante *was a contem-*

porary of, and sailed against, the America *in 1851. Of course, she was too small in tonnage to compete on equal terms.*
(C) Sketch 1 shows the original rudder of Eric Hiscock's 39 ft sloop Wanderer V, *with a rake angle of about 50 degrees. Sketch 2 shows the way a new rudder was made with a sternpost rake of about 10 degrees, because the original was not suitable.*

smallest crew. The yachts were not pure racers yet and the owner, together with friends, frequently lived aboard for the summer. These criteria would certainly be approved by the cruising man of today.

The turning point came soon when the formula was used as a measure of speed potential of the racing boat to calculate time allowance. It will be seen that the BOM formula taxes beam heavily in the sense that its dominating contribution to size, and so its adverse effect on the time allowance, is out of proportion to its contribution to speed. The fact that *length* not beam is the element of size which gives speed was soon forcibly demonstrated; and before the advantage of substituting untaxed depth plus ballast (for stability sake) for heavily taxed beam was discovered, the first rule cheater had arrived.

This was the cutter *Cygnet*, built in 1846 and shown in Fig. 23A. By introducing the raking sternpost, a much longer waterline (LWL) was obtained on a given length of keel (L) which enters the formula. Thus, as compared with older types of hull with near-vertical sternposts (Figs 10, 20 and 22) the *Cygnet* was underrated. The ill-effect of measurement rules was becoming apparent right from the beginning, and changes in hull shape, inspired by the rules, were more and more frequent and radical.

At first, the length reducing device of raking the sternpost was applied in moderation, 20 to 30 degrees being the utmost angle given. But soon after, boats were built with a rake angle of about 50 degrees, as shown in Fig. 23B. Such a development, if carried to extreme, may lead to steering deficiency of the rudder.

It is perhaps interesting to note that quite recently (1982) Eric Hiscock reported that his *Wanderer V*, originally designed with 40 degrees rake of the

---

* *Cygnet*'s tonnage was measured according to the contemporary measurement rule i.e. the BOM rule (2).

sternpost (shown in sketch 1 of Fig. 23C), had suffered some steering defects and 'the yacht was found to carry very heavy helm'.[23] After some unsuccessful attempts to correct hull balance (by shifting the rig and recutting the mainsail) Hiscock concluded that 'much of the helmsman's effort was being wasted in trying to drag the stern down into the water'. *Wanderer V* was 'therefore returned to the builder's yard and had another sternpost built with a rake of only 10 degrees' (sketch 2 in Fig. 23C). 'The operation was largely a success in that the Aries vane gear could now steer in most conditions which it had not been able to do before.'

Here we have an example of a lost cause; the raking sternpost, initially introduced in a spirit of cheating the rule, has been preserved through more than a century to become a tradition which no longer serves a purpose. On the contrary, unconsciously applied to the cruising boat it may adversely affect her seaworthiness.

In 1855 the Royal Thames Yacht Club revised the BOM formula by increasing the reduction of L from 3/5 B to full B in an attempt to reduce the handicap advantages enjoyed by yachts already built with excessive rake. The formula being:

$$\frac{(L - B) \times B \times 1/2\,B}{94} = \text{tonnage} \tag{3}$$

This became known as the Thames Measurement (TM) and survived unchanged till the first half of the 20th century as an accepted definition of tonnage. When one spoke of a 5 tonner, it was not difficult for a contemporary yachtsman to visualise the size of the boat; and also, to a certain extent, estimate the cost of building the average cruising yacht as so much per ton.[24]

Length for any given tonnage subsequently showed a rapid increase, whilst the heavily taxed breadth necessarily decreased, so that yachts became narrower and narrower. Perhaps the irritable Dr Johnson's* dictum that 'questioning is not a mode of conversation amongst gentlemen' partly explains the indifference amongst yachtsmen looking at their boats '. . . nearly approaching Euclid's definition of a line as having length but no breadth'. This comment, made by the famous Scottish designer G. Watson[25], refers to the type of boats shown in Fig. 24A and B.

The *Evolution*, depicted in Fig. 24B, was the logical outcome of the tonnage rule (3) and of the progress made in the meantime in hydrodynamics and popularised by William Froude. Since Froude's experiments on friction and wave resistance (published in the 1870s) many doubts on the matter of basic design factors contributing to speed performance vanished. As G. Watson admitted, Froude had 'the happy knack of writing so that the proverbial schoolboy could understand him; and the schoolboy could see the value of resistance to motion through water weighted out simply and accurately as a pound of currant buns'.

Various tonnage cheaters were suggested, in which either the length

---

* Dr. Johnson was the well known author of an English dictionary published at the end of the 18th century.

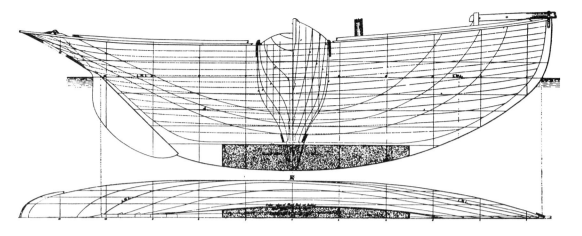

A. A hull built to the TM Rule

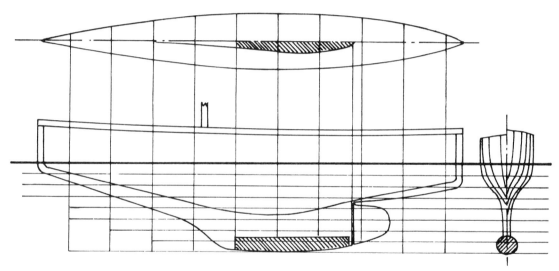

B. EVOLUTION

LWL	50,75	ft.
Beam	6.4	ft.
Draft	10.0	ft.

Fig. 24. *(A) A product of the Thames Measurement Rule. By substituting untaxed depth for the heavily taxed beam, boats 'more and more nearly approached Euclid's definition of a line as having length but no breadth'. Because of their extremely narrow beam (their length/beam ratio sometimes approached as much as 8; see Fig. 24(B)), these boats were called 'plank-on-edge' designs.*

(B) Evolution *(10 tons), designed by E.H. Bentall in 1880. Stability was chiefly obtained by incorporation of an enormous outside lead ballast keel. Her arrival was regarded by contemporary critics as the lamentable result of an absurd system of measurement, and the end of the 'plank-on-edge' era.* Evolution *was built to the Thames Measurement Rule (3).*

A. *Vanderdecken's tonnage cheater*

B. *Side view of VARUNA*

C. *Half-model of a VARUNA-like hull*

Fig. 25. *(A) Vanderdecken's tonnage cheater, suggested in Bell's* Life *magazine in 1852.*
(B) Side view of Varuna, *built in 1892, reveals an attempt to cut drastically the wetted surface of the hull.*

(C) Half-model of a Varuna-*like hull found by the author, lying forgotten on a shelf of an old store (not open to the public) of the Maritime Museum at Greenwich.*

measurement or skin friction were deliberately reduced. Some of them are shown in Fig. 25A, B, and C; in sketch A there is presented Vanderdecken's cheater in which the sternpost is situated nearly amidships; in sketch B the side view of the *Varuna* built in 1852 is shown. The aim was to reduce the friction surface to a minimum.

Only some of the many proposed ideas were actually tested in full scale, others were rejected – the jump was too big a one for contemporary yachtsmen. Some of these ideas were rediscovered later and triumphantly declared by the next generation as outstanding and original achievements.

English yachtsmen could not help looking upon *Evolution*-like boats with horror. Blatant evasion of rules had caused angry voices to be raised against it – to quote one of them 'This absurd system of measurement . . . culminated in a design for a monstrosity well named a plank-on-edge . . . or a capsized soap-box . . . so contrived that although carrying some nine or ten tons of lead in her keel, she only measured one ton by rules. So narrow was this vessel to be, that it was said a broadshouldered man would have to turn edgeways to get below'.[26]

It is perhaps not without irony that the growth of knowledge about hydrodynamic factors affecting boat speed contributed to the development of these unseaworthy craft. The theories and findings of J. Scott Russell, W. Froude, O. Reynolds and others helped to initiate a cascade of profound changes in hull shape, which eventually led to evolutionary blunders that provided rich opportunities for conflict with the sea.

One more important event, responsible for the avalanche of radical changes in hull shape, ultimately leading to unseaworthiness, was the impact of young 'educated' yacht designers not previously associated with boat-building. Their approach to naval architecture was different from that of practical men who, called 'modellers' and brought up in the shipyards of their days, knew practically nothing about tank experiments, or the theoretical achievements of W. Froude and others. Such a man was George Steers who designed the *America* schooner. With a technical education unknown to the older 'modeller' the young generation of designers came to their work with a theoretical knowledge of naval architecture. To quote from the Badmington Library: 'These boys were bold, ambitious, sometimes radical to the point of recklessness; they cared nothing for precedent and where the older and experienced men were content with short cautious steps, the new generation moved by strides, fining lines, moving centres aft, cutting away the fore-foot in a bold sweep from end of the waterline to the heel of the sternpost, and finally hanging all ballast on the keel.'[25]

Fig. 26. *(A) Midship sections show decrease in beam and increase in depth for yachts built under the 94 and 1730 Rules. The effect of rules on main design features is reflected in the table below.*

(B) Midships sections of a hull built under the sail-tons rule, demonstrate a reversed trend as compared with sketch (A). The powerful influence of measurement rules on the shape of hulls is clearly visible.

	Diamond	Vril	Trident	Olga	Doris	Oona
LWL (ft)	25.25	28.3	32.0	33.0	33.7	34.0
Beam (max)	7.2	6.6	6.0	5.7	5.6	5.5
Draft (max)	4.5	5.2	6.25	6.33	7.0	8.0
Displacement (tons)	4.92	7.18	8.9	10.4	12.55	12.5

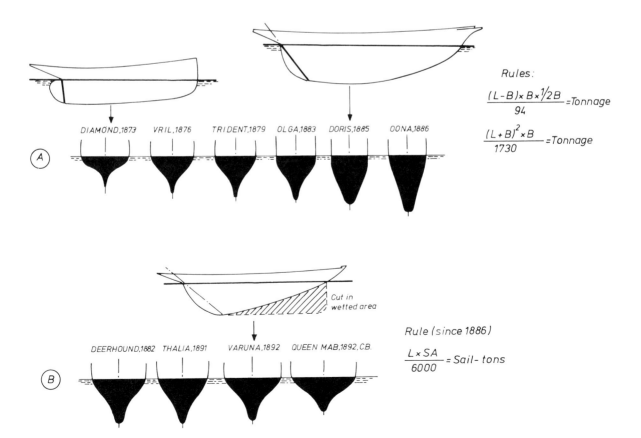

Rules:

$$\frac{(L-B) \times B \times \frac{1}{2}B}{94} = Tonnage$$

$$\frac{(L+B)^2 \times B}{1730} = Tonnage$$

Rule (since 1886)

$$\frac{L \times SA}{6000} = Sail\text{-}tons$$

Changing in midship sections

Figure 26A illustrates rapid and radical changes in midship sections between 1873 and 1886; these were due to the effect of the tonnage rating rules which, at that time, penalised beam but not draught or ballast.[24] Also, at the same time, the hull shape underwent another change towards smaller and smaller wetted surface. Lateral plans of two yachts *Diamond* (1873) and *Doris* (1885) illustrate the trend. This was due to the impact of uncritically applied science, undesirable when viewed from the point of the ultimate purpose and the aim to be achieved through cutting away. While the wetted surface area plays a significant part in the resistance of all water-borne vessels, yet undue importance may be placed upon friction. Wetted surface can be cut down so much that no sufficient lateral area is left to hold the boat to windward.

A notable example of this was the *Thistle*, a Scottish Challenger for the 1887 America's Cup. George L. Watson, her designer, apparently much impressed by Froude's theories, cut down the wetted surface so much that the *Thistle* (shown in Fig. 27) had insufficient lateral plane and although she sailed as fast as the American defender she drifted bodily to leeward. As a result, the American *Volunteer* won two races beating *Thistle* by margins of about 19.5 and 12 minutes; the differences being 6.2% and 3.4% in the elapsed time. The above example illustrates, though indirectly, the wisdom of old fishermen who were so reluctant to cut the forefoot of their vessels (see caption to Fig. 10).

An interesting point is that the effect of a centreboard, or any lateral area for that matter, on weatherliness, recognised in America and successfully applied in earlier Challengers, was not readily understood in Britain. T.W. Lawson in his book expressed in this context the following remark 'Englishmen find in defeat only a spur to further efforts, without applying always those lessons drawn from experience which might shorten the way to victory'.[20] True indeed! Particularly so when one looks upon the America's Cup history from the 1983 perspective.

Changes under the influence of tonnage rules

Referring again to Fig. 26A it is seen that, under the influence of the tonnage rules, length, depth and displacement merrily grew and grew while beam had been shrinking and shrinking till the 'knife-blade' type of hull which finally developed, could no longer be tolerated. It became generally acknowledged that a well designed yacht had to fulfil other important conditions besides speed, namely seaworthiness and safety against capsizing. Even the rich, purse-proud men (to use the language of those days) who might put 500 or 2000 sovereigns of lead on a yacht's bottom, agreed that the existing rule was not making that vessel a fine boat at sea, but only a *cup hunter*. Nothing less than a completely new rule would save the situation.

To lessen the bad effect of highly taxed beam, an argument was set forth for

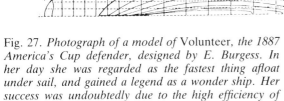

Midship
section

Thistle (G. L. Watson, 1887)

Fig. 27. *Photograph of a model of* Volunteer, *the 1887 America's Cup defender, designed by E. Burgess. In her day she was regarded as the fastest thing afloat under sail, and gained a legend as a wonder ship. Her success was undoubtedly due to the high efficiency of her centreboard in producing lift – a factor of dominant importance in sailing close-hauled. The lines of* Meteor (ex Thistle), *the Scottish challenger designed by G.L. Watson are also shown.*

the use of length alone as the only size dimension that should be taken into account in measuring boats for their speed potential and time allowance. The reasons were as follows: if the breadth or depth of a boat be increased, she is capable of carrying a greater amount of sail, but at the same time her water resistance is also increased, so that there may not be any gain in speed. Indeed, went on the argument, if carried to excess increased beam may incur substantial loss of speed. The conclusion was that breadth and depth measurements should have nothing to do with rating. By leaving them (and sail area) out of account in measuring, so that designers would fix them at such proportions as would give the greatest speed for length, it was postulated that a safer boat, and one better adapted to all kinds of weather than any other, might be developed.[22]

Mean length rule

This idea that yachts should be sailed on the basis of length measurement alone has been advocated over and over again until recent times. A short recollection (from Ref. 22) may well illuminate possible pitfalls associated with over-simplification. The arguments used in discussions preceding the introduction of the short-lived 'Mean Length Rule' in the USA in 1889 deserve to be remembered. A meeting which was specifically called to discuss the measurement question was well attended by a representative assembly of yachtsmen. One of the Nestors of New York yachting, a man whose expert knowledge of sand-bagger yachts entitled him to speak with authority and to be heard with attention, was called on for his opinions. His remarks were brief but very much to the point: 'You want a plain and simple rule, with no hieroglyphics and no plus in it. Who knows what plus is? I don't know what plus is. You take the length overall and the length on the waterline, add them together and divide by two, and you have a plain, simple rule with no plus in it.'

The argument was unanswerable, the vote was democratically taken and the 'Mean Length Rule' unanimously adopted. The introduction of sail area as a factor was at the time bitterly opposed, the slogan being 'A tax on sail is a tax on skill'. How strange this sounds in the present day. Needless to say, the Mean Length Rule, being wide open to abuse, did not enjoy a long life. A rule based on hull length only is bound to develop a form of excessive sail-carrying power in relation to length.

Length/sail area rules

After years of fruitless agitation in the London magazine *Field*, under the editorship of the outstanding British naval architect Dixon Kemp, sail area had been reluctantly recognised as a factor which should be incorporated into the rating rule. Dixon Kemp's proposal was not, however, immediately accepted in his own country but was first adopted in the USA. In 1882 the Seawanhaka

Corinthian Yacht Club of New York decided to adopt Dixon Kemp's suggestion in the form:

$$\frac{L \times S_A}{4000} = \text{‘Sail-tons’} \qquad (4)$$

After a trial season the form of the rule was changed in 1883 to what has since been known as the Seawanhaka Rule:

$$\frac{L + \sqrt{S_A}}{2} = \text{Rating length} \qquad (5)$$

In Britain, however, the privilege of crowding unlimited sails on a given hull length was still cherished as 'an inalienable right'. Typical arguments put forward against Dixon Kemp's rule were similar to those heard earlier in America, for example: 'I should like him (Dixon Kemp) to tell us why the matter was complicated by introducing the sail area, when the length of itself alone would have given a basis for time allowance, and the shipbuilder would have been left free to make the best ship that could be built, whereas now he is again hampered, though in a less degree than under the old tonnage laws.' An interesting point is that this illogical argument was used despite the evident fact that there was no doubt even in those days that sailspread was, apart from the length, the prime speed producing factor. Besides, extra sail area meant extra cost for the sails themselves. In these circumstances, it was considered desirable to place a tax upon sail area.

It has been said, and repeated over and over again, that the proverbial last straw to hasten a change of the rule was the wrecking of the 5 tonner *Oona* on her trial voyage in May 1886; the boat was lost with all hands, including her young designer W.E. Patton. With a lead keel of 9.6 tons on a displacement of 12.6 tons she was probably the most extreme boat built to the 1830 tonnage Rule, having a beam of only 5.5 ft on LOA 46 ft.[24] Her midship section is shown in Fig. 26A.

On 16th November 1886 the Yacht Racing Association adopted the Dixon Kemp rule in the form:

$$\frac{L \times S_A}{6000} = \text{‘Sail tons’} \qquad (6)$$

with length measured on the load waterline and the unit of rating approximating as closely as possible to the preceding 'tons'. Thus, for example, an existing yacht of 20 tons was still in the 20 Rating Class.

The new rule quickly reversed the trend observed earlier under the tonnage rules as depicted in Fig. 26A, and the growth of beam (followed by the reduction in displacement) is indicated in Fig. 26B. Soon after Dixon Kemp's rule was accepted it had shown its weakness. After all every rule, including our present International Offshore Rule, is to a certain extent based on a contemporary understanding of hydro- and aerodynamics, which is one of a deficiency in knowledge, not to say mitigated ignorance. And since knowledge is an open-ended process, so is rule-cheating; and this all too often leads to unseaworthiness. A designer is as unlikely to make a successful yacht if he ignores the implications of the measurement under which the yacht is to race, as he is by failing to recognise the developments made in science or, say, the laws of nature which govern water resistance, stability and sail driving power.

Ultra-light displacement

Although the length/sail area rules (Eqs 4, 5 and 6) put an end to extremely narrow beam and, to some degree, to heavy ballast, they initiated a new trend in design towards ultra-light displacement. With length measured on the waterline, the overhangs gradually became longer and longer to gain maximum sailing length – a term often used in respect to the *effective waterline length* of a hull when under way and/or heeled.

It became apparent that long overhangs could be more usefully adopted with a shallow bodied hull than with a narrow and deep one. However, a moderate overhang on a fairly deep narrow hull, which evolved in the 1890s, was also distinctly advantageous as it gave a fine, easy and at the same time lifting bow at sea. Untaxed beam became considerable, freeboard low, and displacement gradually decreased in an attempt to drive the hull faster and faster under a given rated sail area.

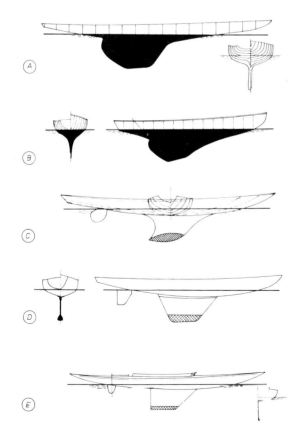

Fig. 28. *(A) Sketch (A) shows the type of yacht built during the later period of the Seawanhaka Rule (1882), and is an example of what the rating rule, together with a gradual growth in knowledge of hydrodynamics, tended to produce. According to W. Froude and others, the most important factor affecting the total resistance of a boat at low speed is the wetted area of the hull, i.e. the friction resistance component; at higher speeds, the wave-making component predominates. The science of aerodynamics did not yet exist, and the effect of the induced drag component (i.e. the effect of leeway) on performance was not known at that time.*
(B) Faugh-a-Ballagh; a 2½-rater of 1892. LWL = 27.5 ft; sail area = 543 sq ft.
(C) An example of a 1-rater designed by J.M. Soper.
(D) Wenonah; a 2½-rater designed by Nat Herreschoff (1892). LWL = 25.05 ft; sail area = 577 sq ft.
(E) Wee Winn; a ½-rater designed by Nat Herreschoff. LWL = 15.6 ft; sail area = 178 sq ft.
In the search for speed, the designers of the boats shown attempted to reduce both components of total resistance (friction and wave drag). It was believed that success of hulls of these forms was due in a large degree to their long overhangs, which produced a so-called 'sailing length' greatly in excess of actual waterline length measured for rating purposes. In other words, long overhangs were deliberately introduced in an attempt to achieve a hull that would sail faster than the rule-makers thought that it should. Steering difficulties of boats with a rudder attached to a short keel, such as those in (A) and (B), were improved by adopting a new configuration – a fin-keel and independently hung rudder. It is interesting to note that the same problem reappeared about 60 years later, in an acute form, in the 5.5 metre class – and for the same reason.

Figure 28 shows some of those boats, aptly called 'skimming dishes'. That such a type of boat with a shallow body is fast in a fresh breeze (for a given water-line length and sail area) is beyond dispute, but this is almost all that can be said in its favour. In the contemporary judgement of most yachtsmen, these boats were expensive to build, expensive to handle and without head-room, or indeed room of any kind inside the smaller classes; they would thrash themselves to pieces in any head sea. 'A season, or at most two, sees the end of their success as racers; then they must be broken up, or sold for a mere song as they are quite *useless for cruising*.'[25]

Figure 29 depicts the most extreme skimming dish ever built as a potential defender of the *America*'s cup. Her career was short and sour. Launched on 18th May, 1901, she was a pile of scrap by the end of September 1901 – after only six races. The hull, although strengthened and re-strengthened, leaked badly and was never strong enough to carry such an enormous sail area and the lead-mine (80 tons) at the bottom. She was equipped with two rudders – the conventional one shown in Fig. 29 and a separate spade rudder fitted aft (similar to that shown in Fig. 28C) – but she was hardly controllable and her skipper regularly had to call for more hands to the wheel.[27]

Separated fin-keel and rudder

It appears that the concept of separated fin-keel and rudder so popular nowadays and dominating in all sort of boats, offshore cruiser-racers included, was initially developed by N.G. Herreshoff and the first of this style of craft, called *Dilemma*, was built and launched in 1891. *Wenonah*, also designed by N. Herreshoff (Fig. 28D) and built a year later, won 17 first, 2 second and 1 third prizes, out of twenty starts. However, it was admitted in those days that 'the value of the fin-keel type in adding to the resources of yachting is limited; the type does not contribute anything of living value to yachting, it serves only as a means to show that old types can easily be beaten, but it takes a machine to do it.'[25]

Their sail-carrying power was obtained by a heavy cigar-shaped bulb attached to a steel plate, similar to that used some 10 years earlier in *Evolution* (Fig. 24B). Separate rudders situated well aft gave them ease in turning on a sixpence. With displacement cut to a dangerous minimum, insufficient scantlings and accomodation within the hull nearly eliminated, the skimming dishes (Fig. 28) were undesirable from anything but a racing point of view. So strong was the reaction of respectable yacht designers and builders (among others Fife, Nicholson and Watson) against this kind of development that in a letter written in October 1892 addressed to the Yacht Racing Association, the following view was put forward 'We take it that the general yachting public require in a yacht: that she shall be safe in all conditions of wind and weather; that she shall combine the maximum of room on deck and below with the minimum of prime cost, and that she shall be driven as fast as may be with the least expenditure of labour – i.e. that she shall have a moderate and workable

Fig. 29. Independence *was arguably the most extreme skimming dish ever built. Work on her began on 30th December 1900, the keel was laid on 26th January 1901, and she was launched on 18th May the same year. By September 1901, after only six races, she had been scrapped at a cost of $3,500, on top of some $210,000 paid by T.W. Lawson to have her built (Ref. 27). One of the avowed demands of the Wall Street* 'Bear' *had been absolute and unlimited speed. The boat's total sail wardrobe was 67,000 sq ft (more than one and a half acres), and she could set 19,000 sq ft at any one time.*

LOA	141 ft	Draft	20	ft
LWL	90 ft	Displacement	146.75	tons
Beam	24 ft	Ballast (lead)	80	tons
Freeboard	4 ft	Wetted area	2,913	sq ft

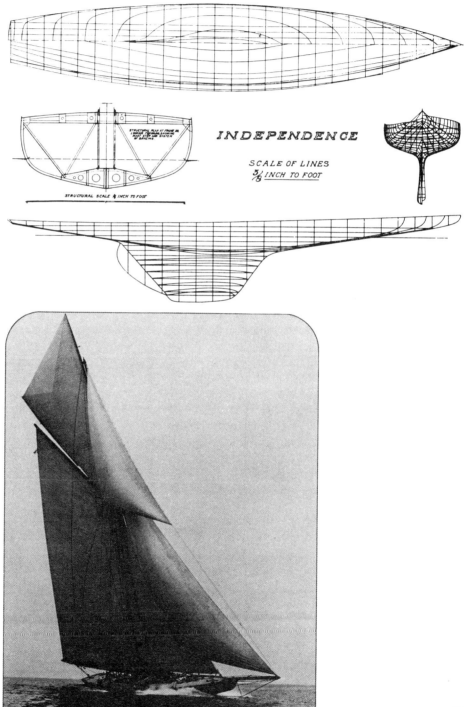

INDEPENDENCE

SCALE OF LINES
$\frac{3}{8}$ INCH TO FOOT

sail area. Therefore, as but few men can afford to build for racing, and for racing only, and as the racer of today is the cruiser of a few years hence, any rating rule should by its limitation encourage such a wholesome type of vessel.'

It had also been suggested in the letter that both the length and sail area (as being the leading speed producing factors) should be preserved but the rating rule be modified so as to make it the interest of builders to produce a *bigger-bodied* boat.

D. The sea-going cruiser-racer

'Yacht measurement and its necessary companion time
allowance, form the spice of the sport of yacht racing and
cannot be overlooked'

Nathaniel G. Herreshoff

'the art of shipbuilding can never be carried to the last degree
of perfection, nor all possible good qualities be given to the
ships, before we at the same time possess in the most perfect
degree possible, a knowledge of the theory and practice.'

Frederick de Chapman
Treatise on Ship Building 1775

A number of excellent, comfortable, sea-going boats were built along the idea of a bigger-bodied hull and some of them are shown in Fig. 30B-D. Lessons learned by designers during the transition period from the cubic content rules (Eqs 1, 2 and 3) to the length/sail area rules (Eqs 4, 5 and 6) played a significant part in this development of a new type of yacht. The *Jullanar* (Fig. 30A) was an initial inspiration. This remarkable boat, with her forefoot cut away to reduce wetted surface, set a profile pattern (called by some early critics 'gratuitously ugly') which was more or less faithfully followed in almost all later designs.

While beam, under the length/sail area rules was still increasing (Fig. 26B), some prominent designers came to the conclusion that beam had already exceeded the limit where it improved a yacht as a comfortable sea-going craft. And that a better, wholesome all-round boat could be produced with somewhat less beam and somewhat more displacement. That was in broad terms the philosophy behind the hull forms given to *Minerva, Gloriana* and *Britannia* (Fig. 30B,C,D). With their advent the old, slow plank-on-edge type of yacht finally died, and a new faster and more seaworthy type had appeared. The evolution of this new type of yacht from 1888 to 1893 was so rapid that some contemporary journalists, B. Heckstall-Smith (secretary of the YRA) amongst them, ventured to use the word 'discovery' when referring to those yachts.

The root of the change can best be appreciated by comparing the midship sections of, say, *Britannia* with that of *Oona* in Fig. 26A. The former was designed to *skim* over the waters and waves, while the latter was *ploughing*

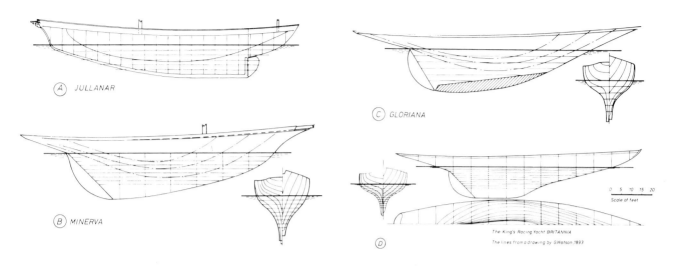

Fig. 30. (A) Jullanar *designed by E.H. Bentall in 1875. She may be regarded as an example of the influence of Froude's theory of resistance on yacht design. The yacht builder John Harvey, a founder member of the Institution of Naval Architects (now with royal status), played a significant part in her design, though he has not often received credit for it.*

LOA	110.5 ft	Draft	13.5 ft
LWL	99.0 ft	Displacement	126 tons
Beam	16.0 ft		

(B) Minerva *designed by W. Fife in 1888, under the Seawanhaka Rule. She was one of the most successful yachts of her time, her midship section being a good compromise between the requirements of the old Tonnage Rule, and the new Length-Sail area Rule. Contemporary opinion was that a suggested tax on draft would have been a doubtful policy, bearing in mind that 'draft gives grip and power to windward, and seaworthiness'. This belief is well reflected in* Minerva's *lines.*

LOA	54.0 ft	Draft	9.0 ft
LWL	40.0 ft	Sail Area	2,724 sq ft

(C) Gloriana *designed by Nat Herreschoff in 1891. This notable yacht is less radical than she appeared to be on her sensational debut in 1891. The popular belief was that she lengthened her sailing lines as she heeled; in fact, in common with many other yachts of the day, she actually lost as much forward as she gained aft. The knuckle of the fore-foot, just under the forward end of the waterline (as also seen in* Minerva*), was cut away to give an even longer overhang. The measured length thus saved gave some rating gain, which could be traded-off for more sail area.*

LOA	70.0 ft	Draft	10.25 ft
LWL	40.25 ft	Sail area	4,100 sq ft
Beam	13.0 ft		

(D) Britannia *designed by G.L. Watson in 1893. One of the critics of the period said that 'with an immense lead keel, she was covered with a cloud of more or less inefficient sails'. Nevertheless, in a career lasting more than 40 years, she sailed in 635 races and won no fewer than 231 of them (with a further 129 second and third flags).*

LOA	122 ft	Draft	15 ft
LWL	87 ft	Displacement	153 tons
Beam	23 ft	Sail area	10,800 sq ft (gaff)
			9,250 sq ft (b'dan)

through. That in everyday language, was the so-called discovery and, indeed, it characterised many fast seaworthy boats built later on both sides of the Atlantic. And because it is an undeniable fact that the hydrodynamic resistance of a vessel largely depends on the 'size of the hole she makes in the water' the heavy, plank-on-edge, *Oona*-type of boat, with lead-mine and all, were slow when compared with those of greater displacement similar to *Gloriana* or *Britannia*, but a lower displacement/length ratio and larger sail area.

Although the *Dorade*, shown in Fig. 31 and designed in 1930, has been regarded as the first of the modern breed of ocean-racers, she was in fact an interpretation of the displacement trend set some 40 years earlier. Referring to Figs 26A and 30C, it is worth noting that the builders of displacement type boats had regressed, in a way, through reverting to midship sections similar to, say, those of *Vril* (1876), which became obsolete in Britain due to the increasing influence of the tonnage rules. As Bacon says in the essay *On Innovations*, 'the forward retention of custom is as turbulent a thing as an innovation.'

However, the designers had not gone the whole way back and the reason lay in an appreciation of the effect of ballast on performance due to increased stability. Lead-keels were at first regarded with a great deal of disfavour and suspicion. In his treatise *Yacht Architecture* published in the 1850s, Lord Robert Montague made the following point: 'Whenever the ballast is stowed, it should above all things, be placed upon springs; in order to make it a *live* not

Fig. 31. Dorade *designed by Olin Stephens in 1929. An interpretation along the lines set earlier by the four yachts shown in Fig. 30. In 1931* Dorade *won the Trans-Atlantic and Fastnet races; in 1933 she cruised across the Atlantic and won another Fastnet.*

LOA	*52.0 ft*	*Draft*	*8.0*	*ft*
LWL	*37.25 ft*	*Displacement*	*14.75*	*tons*
Beam	*10.25 ft*	*Sail area*	*1,100*	*sq ft*

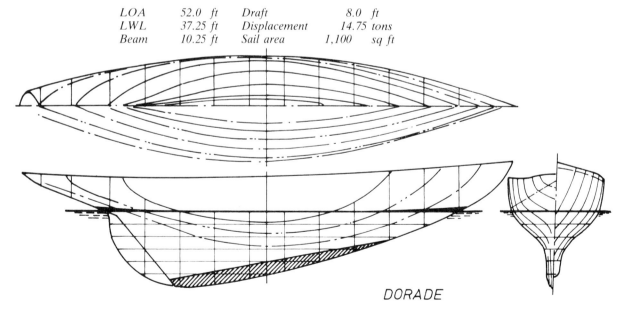

DORADE

dead weight'. Lord Montague explained his view by giving a number of examples; let us quote two of them: 'At Malta there was a race between little sailing boats; one boy slung his ballast under the thwart of his boat, there was a slight tumble in the sea, the boat joggled up and down, but forged away from all the rest and won the race.' And another example: 'The true-blooded *Yankee*, a famous cruiser, was one of our 10-gun brigs, but her ballast had been taken out and stowed upon broom stuff (which gave it spring) and light tops were substituted for our heavy ones. Instances might be multiplied to show the advantages of live *weight*'.

Vanderdecken in his book *The Yacht Sailor*, written in the 1850s says that: 'In belts of calm and veins of wind, a hammock hung to a handspike laid athwart the skylight coamings, half filled with shotbags and kept on a gentle swing fore and aft, I have seen productive of astonishing results'.

By way of digression one may note that, the so-called *new* technique, aptly named *kinetic sailing*, which was developed in the 1960s and involved crew body movement in small racing classes to improve boat performance, is not as new as one might expect to be the case.[28]

Form and weight stability

The prevailing belief shared by yachtsmen up to about 1870 was that a lead-keel made a boat pitch and roll heavily in a seaway; thus 'no yacht was to be found with more than about a tenth of her ballast on the keel, and the majority had none at all.'[26] The kind of stability acquired by the yacht built on such a belief, with midship sections of the *Diamond*-type shown in Fig. 26A, was mainly *form stability*.

Increasing knowledge of the good effect of keeping ballast out of the ends of the hull and, curiously enough, the bad effect of the tonnage rules, rapidly led to a larger quantity of lead being placed outside until, at last, the whole ballast was on the keel. This lowering of the ballast, and consequently of the centre of gravity, enabled the designer to dispense with a considerable amount of beam (otherwise necessary for stability) and add to the length. Such practices went on until the resulting plank-on-edge type of yacht, relying almost entirely on the weight stability, finally reached the end of the development road conditioned by implications of the tonnage rating rules. Figure 26A, together with the associated table of dimensions, clearly illustrates this development.

Two different types of stability, directly dependent on the midship sections of the hull and weight distribution, that is, *stability due to form* and *stability due to ballast* are of high importance both for speed and seaworthiness of the boat. This cardinal point will be touched upon briefly by considering, as an example, two distinctly different types of yacht competing in the America's Cup races prior to 1895. A case much relevant to the current state of yacht design bearing in mind that in those days, as well as today, America's Cup designs tend to influence yacht types beyond their own restricted sphere. Representatives of those yachts, their lines and dimensions are given in Fig. 32A and B.

(A)

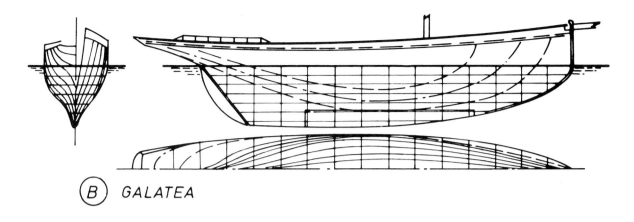

(B) GALATEA

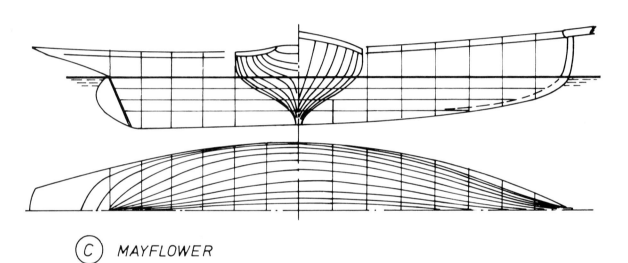

(C) MAYFLOWER

Fig. 32. *(A) Influence on yacht design of national tradition and the rule (which to a certain extent incorporates tradition). On the right the English deep and narrow cutter* Galatea; *on the left the American broad and shallow centreboard sloop* Mayflower; *respectively challenger and defender in the 1886 America's Cup races. The table below gives their dimensions.*

	Galatea	Mayflower	
LOA	*102.6 ft*	*100 ft*	*(B) Lines of* Galatea.
LWL	*87.0 ft*	*85.7 ft*	*(C) Lines of* Mayflower.
Beam (max)	*15.0 ft*	*23.5 ft*	
Draft	*13.5 ft*	*9.0 ft*	
Draft with c/board	*N/A*	*20.3 ft*	
Outside ballast (lead)	*81.5 tons*	*42.0 tons*	
Sail area (SA)	*7,505 sq ft*	*8,500 sq ft*	
Displacement (Δ)	*157.6 tons*	*110.0 tons*	
$\Delta \div \left(\dfrac{L}{100}\right)^3$	*239.3*	*174.8*	
$\dfrac{SA}{\Delta}$	*47.6*	*77.3*	

The story of early America's Cup contests is one of narrow, deep-draught English challengers perpetually defeated by traditional beamy, shallow-draught defenders which usually carried centreboards. *Galatea* and *Mayflower*, respectively challenger and defender in the 1886 contest, provide the opportunity of comparing the relative merits of these two types of boat which had been developed on either side of the Atlantic.

For reasons, irrelevant to the present purpose, for 40 years after 1845 the Americans did not alter the basic concept of the centre-board type of yacht as represented by the *Mayflower* shown in Fig. 32. These yachts for any given length were capable of greater speed than the British challengers in moderate breezes and pretty smooth waters, simply because they were of much lighter displacement and larger sail area. Large additions to displacement without concomitant increase in sail driving power (as in fact was the case of the British challengers) had a prejudicial effect on speed, mainly on the account of the enormous wave-making which large displacement incurs. In average summer conditions, the American skimming type of boat had the advantage in speed, particularly when sailing off the wind in fairly calm seas. But in close-hauled conditions when pressed hard in heavy winds, the advantage was just the other way, particularly in a short rough head sea. Thus on the average, over a wide enough range of weather conditions, there would not be much difference in performance between the two despite their radically opposed concepts in design.

Unfortunately for the British, however, it was made plain that the weather conditions usually prevailing during the America's Cup races were not of the kind in which a heavy displacement narrow boat could win a majority of races. And the British, according to Lawson's remark quoted earlier, were reluctant, or could not be persuaded, to learn the lesson. The reasons why the American type of boat always won seem to be more obvious today than they were before. The table attached to Fig. 32B reveals the truth directly or by implication. Thus, for instance, the driving power of the defender *Mayflower* expressed in terms of sail area per ton displacement, was about 62% higher than that of the challenging *Galatea*; as a result, *Mayflower* won two races and the cup by margins of 3.5% and 6.4% in elapsed time. This gives some idea of what the terms 'fast' and 'slow' really mean in practice; we are dealing only in fractions of a knot.

The superiority of shallow centreboarders in speed was, however, dearly achieved in terms of stability and, indirectly, in seaworthiness. While the narrow, deep English type of boat had practically an unlimited range of *weight stability*, increasing within the practical range of the heel angles, the shallower and broader yacht of the American type reached the maximum of her *form stability* at a heeling angle of about 30 degrees; this type of shallow boat was unfit for serious cruising purposes. Due to their size small skimming-dish classes in particular were more vulnerable at sea than were the bigger ones of the America's Cup defenders' size. 'The capsizing of small open boats and yachts,' wrote W.P. Stephens, 'even when attended by fatal results, was too common to attract much notice; and the larger yachts came in for a full share of very narrow escapes and an occasional disaster.'[22]

Phillips-Birt in his book *Sailing Yacht Design* records that the greatest of the disasters which occurred was to the *Mohawk* in 1876, a schooner 140 ft in length and drawing only 6 ft, which was lost when lying at anchor with her sails set; she was struck by a squall and capsized, drowning her owner and his guests.

By contrast, the English deep and narrow type of boat was fundamentally stable. Capsizing, in so-called intact stability conditions (no damage and flooding of the hull), was virtually impossible, since at no angle of heel did these heavily ballasted hulls lose their positive righting moment. This is the typical characteristic of weight-conditioned stability.

There was also another noticeable dissimilar pattern in behaviour between British and American type boats. While the former usually remained in immaculate rigging condition after a race, the latter used to emerge in various stages of disarray, the result of the high accelerations and stresses suffered and generated by their hulls – 'stiff and unyielding until the moment came when they were in danger of capsizing'. This is the typical feature of form-conditioned stability, characterised by large initial stiffness – inflicting high accelerations in rolling – but with a reducing range of positive stability beyond 30-40 degrees of heel.

In those days, and even today, the effects of stability on seaworthiness were not understood and the criticism addressed towards heavily ballasted British yachts was, from the stability point of view, naïve (although in some respects correct because their lack of reserve buoyancy made them wet and even dangerous in heavy sea conditions). At the time when *Genesta* (Fig. 33) was to challenge for the America's Cup in 1885 under the condition that 'vessels intending to compete for this cup must proceed under sail on their own bottoms to the port where the contest is to take place', many wild speculations and prophecies were published by renowned authorities in the USA. Let us quote: 'I have doubts that the English yachts will get here . . . an Atlantic passage will

	Genesta	Puritan
LOA	96.4 ft	94.0 ft
LWL	81.6 ft	81.1 ft
Beam	15.0 ft	22.6 ft
Draft (hull)	13.5 ft	8.7 ft
Draft (with C/B)	N/A	20.0 ft
Ballast	70 tons	48 tons
Sail area	7,150 sq ft	7,983 sq ft

Fig. 33. *Lines of* Genesta, *the British challenger for the 1885 America's Cup contest. Her dimensions, together with those of her American rival, are given opposite.*

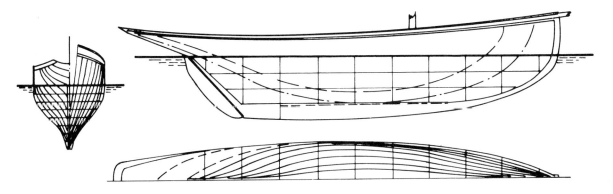

GENESTA

jerk the sticks out of them'. And another one: 'The attempt to sail over here, except in the finest weather, would be dangerous, rash and foolhardy . . . for these sharp, lead-loaded sailing machines have no reserve buoyancy, and when pressed they must pound . . . you will not see any of these diving-bells over here yet awhile'. However, those 'diving bells' arrived safely, amongst them *Genesta* and the excellent *Madge*, with their sticks in place. *Genesta* crossed the Atlantic again on her bottom back to England, where she arrived safely after a stormy passage of nineteen days ten hours, nearly the entire voyage being made under close reefs.

E. Dual-purpose rating formulae

'Speaking generally, it is not the case, as the rest of the world
think, that reason is the principle and guide to virtue but
rather feelings. For there must be produced in us (as indeed
is the case) an irrational impulse to the right, and then later
on reason must put the question to the vote and decide it'

Aristotle 'Magna Moralia'

Gradually, with increasing understanding of the good and bad effects of the diametrically opposed concepts of design – as represented in Fig. 32B – on yacht behaviour, the merging of these two extreme types began to the mutual benefit of yachtsmen on both sides of the Atlantic. The design pattern and underlying philosophy imprinted in the hull forms shown in Fig. 30B, C, had ultimately been accepted, and attempts were made to devise a rating rule which would safeguard the proper form of the hull. By that time it became evident that, in order to avoid the proliferation of freak and unseaworthy boats, the measurement rule must *govern not only the size of the boat but also the shape of the hull* – its midship sections in particular.

On 1st January 1896 the Yacht Racing Union adopted the new formula:

$$\frac{L + B + 0.75\,G + 0.5\,\sqrt{S_A}}{2} = \text{Linear Rating} \tag{7}$$

proposed by R.E. Froude (the English hydrodynamicist, son of the famous William Froude). The new and unique measurement factor G represented the skin girth taken from waterline to waterline, as shown in sketch A of Fig. 34. This was considered as a safeguarding clause sufficient to penalise the light displacement skimming-dishes with hard bilges, and to encourage a healthy seagoing type with soft bilges and fullness of hull sections to provide better headroom. It is seen that the G factor is larger for the skimming-dish type of hull than for that with fuller midship sections of the same depth; therefore it unfavourably increases the rating of the boat.

As a matter of fact the linear formula (Eq. 7) was a modification of an earlier French formula, often called the *Girth Rule*, proposed by M. Godinet in 1892,

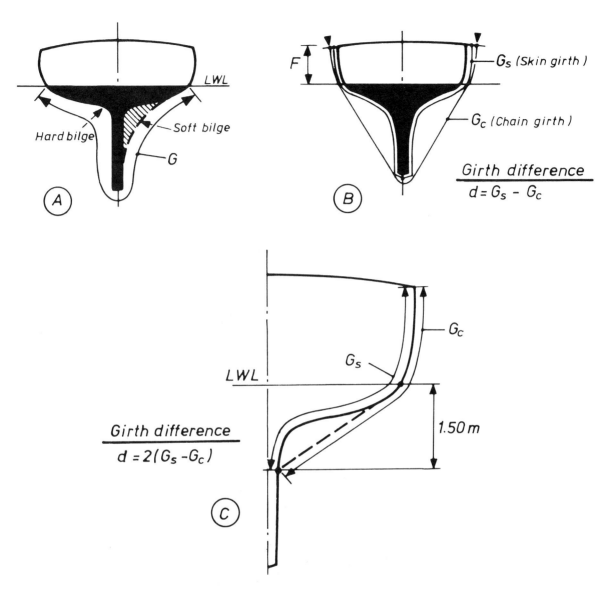

Fig. 34. *Methods of measuring the girth factor and girth difference (d).*

which in its simplest form read:

$$\frac{(4\,L - G)\,G\,\sqrt{S_A}}{520} = \text{Rating} \qquad (8)$$

G being the skin girth from the top of the deck planking port round the keel to ditto starboard, plus maximum beam. The result, given in cubic form, was converted into the English rating by the divisor selected (in this case 520). It is evident that the G effect on hull shape in the French formula is much stronger than that in the modified form of the English formula, in the sense that skimming-dishes were more heavily penalised.[25] The idea was a very simple one, so simple that it would have tempted Sherlock Holmes to say: 'Elementary, my dear Watson, elementary!'.

At first, unlike the Germans and Scandinavians, the English yachtsmen were rather disinclined to adopt the basic premise of the French rule (the G factor) perhaps because the French approach had, shall we say, a certain logicality. Unfortunately, as we shall see, English rule-makers tend to think and act like politicians rather than like scientists who usually exercise logic and reasoning faculties.

The author believes that he will be forgiven for a short digression and for taking advantage of his continental predisposition in dealing with such difficult problems as rating rules. There is a belief prevalent, not only among foreigners, that the Anglo-Americans are somewhat illogical. They appear to scorn the 'horrid clarity of Voltaire' i.e. the type of intelligence based on the Cartesian logic which analyses, discriminates and formulates reasonable concepts or solutions. No one has put this point of view better than the men who embodied the best qualities of their country – Stanley Baldwin, Austen Chamberlain and Winston Churchill. In a speech published in *The Times* with the subheading: 'Constitution and logic' Baldwin maintained that 'one of the reasons why our people are alive and flourishing, and have avoided many of the troubles that have fallen to less happy nations, is because we have *never been guided by logic in anything we have done*'.[30]

At the Assembly of the League of Nations Austen Chamberlain made the following remark: 'We (the English) are prone to eschew the general, we are fearful of these logical conclusions pushed to extreme, because, in fact, human nature being what it is, logic plays but a small part in our everyday life . . . In the face of any great problem, we are seldom really guided by stern logic of the philosopher or the historian'.[31] Winston Churchill similarly remarked that: 'Logic is a poor guide compared with custom. Logic . . . has proved fatal to the parliamentary government'.[32]

This deliberate absence of pejorative logic, 'the glorious incapacity for clear thought which is one of the distinguishing marks of our race' – to use Lord Selborne's words – is itself a method. 'We'll muddle through somehow', the Englishman believes with some degree of proud complacency. Men have diverse interests, diverse aims and diverse problems to solve, and these cannot always be harmoniously solved by 'dead logic formula'. Consequently the English and perhaps to a lesser degree the Americans (by hereditary token) are always tempted to adopt a piecemeal or 'tinkering' solution, leaving unsolved problems to be dealt with later, and not much bothering about side-effects of their immediate action.

'Muddling through' may work well as long as one can afford a good many faults, or in party politics, where the principal qualification of the leader is not his capacity to reason logically but his appeal to the elector's gullibility, and his capacity to hit 'below intellect'. However, such a primitive device may no longer be appropriate, could even lead to catastrophe, when dealing with a cunning and relentless enemy. Certainly, we would be living in a better and safer world today had our 'wise men without gift of foresight' given logic and reason a chance at the right time.

Reverting to the rating rule influence on design, the Girth Rule (Eq. 7) failed in its original form to safeguard the desired end – the promotion of a larger area of midship section. Subsequently, the rule was amended by the addition of 'chain girth' to 'skin girth' measurement and the further addition of the 4 d term (four times girth difference as shown in sketch B in Fig. 34) to the pre-existing formula (Eq. 7). The new rule, proposed by a Danish yachtsman Alfred Benson, was adopted in 1901 in the form:

$$\frac{L + B + 0.75\,G + 4\,d + 0.5\,\sqrt{S_A}}{2.1} = \text{Linear Rating} \qquad (9)$$

where $G = G_c - 2\,F$ and is the chain girth deck to deck, minus twice free-board, F (see Fig. 34B).

The new factor d was the tax which had to be paid by the skimming-dishes. The term 4 d was a strong enough penalty and therefore made it worthwhile to fill out the garboards to produce fuller, and thus more habitable hull sections. It can easily be seen from sketch B of Fig. 34 that, length and sail area being equal, hulls having fuller sections (and thus a smaller value of d, which is multiplied by four in the formula) would result in an advantageous, lower rating in comparison with flat-bottom, bulb-keel yachts. The girth rule in the form given in Eq. 10 below practically eliminated unseaworthy hulls of the skimming-dish type from competition.

After some modifications introduced in 1906 and 1919, the girth rule became accepted as the International Rule in the form:

$$\frac{L + 0.25\,G + 2\,d + \sqrt{S_A} - F}{2.5} = \text{Linear Rating} \qquad (10)$$

It should be noted that the beam (B) was dropped as a penalty, and the effects of girth (G) and the girth difference (d) on the rating were moderated. In addition, a premium on freeboard (F) was introduced. In 1933 the International Rule, the descendant of the Girth rule, was further modified to its current form:

$$\frac{L + 2\,d + \sqrt{S_A} - F}{2.37} = \text{Linear Rating} \qquad (11)$$

which, after more than 80 years is still in use as the rule which controls the 12 metre yachts participating in the America's Cup contests. The method of measurement of the d factor in formula 11 is illustrated in sketch C of Fig. 34. This is the difference between the skin girth G_s (from a point 1.5 metres below the load waterline to the deck) and the chain girth G_c (bridging any hollows in the hull by a straight line). Measurements are taken at the section located at 55% LWL from the fore-end of the LWL. The d factor, together with some restriction on minimum displacement, insures that the 12 metre, or any other class built to the formula of Eq. 11 for that matter, will never be an ultra light displacement, flat-bottom type of boat.

The Girth Rule (Eq. 9), which ultimately evolved into the International Rule (Eq. 11), is unique in the sense that it is the only rule in which an attempt is made, albeit shyly, to resolve the conflict of purpose between speed and seaworthiness. That is, on the one hand to establish the speed potential of the boat for handicap purpose, and on the other to safeguard a desirable seaworthy hull form. All other rating rules, produced before or after, were formulated without due appreciation of the side effects of the hull geometry on the seagoing characteristics of the boat.

The measurement rule (Eq. 9) was a result of extensive, truly international discussions on the purpose of the rule, which preceded its mathematical form. These are reflected in R.E. Froude's paper of 1906.[33] 'The principle to which the situation points, is that the legitimate purpose of a measurement rule is simply to measure size, without fear or favour; in order that, the element of size being eliminated either by classification or time allowance, the yachts which win shall be those which are fastest for their size, and that the model evolved under these conditions of competition, shall be the *speediest* model. Here, then, *prima facie* we seem to find ready to hand a definition of the ideal principle which should govern the competition of a good measurement rule.'

Froude continued: 'This much premised, however, experience at once confronts us with grave difficulty in putting this ideal into practice. For it is a matter of notoriety that, as regards many of the most conspicuous developments which come to the front under various measurement rules, the model evolved owes its success, palpably, to what we may call *measurement cheating* qualities rather than to *genuine speed qualities*.'

Furthermore, Froude and his contemporaries, among them Alfred Benson, were fully aware that if the sport was to continue to be yacht racing, and not merely sailing machine racing, the principle had to be suitably modified by introducing a collateral aim in addition to that of speed. 'Speed must still, indeed, be an aim; but not speed without qualification.' Consequently, the principal aim of the measurement rule was modified, in the sense that speed became somewhat related to habitability of the hull. For the first time measurement was introduced in the girth difference term (d) which could not be accused of having as its sole ostensible purpose measurement of the size of the boat and, so, her speed potential. By introducing the d factor as a premium, the rule-makers believed that it would secure a certain habitability of the boat with adequate head-room and, it was hoped, seaworthiness. Thus, the *dual purpose rating rule* was conceived – although in an embryonic form – to promote a wholesome yacht suitable both for racing and for cruising.

F. Back to square one?

*'Traits such as hypocrisy and deceit and even self-deceit may
be a fundamental aspect of human nature that can't be
eradicated altogether'*

E. Wilson
'Sociobiology'

Numerous rules were subsequently proposed and with the same object in mind: that the designer's talent could and should be used for the improvement of dual purpose yachts and not for the mere evasion of the measurement rule. All that has been written on this subject during the last hundred years or so would not equal in bulk the volumes that have been written on the principles of yacht architecture; and the discussion still continues with no end in view. The history of rating rules is an almost unbroken record of failures. It must be admitted, however, that none of the rules has been so bad that it failed altogether to attract ardent defenders. There are always people with vested interests, even in a bad rule.

There is no need to continue this familiar story down to the present time. Suffice it to say that the International Offshore Rule (IOR) introduced in 1970 in the form:

$$0.13 \left(\frac{L \sqrt{S_A}}{\sqrt{BD}} + 0.25\,L + 0.2\sqrt{S_A} + \text{draft correction} + \right.$$

$$\left. \text{freeboard correction} \right) \times \text{EPF} \times \text{CGF} = \text{Linear Rating} \qquad (12)$$

where
  EPF is engine and propeller factor and
  CGF is centre of gravity factor
  stems in its basic form, from the older RORC rule.[34]

The rationale of formula (12), different in principle from the Girth Rules (9, 10 and 11), is that the length L and the sail area S_A are both regarded as factors of speed, while displacement, represented in formula (12) by the product of beam (B) and depth of hull (D) is a measure of effective work done in the propulsion of a boat. Thus, the IOR formula is, in fact, an attempt at a *speed formula* and nothing else. The philosophy which led to the girth formulae and the lessons learned in the past were forgotten. Inevitably, unresolved conflict of purpose has returned once again. The fact is that, almost by definition, a dual purpose yacht cannot possibly be designed on the premises which led to the IOR formula, which is intended to measure speed potential only. Scantling allowances alone cannot safeguard seaworthiness.

Soon after the International Offshore Rule (Eq. 12) came into force it ran into difficulties. The hard fact is that any rating rule inevitably becomes a building rule, favouring particular design features of the hull. Thus, recently observed trends in yacht design (as compared with older yacht forms such as those shown, for example, in Figs 30B, C and 31) are:

(1) lighter displacement
(2) greater beam and flat bottom
(3) reduced lateral area of the hull (separated fin-keel and rudder)
(4) higher centre of gravity
(5) increased freeboard (particularly conspicuous in small classes)

All these features, although advantageous from the viewpoint of speed for a given rating (not necessarily for given size of the boat) have a deleterious effect on seaworthiness, as we shall see.

The fact that this undesirable development towards an unseaworthy kind of boat strongly accelerated after the IOR was introduced, does not indicate that the latest rule is particularly bad in this respect. As a matter of fact, the current rule is not much different from either the RORC or CCA rule which were brought together to procreate the new rule[34]. The main reason why the RORC and CCA rules did not produce such an unhealthy type of boat as that which dominates the racing scene today is that the hidden seeds contained in latent form in those rules (and particularly in the RORC rule) had no favourable social climate in which to germinate.

The International Offshore Rule which, as already mentioned, is in fact a speed rule, serves the purpose and is gladly acknowledged by the majority of contemporary yacht designers. It has been said that 'the newer ocean racing skippers and crews are so much better than their forebears that one should not weep for what has gone by'. Perhaps in some respect they are better, certainly they are faster.

Although, in the matter of seaworthiness the new rule IOR has the same object as the past RORC rule – 'to encourage the design of sailing vessel in which speed and seaworthiness are combined' – the liberal encouragement given by the IOR to the design development of fast boats has unfortunately resulted in their increasing unseaworthiness. Thus the present rule, as with many other rules before, has failed as a dual-purpose rule. It would nevertheless be difficult to get an agreement in any representative group of yachtsmen or designers on why it happened and how to correct this unwholesome situation.

One might reasonably expect that if a human project or intention fails, it will sooner or later be corrected or terminated. Logically, no failure should survive. Unfortunately history shows us that it can be repeated time and time again by new people; so the life span of a failure can be extended. The International Offshore Rule appears to be an example of such a surviving failure. Why? The recognition of failure surely entails that the failing concept ought to be corrected or abandoned. This implies that if the corrective action is to be successful, the source of failure must be identified.

Until very recent times no attempt was made to trace the source of unseaworthiness. That this was so has been made clear in one of the statements of the 1979 Fastnet Race Inquiry report: '48% of the fleet (112 boats) reported that on one or more occasions the yacht was knocked down to horizontal during the storm. Knockdowns to horizontal have always been a potential danger in cruising and offshore racing yachts in heavy seas; *therefore no attempt has been made to analyse the causes or effects.*[4]* The last sentence (the italics are mine) is a rather despairingly passive conclusion and reflects the half-jokingly called Flagles' Law of the Perversity of Inanimate Objects: 'Any inanimate object, regardless of its composition or configuration, may be expected to perform at any time in a totally unexpected manner for reasons that are either completely obscure or wholly mysterious.'

It cannot of course be denied that an unpredictable sequence of events can overwhelm even the most seaworthy boat and the most experienced and prudent seaman; and in this sense the knockdown or capsize is always a potential danger for those at sea. However, the predictable consequence of badly designed unseaworthy boats or crew improvidence are too readily included in this 'unpredictable' category of disasters mentioned in the excerpt taken from the Fastnet report. One is consequently bound to regard knockdown and complete capsize, with their totally mysterious causes, as phenomena which almost by definition are not amenable to scientific enquiry. A contrasting attitude, incidently shared by the author, would be to consider rolling and broaching, which ultimately may lead to capsize, as dangerous foes which nevertheless might successfully be dealt with (in terms of reduced probability or frequency of occurrence) provided we have enough intelligence of the enemy's intentions, methods and tactics.

Résumé and concluding remarks

If what has been said so far is not to be purely a relation of facts, but an attempt at a solution to a problem, we must try to identify the logical flaw in the past and current measurement rules which has made the dual-purpose wholesome type of yacht – suitable both for racing and for cruising – such an elusive, almost impossible goal to achieve in practice. From our brief, but sufficient, perusal of the past rating rules it becomes evident that, with one exception, all measurement formulae were intended to be *speed formulae*. In fact these formulae are nothing but simple, or rather simplistic, mathematical expressions, wherein certain variables called length, breadth, depth, sail area, girth, displacement and, more recently, stability enter the equation and, according to the *valuation* given to them by the rule-makers, are hoped to determine the speed potential of the boat for handicap purposes. By 'valuation' we understand the assumed effect of given variables, such as length or beam, on speed. These variables are broadly divided into two categories: the speed-producing and speed-reducing factors. Thus, length is regarded as a speed-producing factor whilst displacement is seen as a speed-reducing factor. The effects on speed of some variables, such as beam, are too complicated to be given values by any straightforward reasoning. Greater beam increases initial stability and allows a large sail area and so increased speed; on the other hand, it makes the hull less slender and so it incurs a wave resistance penalty. But a heavy displacement type of boat, whose wave resistance largely depends on the

---

* Such a statement is so general that it cannot possibly be wrong; undoubtedly this is true but not very helpful.

size of the hole she makes in the water, usually pays a higher penalty than does a light displacement skimming dish of the same beam. As shown earlier, beam is a poor measure of the boat's size for any handicap system and may be abused to cheat the rule. Besides, it will be shown that beam largely determines the type of stability and, as such, is an important factor of seaworthiness. Depending on whether beam is the numerator or the denominator of the formula, or is not included in the measurement formula at all, different types of boats, some of them safer at sea than the others, will result and Figs 24–26 illustrate the point.

Because of the valuation or taxation attached to every variable in the formula, the rating rule becomes a frame of reference for the designer and, inevitably, influences the shape of the hull. To phrase it differently, the rating rule is a kind of textbook for the yacht architect and he tends to, or even must, design a yacht to the book to be successful. This practice can be dangerous because the evolving shape of the boat, disproportionally fast to the rating assessment, may not and usually does not satisfy those requirements which would be demanded if seaworthiness were truly to be achieved through the measurement rules.

G. Where there is a will there is a way

'Concern for man himself and his fate must always form the chief interest of technical endeavours . . . never forget this in the midst of your diagrams and equations'
Albert Einstein

Seaworthiness, admittedly desirable, is not feasible as long as the factors of hull geometry related to seaworthiness are not included in the measurement formula. The fact that seaworthiness is demanded in the preamble to almost every rating formula is nothing but wishful thinking, and as such is of little or no help at all. It is only by imposing a fair premium on the seaworthiness features of hull shape that the desired goal can be practicably achieved. So far, there is no frame of reference or set of criteria ascribing proportional values to those desirable features in hull shape that contribute to safety and sea-worthiness; in principle it should be equally important to that frame of reference whereby speed potential is estimated. And this *lack of a seaworthiness frame of reference, supplementing the speed reference frame*, is the cardinal logical flaw which precludes development of a dual purpose rule and thus of a reasonably seaworthy cruiser-racer.

An integral part of offshore racing as well as cruising is impending danger; thus the hull shape, together with its appendages and other characteristics, must correspond to efficient and safe function in order to meet this danger with a high probability of survival. Unfortunately, seaworthiness requirements have usually been contradictory to those of speed imposed by the measurement rules, so that the designer is forced to trade-off among the contradictions. The flat-out racer versus the cruising type of boat controversy is bound to arise.

The intense preoccupation with speed, which dominates today, permits no half-way approach. The designers' as well as the builders' reputations are made by the racing success of their creations. Inevitably, the design conflict between speed and seaworthiness is nowadays always resolved in favour of speed performance.

Of course, if there were two frames of reference built into the rating rule, the designer's job would be much more difficult, since a positive value for one frame of reference might be negative for another. And where there are two objectives it is impossible to maximise both. It can be mathematically proved that two or more interrelated variables (those related to speed and those related to seaworthiness) cannot be maximised at the same time; compromise is therefore unavoidable. This is the only way in which the laudable principal object of the Royal Ocean Racing Club 'to encourage the design, building ... of sailing vessels in which speed and seaworthiness are combined, by any means including scientific research and practical demonstration' might realistically be achieved.[35] Anything else is hopeless tinkering and attempting to muddle through, with only the excuse, or consolation, of a hundred year old tradition.

A fundamental question arises with respect to the second frame of reference which should be established in non ambiguous terms if seaworthiness of sailing boats is to be safeguarded by the measurement rules. What are these desirable geometry factors of the hull or its other characteristics, which make one boat safer than another when facing the environmental hazards of weather and waves?

Textbooks on yacht design are of little help in eliciting these factors. In more general references on the subject, the following hints are given: 'The effect of hull form on seaworthiness and seakindliness is very important. These qualities depend upon distribution of weight and displacement, combined with proper hull proportions and hull form.'[36]

'A vessel may be absolutely seaworthy and yet extremely uncomfortable. Seaworthiness is a quality difficult to define in precise terms, but naval architects and practical seamen can usually be found to possess *strong views about unseaworthiness*. Controversy usually centres around ship motion and behaviour in a seaway. The only point at issue is that of safety . . . all authorities concerned with safety of ships at sea are fully agreed that *satisfactory stability* is the most important. As to what exactly constitutes this elusive virtue, i.e. the standard which should be laid down, is a matter of judgment and experience in any particular case. Inevitably, this means that there is room for argument on matters of important detail.'*

Without making wicked comments on whether *absolutely seaworthy* craft may or may not be comfortable, strong views about unseaworthiness (read again one of those strong views expressed by a prominent designer and quoted on page 7) or the observation that satisfactory stability is an elusive virtue, are too vague to be of practical help in settling the matter of what are the primary factors of seaworthiness.

Under the heading *Seaworthiness and Proportions*, the following remarks are

* From: J.A. Hind's *Stability and Trim of Fishing Vessels*, Fishing News Books Ltd, 1982.

expressed in Barnaby's book *Basic Naval Architecture*: 'Seaworthiness is a quality that is profoundly affected by many factors other than mere size. A small yacht can be as seaworthy as anything afloat, though she may be extremely uncomfortable. A large vessel can be comfortable in a seaway, yet essentially unseaworthy. Most of the points that contribute to seaworthiness permit little doubt or argument. Naval architects and seamen all agree on the desirability of good sheer, ample freeboard and stability range, strong construction, well-protected deck openings and reasonably deep draught. The most debatable point is the initial metacentric height (GM) that should be provided. This can be illustrated by the case of two yachts that were virtually sister ships, differing only in the height of the GM. The captain of the first yacht reported her to be a magnificent seaboat extremely dry, and "stiff as a church" in sudden squalls. Her owner thought she was much too quick and lively in a seaway . . . the second vessel was given less GM (reduced stability). The same captain transferred to the new yacht and, in accordance with best seafaring tradition, greatly preferred his old ship. His new command was wetter and more sluggish in a seaway and, for these reasons, he considered her a worse seaboat.'[37]

Again, we have a number of statements or observations (some of them contradictory) which, although they agree that the shape of hull, its stability, weight distribution, etc., matter most, are too general, dim and too subjective to be considered as the basis on which the problem of seaworthiness as a frame of reference could be solved. It is impossible on that basis to answer many questions: Are the contemporary yachts of good proportions? Is their stability sufficient, and if not what should be done? Have they reasonably deep draught etc. to deem them seaworthy?

No better postscript to this chapter could be given than that of quoting a prominent Victorian scientist, James Syme. His opinion, expressed some hundred years ago in a different context, is surprisingly relevant to our present predicament: 'At no time in the history . . . has there been so much occasion for information as at present, since the profusion of vague and verbose compilations, together with the mass of crude speculation and reckless misinterpretation with which the press has of late years teemed, has so bewildered the minds of most men as to render them incapable of discriminating between good and evil of what they read. There hence results a painful feeling of uncertainty with constant straining after novelty, as the wheel of fashion revolves so that some doctrines, instead of becoming more firmly established through time, are apt to be relinquished and replaced by the silly suggestions of presumptuous folly.'

It appears that some hurdles need to be surmountd before one can acquire an intelligible notion of seaworthiness and its really commensurate factors, in order to reduce the ratio of speculations to facts. Otherwise we may be left with another paradox so aptly expressed by Sir Rowland Baker's observation: 'What is wrong with our ships will just make heroes out of ordinary mortals, there is not any possibility of curative action.'

*'Nothing ever becomes real till it is experienced
– even a proverb is no proverb to you till your
life illustrated it'*

John Keats

*'Nobody will use other people's experience nor
have any of his own till it is too late to use it'*

Nathaniel Hawthorne

4 Boat Motion in a Seaway

The problem of seaworthiness is ultimately bound up with that of boat motion in a seaway. As a result of the combined action of forces of different origins, aerodynamic, hydrodynamic, gravitational, inertia and buoyancy, the boat driven through rough seas is subject to a variety of more or less violent motions. There are six of those, the first three of which are rotational oscillations about some axis and the second three are translational or linear.

(1) **Rolling.** The boat heels rhythmically first to one side then to the other about longitudinal axis (Fig. 35). Rolling can be caused and magnified by a number of influences, mainly wave action normally accompanied by aerodynamic excitation. Figure 36 illustrates an aerodynamically induced roll.

(2) **Pitching.** This is the periodic motion of a boat which buries the bow and then causes it to lift about the transverse axis marked (see Figs 35 and 37). It is characteristic of some sailing boats that, when closehauled in a headsea, they tend to develop a sustained oscillation in pitch which may effectively stop all headway; such a yacht may be referred to as 'pitching twice in the same hole'. Figure 37 depicts the heavy pitching motion which usually takes place if the natural pitching frequency of the boat is nearly the same as the frequency of the wave system.

(3) **Yawing.** Lurching or swinging to either side of the course is the tendency for a boat to veer off the desired course. If rhythmic yawing is aggravated by poor steering it may end in a violent broach, involving a rapid swing into wind. A sailing boat is inherently directionally unstable about the vertical axis (see Figs 35 and 38B), because she has no inbuilt stabilising

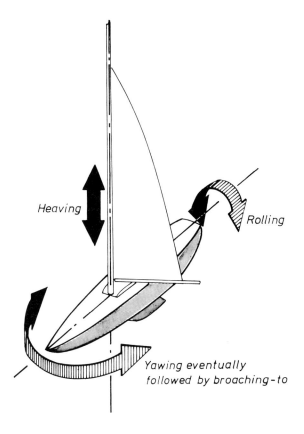

Heaving

Rolling

Yawing eventually
followed by broaching-to

Fig. 35. Rolling, Heaving and Yawing Motions.
*Cruising men expect that a well-designed boat should
be seakindly in these most important motions, with
accelerations as low as possible and stresses on both
structure and crew correspondingly minimal. In general,
increase in boat size (displacement) improves seakindliness and seaworthiness.*

properties tending to damp out yawing automatically. If course stability is desired, it has to be provided through the use of automatic steering (electrically operated and compass-related), or by means of a vane gear (wind operated and related to wind direction); either of these will keep a steady course without 'hunting' and thereby relieve the helmsman of much tedious watchfulness in reasonable conditions, but such aids do not have the power nor, indeed, the ability to anticipate, which are required to prevent or control a broach. Figure 39 illustrates an aerodynamically induced yaw, aggravated by poor rudder control, leading to a broach.

(4) **Surging or surfing.** This is the tendency of a boat sailing downwind to accelerate on the face of a wave and decelerate on the back of the wave and in the trough (Fig. 38A). These alternating accelerations and decelerations are due to the action of the orbital current (U_o) in different parts of the wave, and are augmented by a gravity force component (F_d) due to the boat's weight (W) so that $F_d = W \sin \alpha$ where α = steepness of the wave in degrees. The resultant speed over the sea bottom of a surfing boat is therefore composed of a speed (V_s) which would be attained for the course sailed and wind strength, plus the effect of the orbital velocity (U_o) and (F_d). With a wide, hard-bilge stern and slim bow (with low

Fig. 36. *Two consecutive pictures of the same boat rolling due to aerodynamically induced self-excitation. Such unseaworthy behaviour is more the rule than the exception with contemporary racers of the type marked* B *in Fig. 7. Self-excited rolling requires a source of energy (wind), and also some physical process for extracting that energy and converting it into a rolling motion.*

Fig. 37. *If resonant conditions occur, pitching may become violent, and the boat may even 'plunge twice in the same hole'. This can happen when oscillation is reinforced by a succession of waves, not necessarily of large amplitude, but having a frequency of encounter which matches the natural period of pitching of the boat. The common practice in dealing with this, is for the helmsman to bear away from the wind to keep the sails full and the boat moving. This may result in a considerable decrease in speed made good to windward, as compared with a boat which is not so prone to pitching (and thus does not need to bear away so much).* Practical Boat Owner

buoyancy reserve) there is a danger of digging the bow into the back of the wave ahead when running before wind and sea. If this happens in high breaking seas, the stern may be lifted so high that pitch-poling may follow, even if the boat is running under bare poles. Figure 40 illustrates a catamaran burying her bow when driven hard.

(5) **Swaying and Drifting** shown in Fig. 38C is an oscillatory form of sidling in which the boat moves bodily alternately to port and starboard of a mean heading. Usually, a boat making no headway will tend to set herself roughly broad-side on to a swell. The wind forces operating on the boat's superstructure will affect her attitude relative to the wind and wave crest, and cause her to drift to leeward with the hull centreline lying at an angle to the direction of drift (depending upon her configuration and the forces and moments acting upon her). It involves, therefore, a combination of advancing (or backing) and sidling. This is usually an uncontrolled or involuntary motion, when a boat is completely disabled in a storm at sea. The drift can, however, be controlled to a certain extent by applying the so-called heave-to or lie-to routine, whereby the trysail is sheeted fairly close, the storm jib kept aback, and the tiller lashed to leeward. In such a situation the boat fore-reaches at about quarter of a knot (although she may drift considerably), but lies relatively comfortably when riding out a storm.

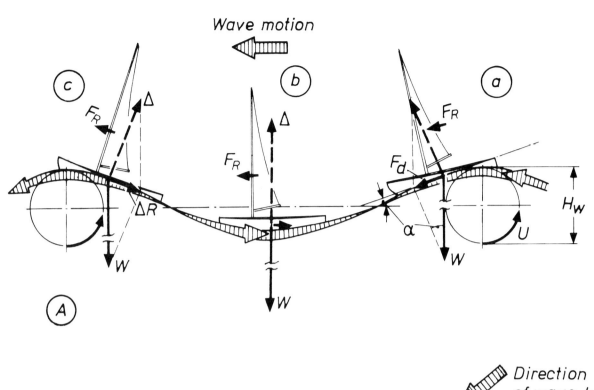

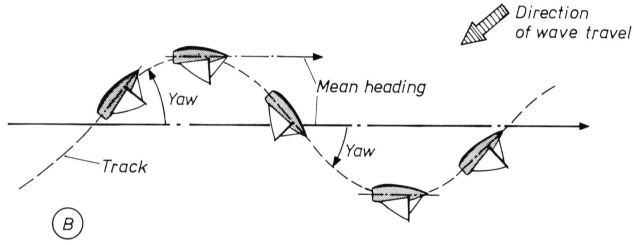

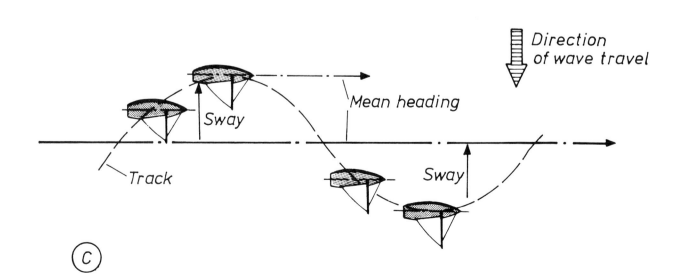

Fig. 38. *(A)* Surging. *A side view of a boat running down wind in following seas. The mass of water in the crest of a wave moves forward in the direction of swell (position a and c in sketch (A) see also Fig. 90) and backward in the trough (position b). Therefore a boat heading into a swell, or running before following seas of similar wave dimensions, will not proceed at uniform speed, but will be subjected to a periodic acceleration and deceleration as she rides over the crests and troughs. Because of water resistance, there will be a phase lag in time between her period of surge and period of encounter with waves. Thus, the boat will be alternately accelerated and retarded out of phase with the waves, and she will tend to bury her bow in the wave crest. If the boat displacement (mass) is small, her forward momentum (mass × speed) will also be small and consequently the changes in speed during each surge will become noticeable. Surging backward and forward is also affected by the action of wave slope thrust and drag. The wave slope is measured by the angle α; the greater the α the more rapid the surging. As compared with sail propulsive force, F_R, the driving component, F_d, due to boat weight, W, can, on a wave slope α = 20°, be a more substantial proportion of the boat's thrust – it may temporarily be in the order of ten* times greater than the aerodynamic driving force F_R, without incurring heavy loads on the rig. Free running tests on radio controlled models in waves, indicate that a long keel model is much easier to hold on course than a model with a high aspect ratio fin-keel once established with her stern to the wave crest, the *heavier displacement boat seemed to be at an advantage in gathering speed during the slide down the wave face.*

(B) Yawing (Bird's Eye View). *When travelling obliquely to the wave crests (bow or quartering seas) the boat yaws alternatively to port and starboard of the mean desired course. In rough seas, wave action may overpower all control that can be exercised by the most careful helmsman. Subsequently, the boat may swing broadside to the seas, with her longitudinal axis parallel to the crests (broaching) and capsize.*

(C) Swaying (Bird's Eye View). *In its pure form, swaying is an oscillatory motion in which the boat moves alternately to port and starboard of a mean heading.*

In a seaway, the motions a, b and c discussed above, together with rolling, heaving and pitching (Figs 39, 41 and 43) are almost invariably superimposed and unsteady in character, changing with time from one instant to the next.

Fig. 39. *Aerodynamically induced rolling leading to complete loss of rudder power, rapid yaw, and broaching; note that the whole of the rudder comes out of the water. Contemporary, beamy, shallow-bodied* boats with a pinched bow, and built to the current rating rule (IOR), are susceptible to such complete loss of steering ability.

Fig. 40. *(A) A fast catamaran in rough seas. The 'bow burying', with imminent possibility of being pitch-poled (see Fig. 40(B)), is a danger for all kinds of sailing craft, not only hard driven catamarans. Boats sailed down by the head are in acute danger that the stern may* *be lifted by an overtaking wave, so that the vessel is carried athwart and rolled over by the sea.*
(B) A catamaran flips right over. Such a danger cannot be entirely attributed to the design of the boat; it can only be met by reducing speed. Beken.

(6) **Heaving.** This is the vertical bodily movement of the whole boat upwards and downwards about the average still water level (Figs 35 and 41A and B). If the boat is heaving and rolling simultaneously, a peculiar coupling effect occurs which eventually leads to rapid magnification of rolling and, ultimately, to capsize. The influence which the heaving motion has upon the instantaneous righting moment of a boat rolling in waves was fully recognised by W. Froude some hundred years ago. Oddly enough, this effect has since been neglected, although the well-known phenomenon of a sailing boat unexpectedly capsizing on the crest of even long smooth-topped waves may be cited in support of the need to take this motion into account in seaworthiness or safety considerations.

When a boat is sailing in rough seas all six of these motions, and their coupling effects, are imposed on the hull in addition to forward movement, although not all to a like degree. Apart from the effect on speed, each of these movements may lead to damage or even cause the vessel to founder. Moreover, and perhaps most importantly, all those unsteady motions affect the mental and physical performance of the crew, and thus their chances of survival in storm conditions.

A. Effect of motion on crew performance

The designer's problem resolves itself into deciding the order of importance of the six motions upon seaworthiness, seakindliness and speed, and in giving proper weight or priority to different features of the design of the boat's form. The principal concern is usually limited to only three of these motions, namely: rolling, pitching and yawing (broaching) which are the most objectionable and may lead to damage or even sinking of the boat in heavy weather.

Experience has shown that when a boat is pitching, heaving or rolling, the ability of the crew to perform its function efficiently may be seriously impaired. Studies carried out aboard the USS *Glover*[38] suggest that the knowledge of human responses to ship motion is approaching the point where it may be used to indicate, in quantitative terms, the probable deterioration of crew performance. Much of the research that has been reported so far has been concerned with *motion sickness* caused by the accelerations and rolling. It appears that there is a close relationship between the mental and physical effectiveness of the crew and the magnitude and frequency of experienced accelerations. These constitute the principal stimuli to motion sickness operating through receptor organs in the semi-circular canals and utricules of the human inner ear (vestibular system) which are known to be accelerometers independently sensitive to both linear and angular accelerations.[39] It is well known that the most disturbing movement of a ship is the corkscrew or 'wobble'; a combination of ascending (vertical accelerations) with pitching and rolling, usually called 'labouring', i.e. angular and linear accelerations combined.

The effect of rolling on crew capabilities is shown in Fig. 42A. It shows broadly three regions of human reaction for various amounts of roll angle, measured from the vertical, for a prolonged period of time. These are from 0 to about 6 degrees, then from 6 to approximately 10 degrees and more than 10 degrees. They correspond to ranges at which the crew may work at various rates of efficiency. It should be noted that a small amount of roll in the order of 4 degrees can be beneficial. That is probably why cradles and rocking-chairs were invented a long time ago.

In the region from 6 to about 10 degrees, rapidly increasing deterioration of crew performance is noticeable – progressing from some fatigue through the requirement for additional manpower to conduct a given task. At more than 10 degrees, normal functions such as eating, sleeping and movement around the ship deteriorate progressively from the difficult to the impossible; if the rolling angle exceeds 30 degrees, the crew may become totally incapacitated.

Fig. 41. *(A) A close-hauled Star class yacht heaving and pitching simultaneously in heavy seas. For reasons discussed in this book, a boat may suddenly be knocked down due to the coupling effect of both heaving and rolling.*
(B) Pure heaving is an oscillatory form of vertical lifting and dropping of the Centre of Gravity (G) about its average smooth-water position.

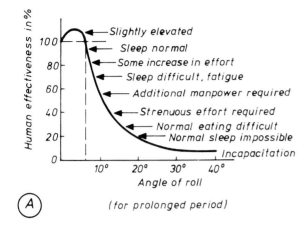

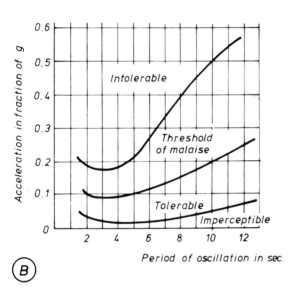

Fig. 42. *Effects of rolling and acceleration when pitching and heaving, on crew capability. A body on the earth's surface is pressed towards the centre of the earth by the pull of gravity force (force = mass × gravity acceleration (g); g = 32.2 ft/sec² = 9.8 m/sec²). It has been established that the maximum acceleration for fishing vessels in waves is in the neighbourhood of one g below or above the acceleration due to gravity g. This acceleration is thus about ten times larger than the value of g at which seasickness occurs (graph B). This gives some idea of the stresses to which fishermen (and yacht crews) are exposed in the pursuit of their occupation. It has been frequently observed that it is not the boat which wins races; it is the people who sail her. If boat motion becomes unbearable, the crew won't sail her to best advantage; they won't win races and, when the worst comes to the worst, the chances of survival can be seriously impaired. Habitability is more than the available space below deck.*

Acceleration

The effect of accelerations experienced by the crew on motion sickness is shown in Fig. 42B. Before the significance of this figure can be properly appreciated, a few words about acceleration in general may be appropriate. Maximum acceleration can easily be felt at the end points of the motion. Thus, for instance, a feeling of acceleration or deceleration is commonly experienced in a lift, swing or motorcar when motion begins, ends or is reversed. Any change in velocity of a moving object involves an acceleration which can simply be defined as the rate of change in velocity (retardation or deceleration is a negative acceleration). These sporadically experienced accelerations are usually relatively small, as compared with the so-called gravity acceleration (g = 32.2 ft/sec²) whose effect holds us firmly attached to Mother Earth. If change in motion velocity is rapid, accelerations must be large. Although accelerations experienced by sailing people in rough weather are not as large as those suffered by astronauts leaving the launching pad at the beginning of their journey into space, they can be sufficiently frequent to affect the ability of a man to perform his crew duty efficiently.

Now let us examine an expression which allows us to calculate the accelerations that may occur, say, on a pitching boat. That which applies to pitching holds true in general terms with other kinds of acceleration or deceleration experienced when the boat is rolling or heaving.

There are three quantities which determine the maximum acceleration in any angular simple harmonic oscillation. Referring to pitching (Fig. 43) these are:

r = distance of the object (be it man or anchor) from the axis of pitching, assumed to be through the Centre of Gravity, G.

φ = maximum inclination (angle expressed in radians) reached by the pitching boat, measured on one side of the horizontal. If φ is given in degrees, then the measure in radians can be obtained by dividing φ by

57.3, i.e. $\phi_{rad} = \dfrac{\phi \text{ degrees}}{57.3}$

Fig. 43. Pitching in Bow Waves. *Pitching accelerations (ap) experienced by the crew at different pitching periods (T_p) are given in the table below (see also Fig. 41(A)).*

It is assumed that the crew is about 12 ft (4 m) from the Centre of Gravity (G), and that the maximum bow emergence in relation to mean water level is about 20 degrees. Also shown is the ratio of pitching acceleration to that of gravity $\left(\dfrac{ap}{g}\right)$.

Table 1

T_p(sec)	2	3	4	5	6	7	8	in sec
ap	41.3	18.3	10.3	6.6	4.6	3.4	2.6	ft/sec²
$\dfrac{ap}{g}$	1.28	0.57	0.32	0.2	0.14	0.11	0.08	

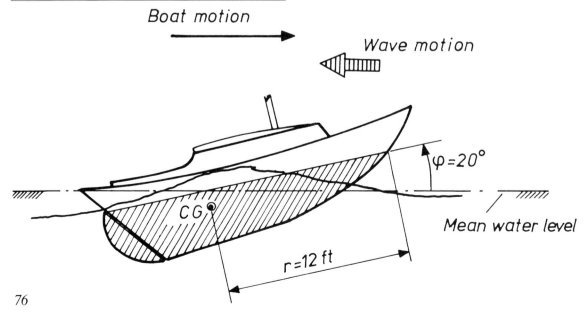

T_p = period of pitching in seconds.
Maximum pitching acceleration (a_p) can be estimated from the expression:

$$a_p = \left(\frac{2\pi}{T_p}\right)^2 r\, \phi_{(rad)} \tag{13}$$

Example: calculate the vertical pitching acceleration experienced by a man who works on the foredeck, some 12 ft from the pitching axis; the boat is pitching to a maximum angle φ of 20 degrees and the pitching period is assumed to be T_p = 4 sec.

$$a_p = \left(\frac{2\pi}{4}\right)^2 12\frac{20}{57.3} = 10.37 \text{ ft/sec}^2$$

Calculated pitching acceleration (a_p) can conveniently be expressed in terms of the gravity acceleration g = 32.2 ft/sec^2 as its fraction:

$$\frac{a_p}{g} = \frac{10.37}{32.2} = 0.32 \text{ g}$$

Along the vertical axis in Fig. 42B there are written the values of actual acceleration expressed as a fraction of gravity acceleration (g). It is seen that our calculated a_p = 0.32 g, for the assumed period of pitching T_p = 4 sec, is well inside the *intolerable* acceleration zone. For a given T_p the threshold of malaise caused by prolonged acceleration is only about 0.1 g.

Of course, a crew sporadically changing sails under intolerable pitching conditions at the bow, possibly aggravated by other types of acceleration due to say, simultaneous heaving and/or rolling, may perform its duty to full satisfaction. But under prolonged stress, due to the effects of unsteady motion shown in Fig. 42A and B aggravated by fatigue and cold, the time may come when crew and boat safety may entirely depend upon heroes – if, hopefully, there are any such amongst the crew.

As seen in Fig. 42B, the region where the periods of oscillation are 3–4 seconds, shows the minimum level of tolerance. A little reflection on formula 13 will suffice to show that the magnitude of pitching acceleration depends principally on the period of pitching (T_p), the shorter the period, the greater the acceleration. For example, Table 1 in Fig. 43 shows the acceleration (a_p) calculated for a number of periods in terms of g $\left(\frac{a_p}{g}\right)$, assuming that the other conditions of Fig. 43 are the same as those in the worked example above, i.e. the distance of object from axis r = 12 ft and inclination angle φ = 20 degrees.

When forces or moments due to the action of waves are applied to a boat, approximately in phase with any type of oscillatory motion (the first three of the six violent motions listed at the start of this chapter), the successive amplitudes of motion may increase progressively by a process known as *resonant magnification*. A necessary condition for resonance to occur is that alternating forces or moments are applied in the same direction as the velocity of motion, and generally in phase with it; so as to add to the energy of each successive roll or pitch, in a manner similar to that of a child's swing. Each time the swing is going towards the vertical position, a person on the ground pushes the swing, thus supplying an impulse (energy) in the direction of motion. If the swing is excited in this fashion the amplitude may grow progressively. In the case of a boat pitching in waves this happens if the period of encounter is roughly that of the boat's natural period (T_p). The amplitude of motion then increases more or less rapidly, until the energy dissipated by damping equals the exciting energy. If the energy added by the wave train continues to exceed the energy removed by damping, the boat will roll or pitch deeper and deeper with proportionally increasing accelerations. The shorter the natural period of pitching, the shorter are the waves in which resonant pitching with high accelerations is likely to occur. Barnaby[37] gives the natural period of pitching (T_p) for various types of ship varying from $0.22\sqrt{L}$ to $0.50\sqrt{L}$ (where L is the length of ship in feet), on the basis that the period (T_p) bears a certain relation to the length (size) for most ships. Because a large proportion of the moment of inertia in pitch (as well as in roll) of a sailing boat is due to the mast, sails and rigging (amounting to about 40% of the longitudinal moment of inertia, and about 60% of the roll moment of inertia), it appears that the approximate natural period of pitch for a yacht can be assumed $T_p = 0.4 - 0.5$ L ft, with the coefficient 0.4 for light and 0.5 for heavy displacement boats. Thus, larger boats are relatively immune from excessive motions and objectionable accelerations likely to be developed in synchronism with short waves. In longer waves their motion may also be large but it is usually slow (because of the greater periods of those waves), hence the accelerations suffered by the crew will be relatively much less exhausting.

Size of the boat, habitability

So far, no attempt has been made to determine the order of importance of the six motions which we postulated at the outset as regards seakindliness and seaworthiness, or giving weight to different features of the design of the boat's form. The main purpose was to draw attention to the perhaps undermined effects of acceleration on crew morale and the relation between size of boat and her motion.

One does not have to be at sea very long to convince oneself that the elements and the size of the boat are intimately related to each other in the sense that, other things being equal, the sea is less kind to smaller boats. And the key factor of seakindliness is the high acceleration to which the small boat is subjected in a rough sea. This leads us to the problem of *habitability* – a design feature to which much lip-service is paid. We might agree that, in broad terms, habitability is concerned with providing the crew with an environment that permits them to function effectively – without degrading their performance because the forces of a hostile sea are not rendered kind to the crew.

In conjunction with the influence of the current rating rule, there has been a steady demand for commodious boats having full standing headroom and

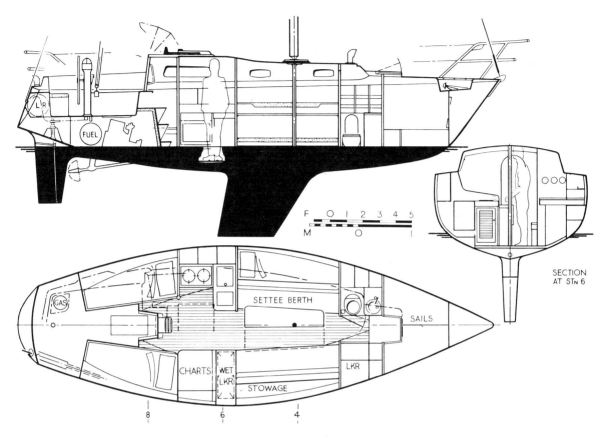

Fig. 44. *A 1975 design competition winner, with an LOA of some 30 ft. Yachts built between the two World Wars had a depth of hull under water about two and a half times that which was above, whereas the reverse is true in most modern designs. Change in yacht design philosophy, encouraged by the International Offshore Rule, started a cascade of aberrations which has paved the way towards unseaworthy boats and the 1979 Fastnet disaster.*

something close to a flush deck whatever their overall length. Figure 44 shows such a specimen – the product on the one hand of pressure of the rating rule, and on the other of demand by a misguided public open to the market cheaply offering large volumetric capacity within a small hull. The use of fibreglass has introduced a freedom of shape, not normally possible in other materials, and this together with an inherent economic inducement towards mass production, has facilitated evolution of the kind of hull shape depicted in Fig. 44.

As compared with other types of boat which retained some relationship to working boats of the past (see Figs 16A–C and 31), contemporary buoyant yachts stand with their freeboards well above water. In the past there was about two or sometimes two-and-a-half times the depth of hull under the water that there was above, whereas the reverse is true in contemporary designs. These relatively small modern, fat, buoyant bath-tube like boats, called cruiser-racers – bobbing about on the water surface, and exposed to the full fury of the sea which manifests itself most intensively at its surface – are vulnerable in rough seas. The periods of all oscillatory motions of these boats when rolling, pitching and heaving are inevitably short and, thus, accelerations are high. Such boats can be habitable and even comfortable in static, marina conditions, but are bound to become uninhabitable in even moderate weather. Bearing in mind that the human element plays a prominent part in seaworthiness, i.e. the way in which a boat is handled may be as important as her design, it is evident in the light of Fig. 42A and B that habitability has more to it than the available headroom and the volumetric capacity within the hull.

The problem of habitability and seaworthiness is tied up with yet another aspect of safety at sea: *watertight integrity*. To quote from one of the yachting magazines: 'Interest in unsinkable boats seems to be world-wide. That should not be surprising, since anyone who goes to sea would prefer not to have his boat sink under him if it were avoidable'. Very true, indeed!

The term *vessel* was derived from the Latin *vas, vascellum*, which means either a container holding water *in*, or any craft (boat) which keeps the water *out*. Thus, a vessel which leaks is useless in either of its semantic meanings. Incidentally, there is yet a third, biblical, meaning of the word vessel – that is a woman.

Sailing has been described as one-third euphoria, one-third boredom and one-third abject terror. Even the most experienced sailors have admitted that fear that the boat might sink has never been foreign to them. A hundred days out from Plymouth in *Gipsy Moth IV* Sir Francis Chichester reported: 'I was coming up from Gabo Island off the Australian coast. It was a fine day with a steady breeze and moderate seas. I was repairing the navigation light on the stern which should be nearly five feet above waterline. Suddenly the light appeared to be about eighteen inches above the sea. I looked aft: the stern also appeared to be nearly under water. She seemed to be sinking, nearly awash . . . I ran below to check how deep she was flooded. The bilge was completely dry!'

B. The 1979 Fastnet Race lesson

Whether the kind of vision or hallucination experienced by Sir Francis is a result of yacht motion and associated accelerations, or some other kind of mental stress suffered by lonely sailors, cannot be answered for sure. The most strange fact is that, in the severe weather conditions experienced during the 1979 Fastnet Race, a large number of crews of smaller boats in classes III, IV and V (rating limits 21.0–28.9 feet), inherently more vulnerable to high accelerations, hastily abandoned their boats although there was no immediate danger of sinking. Full confidence was placed rather in the life raft as a means of survival, than in the old adage – 'stay with your boat'; an adage reflecting the dearly paid experience of a past generation that, even a damaged yacht (but intact in terms of watertight integrity), is a safer place than a life raft.

As a result, seven lives were lost from three life rafts, and in each case the yacht did not sink and was subsequently recovered, of the 24 abandoned yachts only five have not been recovered and one of these five sank under tow. Table 2 shows some of the results in each of the six classes into which the fleet of 303 yachts was divided by rating bands.[4]

Table 2

Class	Rating limits ft	Started	Finished	Retired	No of crew lost	Yacht abandoned recovered	lost
0	42.1–70.0	14	13	1	—	—	—
I	33.0–42.0	56	36	19	—	1	—
II	29.0–32.9	53	23	30	—	—	—
III	25.5–28.9	64	6	52	6	4	2
IV	23.0–25.4	58	6	44	6	7	1
V	21.0–22.9	58	1	48	3	7	2
Total		303	85	194	15	19	5

Note: 136 crewmembers were rescued by outside agencies: helicopters, lifeboats etc.

It should perhaps be remembered that the rating given in Table 2 is a measure of the *effective* sailing length of the boat and not of her actual size, which is larger. The minimum size of boat which might qualify for entry is about 28 ft length and the maximum about 85 ft.

Does the Fastnet Report justify an expectation that definite lessons have been learned from this harsh experience so that a recurrence can hopefully be averted? Some sailing magazines referring to the 1979 Fastnet Report, which followed three months' investigation into all aspects of the Force 10 to 11 storm, have complained that: 'Because . . . a massive survey of nearly 700 owners and crew (235 boats) and countless hours of research and analysis went into preparation of this report, a reader expects to find some clear cut answers. *There are none.* We are reminded instead that accidents and death at sea, like accidents and death everywhere, seldom have a single cause.'[40]

Trial and error is a hard way of gaining experience or knowledge; and errors which lead to catastrophe of the 1979 Fastnet calibre are expensive. Catastrophe, however, if properly analysed through conscious searches for causes or for errors made, may help people to come to their senses so that recurrence can be avoided.

The hackneyed truth is that in order to see and learn one must first look attentively. In successful scientific inquiries this process of 'looking', in the form of deliberate and preferential observation which may ultimately lead to knowledge, is what Sir Karl Popper has called 'theory-impregnated'.[41] In a nutshell, the way in which knowledge progresses – and especially our scientific knowledge – is by guesses, by tentative solutions to our problems or the danger we face, by conjectures, and finally by hypotheses which may turn out to be theories of high predictive power. These hypotheses are controlled by criticism, that is, by attempted refutations which, of course, include severely critical tests. An encouragement to the refutation attempt of any suggested theory or concept characterises the empirical scientific method of enquiry. To quote Popper again: 'Its aim is not to save the lives of untenable theories but, on the contrary, to select the one which is by comparison the fittest, by exposing them all to the fiercest struggle for survival.'

A fortunate aspect of any scientifically conducted enquiry is that it is easier to deal with rationally derived statements, based on solid experimental data and correspondence of theory to the facts, than with personal opinions which not infrequently are of an emotional or political character, or which simply reflect one's vested interest. Thus, it is a fundamental duty of the responsible enquirer, be he scientist or even yacht designer, to make sincere effort to refute his concept or theory – by exposing its weak points, deficiencies or limits of validity – before it is presented as a credible claim. Otherwise, his critics or fellow professionals must do it for him, no matter how ruthless and disappointing such criticism may appear. Only on this condition of an *open critical examination* of our theories, judgments and concepts can science flourish, and so genuine progress be made. In this respect, there is an essential difference between the ethics of a scientist and those of a salesman. We all have our philosophies or theories, we hold them unconsciously or take them for granted and apply them to facts in an attempt to understand why certain things happen, although many of these theories are almost certain to be only partly correct or perhaps even altogether false. The impact of theories we hold concerning our actions and our lives may be, and often is, devastating. This makes it imperative to try to correct and improve our philosophies and theories by creative criticism.

These few general remarks about some aspects of scientific inquiry have been written to give the reason *why* the author should be forgiven if his, perhaps somewhat uncomfortable, interpretation of the Fastnet facts ruffles some feathers.

Figure 45A and Table 3 show the occurrence of knockdowns to the horizontal identified in the Fastnet Report as B1 knockdowns, and also severe knockdowns beyond the horizontal (including a 360 degree roll) called B2 knockdowns and reported in different classes among 235 boats of which 233 constituted the sample base for analysis.

Table 3

Fastnet Class	Knockdown B1 Number	%	Abandoned Number	Knockdown B2 Number	%	Number of participants in each class
0	3	38	—	—	—	8
I	11	28	—	6	8	40
II	14	35	—	4	5	40
III	28	54	6	24	31	52
IV	25	54	8	20	26	46
V	30	64	8	22	29	47
Total	111		22	76		233

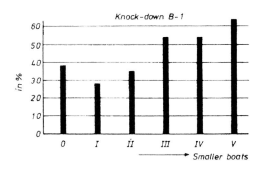

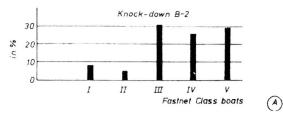

Fig. 45. *(A)* Fastnet 1979. *Percentage of B.1 and B.2 knock downs reported in each class. Table 2 gives the rating limits for classes 1–5.*
(B) Percentage of boats abandoned or retired from the race. Data are based on a sample of 233 boats which were exposed to the storm.

Since the rather horrifying Fastnet of 1979 we read about the 1984 Sydney–Hobart debacle where 106 boats out of 152 starters retired for reasons given in the table below:

Reason	*Number of boats*
Rig failure	26
Hull damage	16
Steering damage	4
Sail damage	13
Seasickness, fatigue, injury	19
Seamanship (prudence)	18
Electric failure	8
Other	2

According to the Official Hobart Inquiry conducted by the Cruising Yacht Club of Australia, the heavier boats fared better than the lighter ones. Search for lighter construction within the hull and the rig leaves less margins for safety, which might otherwise compensate for errors in construction.

In the 1985 Fastnet Race during which westerly winds were mainly in the region of force six to eight and only occasionally as strong as nine, well over half the participating boats retired.

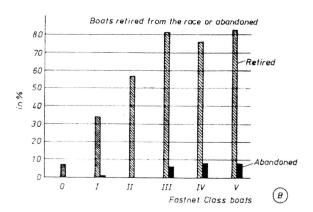

Figure 46 demonstrates the B2 knockdown as interpreted by the cartoonist. Figure 45A supplements Table 3 and Fig. 45B indicates the number of boats which retired from the race or were abandoned.

It has been alleged that, in their quest for faster boats, designers have gone to extremes (permitted or/and encouraged by the rule). These excesses surpass the bounds of common sense, and ignore constraints which should be imposed by the requirement for offshore racing yachts to be able to cope with weather conditions which they might be expected to encounter. In particular, small light

Fig. 46. *'It might be only a B2 knock down to you but it's a bloody capsize to me.'* (Peyton)

displacement, broad-beam, shallow hull forms have been singled out as a target for criticism.

In the light of the Fastnet evidence presented in Tables 2 and 3 and in Figs 45A and B, are these allegations justified? It is seen that the occurrence of B1 and B2 knockdowns, the number of boats retired or abandoned and, finally, the number of crew members lost, are closely related to the size of boat. Forty-eight per cent of the fleet (111 boats) reported that on one or more occasions the yacht was knocked down to horizontal during the storm. However, the smaller boats in classes III–V were much more vulnerable – 74% of them reported B1 knockdowns. The more severe B2 knockdown was reported by 77 boats, but 66 of them, i.e. 86%, were again in the small classes III–V. One hundred and ninety-four boats retired from the race, but 144, i.e. 74%, belonged to the smaller classes, not including 23 of the total 24 boats abandoned; all 15 men lost were crewmembers of those vulnerable classes. As indicated in Fig. 45A and B, B2 knockdowns, the number of retirements and abandoned boats, all have a clear diminishing tendency as the size of the boat increases.

In the face of these facts there is one unquestionable conclusion which cannot possibly be concealed: the Fastnet storm was catastrophic to small boats. It appears that classes III–V were so unseakindly in the Fastnet storm conditions that expert handling (tacitly assumed to be equally distributed amongst all participants, regardless of boat class) was in these small classes no longer available. Apparently, there is indeed a certain limit of violent tumultuous sea motion and accelerations beyond which all, or almost all, human beings become mentally and physically incapacitated. In such conditions when extreme fatigue sets in it is unlikely that cool-headed rational decisions can be taken. Instead, a blind biological instinct – an overwhelming irrational desire to run away from a dangerous environment, to reach an escape route to survival, dictated by some kind of strategy of genes – may take over.

The question is: do these smallest, III–V Fastnet classes, deserve their status of *ocean cruiser-racers*, or should the lower limit of eligibility be raised? The unheralded verdict delivered by Nature herself and by common sense is rather straightforward. Unfortunately this verdict is at variance with the conclusions and recommendations of the Fastnest Report. Let us quote again those most relevant to the subject matter.

'Knockdowns to horizontal' (referred to in Table 3) 'have always been a potential danger in cruising and offshore racing yachts in heavy seas; *therefore no attempt has been made to analyse the causes or effects*' (italics are mine). This logically circular argument makes curious reading in view of evident, and disturbing, correlation between certain design characteristics and the vulnerability of some types of boats to severe knockdowns.

The Report recognises that according to a consensus 'it was the severity of the conditions rather than any defect in the design of the boats which was the prime consideration.' In this context it should perhaps be remembered that 'the race marked the first wholesale failure of one of the cornerstones upon which amateur offshore racing is built . . . the ability of the yachtsmen to cope *unaided* with the weather as it comes'.[42] 'No one' – to quote from reference 40 – 'can accuse the committee of impartiality. It never reaches out far enough.' Its recommendations were, rather, of secondary importance: up-dating life raft requirements, more attention to be paid to companionway closure and cockpit drainage arrangements, and that owners should pay more attention to safety harness requirements. There are also other recommendations concerning crew/skipper experience, race managements, storm sails, life jackets, to mention a few, but they lack any bite. For example, despite an alarming number of separated rudder failures, the committee was content to note that 'there are grounds for concern', and that 'designers are analysing the cause.'

The closing sentence of the Report is as follows: 'The Fastnet is a supreme challenge to ocean racing yachtsmen in British waters. In the 1979 race the sea showed that it can be a deadly enemy and that those who go to sea for pleasure must do so in the full knowledge that they may encounter dangers of the highest order. However, provided that the lessons so harshly taught in this race are well learned we feel that yachts should continue to race the Fastnet course'.

Precisely! But then what? The information given in the Report is extremely comprehensive. From these reasonably reliable facts, unmistakable hints and clues emerge. And from them lessons can be drawn and decision taken. We have a chance which, it is profoundly to be hoped will never arise again, to learn from this worst yachting disaster of all times. Unfortunately, the authors of the Report have shrunk back from demanding definite action. An unforgivable lapse, or one to be lightly taken?

The author believes that seaworthiness and seakindliness begin in the minds of rule makers and thence yacht designers. Although no one can design a sailing boat which is totally immune from violent motions, the severity of hull response can be mitigated before the boat is launched. Naturally, the probability that a small boat will encounter capsizing waves is much greater than the probability that a supertanker would. The Fastnet statistics have clearly indicated that the size of a boat is, beyond any doubt, an important design factor in a survival situation. But not the only one. Experience has shown that the hull form, together with its displacement and weight distribution, is also crucial. Boats similar in size but different in hull shape may vary considerably in their behaviour in the same heavy sea conditions. The Fastnet Report findings, and other tragic although less conspicuous disasters reported since, appear to amount to a devastating indictment of the contemporary ocean racer, as we have come to know it over the last decade or so. However, such a common sense, not to say logical, conclusion has been rejected by the *dominant minority* of the sailing fraternity, who blamed the weather rather than any defect in the design of the boats.

The very essence of human predicament is the split between reason and belief – the first is controlled by the rational mind, the second is governed by emotions and ideologies. Belief tends to distort reality via interpretation by frequently aggressive dominant minorities, into something acceptable to them. This is not to say that such people are self-consciously deceptive. They simply propagate belief, or rather perverted logic, which they may not themselves hold self-critically. From historical evidence we know that aberrant ideas serve well enough to give our actions justifying motives; the homicide committed for selfish, personal motives is a statistical rarity, as compared with the number of people allowed to be killed for unselfish irrational reasons in the name of a belief.

As mentioned earlier, the issue of seaworthiness and safety is unlikely to be resolved through opinion polls, which usually measure the degree of human irrationality at particular moments. The only promising path is through sensible logical analysis of the dynamic aspects of boat behaviour in heavy seas in order to:

(1) establish the primary factors in hull designs which control the boat's motion in rough water, and
(2) provide irrefutable evidence, supported when necessary by experiment,

why and on what conditions a certain type of boat has better chances of survival than another.

This is the object of the following chapters.

'One thing which stands out very clearly in my mind is that, in spite of the fact that man has been building ships for thousands of years, it is still necessary to think and talk in terms of main issues only, if we are going to advance our understanding and knowledge of seagoing qualities in any important respect.'

Dr K.S.M. Davidson

5 Stability and its Effects on Safety

Of the three rotational and three translational motions of a boat in a seaway (Figs 35–41) the most important, affecting seakindliness and safety, is rolling. It is the motion which is most readily apparent and which usually has, apart from pitchpoling, the most serious effects. Rolling is related to the stability of a boat and whenever people begin to discuss seaworthiness, the first notion to come to mind is the hull shape and its *stability*. Usually, what is meant is transverse stability which, it is presupposed, resists rolling and ultimately prevents capsize.

If such an intuitive feeling is correct, if stability is a good thing, then more of the same would be even better. This apparently logical train of thought leads to the conclusion that what makes a boat seaworthy is simply large stability. Furthermore, some people believe that stability, as reflected by the so called metacentric height or righting lever, may be used directly as a measure of a boat's seaworthiness – a rather convenient measure because it can be easily quantified.

A. Hydrostatic stability

Although stability is one feature of primordial importance, its precise role in the context of seaworthiness is still ambiguous. But let us first be sure what we mean by the word. A freely floating hull in undisturbed water is acted upon by two resultant vertical forces (Fig. 47A). The upward force of buoyancy (Δ) (displacement) may be imagined as acting at one point called the centre of buoyancy (B). Similarly, the resultant of all the weights (W) can be envisaged

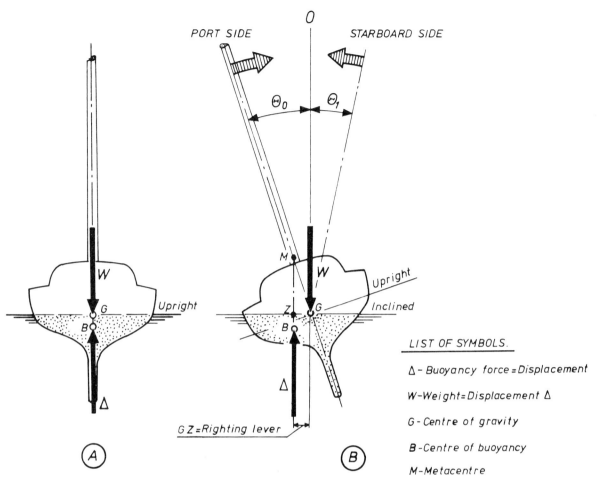

Fig. 47. *Definition of terms and forces operating in hydrostatic conditions.*

as a single force acting vertically downward through the centre of gravity (G). In the absence of other forces, such as those due to wind or waves, hull attitude is determined by the interaction of weight and buoyancy. The hull will settle in equilibrium to an upright position when the buoyancy force (Δ) balances the weight (W) and both forces act along the same straight line.

Figure 47B shows that when a hull is made to heel the centre of buoyancy (B) moves away athwartships from the centre of gravity (G) thus creating a righting moment which tends to bring the boat to equilibrium in an upright position. This amount of leeward shift of B relative to G (i.e. the magnitude of the righting lever GZ) can be regarded as a measure of the *hydrostatic stability* of the boat in question. If the shape of the hull and position of its centre of gravity are known, the righting lever variation with angle of heel can be established and presented in the form of a diagram (Fig. 48). A number of

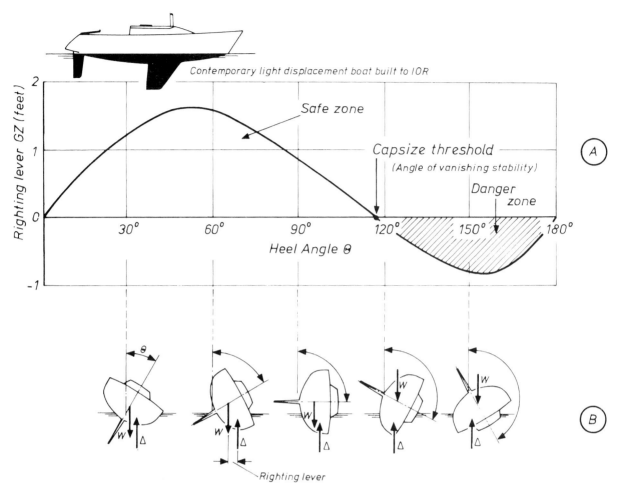

Fig. 48. *The hydrostatic stability curve of a contemporary light displacement boat built to the IOR. Note the area under the positive stability curve, indicated by an arrow 'safe zone', and compare it with the hatched area of negative stability indicated by an arrow* 'dangerous zone'. *The hydrostatic stability of any given boat depends primarily on her displacement (W), the position of metacentre (M) or metacentric height (GM), and the position of centre of gravity (G) in relation to the waterline (see Fig. 47).*

sketches drawn below the stability curve in Fig. 48 illustrate the position of relevant forces Δ and W at angles of heel 30, 60, 120 and 150 degrees.

If the stability curve is known, the magnitude of the righting moment and hence the power to carry sail can be calculated; all we need to know are the magnitude of the righting lever (GZ) at the given angle of heel, and the boat displacement (W) because right moment = GZ · W.

Figure 49 shows the static stability curves for two yachts which participated in the 1979 Fastnet Race. Three features of the stability curve are considered to be of particular significance:

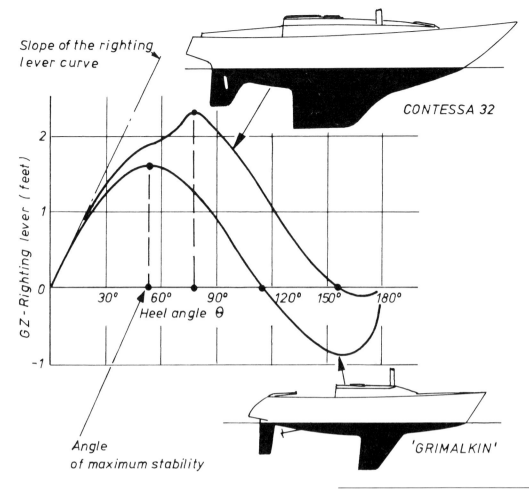

Fig. 49. *Hydrostatic stability curves for a* Contessa 32 *footer, and the Half-Tonner* Grimalkin *in still water; both boats participated in the 1979 Fastnet Race (data taken from the RYA-RORC Report). It is evident that these two boats, different in hull shape, displacement and position of the centre of gravity, have different stability characteristics; this is particularly true of their ranges of positive (safe) and negative (dangerous) stability (see also Fig. 48).*

	Contessa 32	*Half-Tonner*
Displacement (lbs)	10,112	8,320
Keel ballast (lbs)	4,468	1,790
Internal ballast (lbs)	—	1,100
Keel ballast ratio	44%	21%
Total ballast ratio	44%	34%
Draft (ft)	5.5	5.75
LWL (ft)	24.0	24.75
$\Delta/(0.01 \times LWL)^3$	326	245
CG position relative to DWL (ft)	−0.75	+0.65

(1) *The initial stability of the yacht.* At small angles of heel up to about 8–10 degrees, the stability of most yachts as given by the slope of the righting lever curve in Fig. 49, is similar. Beyond 10 degrees of heel, however, these two curves are clearly different. The *Contessa 32* is more stable than the *Grimalkin.*

(2) *The angle of heel (Θ) at which the righting lever curve reaches its maximum value.* Note that the *Contessa 32* has a greater maximum GZ value, largely

due to her low centre of gravity location and raised coach roof.

(3) *The heel angle of vanishing stability* or the capsize threshold (Fig. 48) at which positive stability disappears. Once a boat is heeled past this critical angle, she continues rolling until she is fully inverted. In other words, the boat acquires a negative stability and becomes stable in the *turned turtle* position. Her chances of quick recovery from the upside-down attitude will depend on the range of heel angles within which her stability is negative. Thus the *Contessa 32* would be less likely to remain in the inverted position than *Grimalkin*. She would need to be rolled out through a further 24 degrees in order to regain her upright stability, whereas *Grimalkin* needs to be rolled out through 63 degrees before she will come right side up again.

It can be seen in Fig. 50 that the magnitude of the righting lever at a given angle of heel is determined by the three characteristic centres. Initially, by the position of the centre of buoyancy (B), which in turn specifies the position of the so-called metacentre (M), and thereafter by the position of the centre of gravity (G), which is assumed (in hydrostatic stability calculations) to be a fixed point. As a matter of fact, the position of the centre of gravity may deliberately

Fig. 50. *Different hull forms produce different hydrostatic stability characteristics. In the case of hull A, the predominant source of stability is ballast, located well below the waterline (WL) in the keel. Note that the location of the centre of gravity of the hull, as measured by the distance G–WL, is below WL (pendulum stability). In the case of hull B, its main source of stability is the form of the hull (its width), resulting in a high position of metacentre (M), and hence a large MB factor; the location of the G of this hull, as measured by G–WL, is above the WL. These differences are reflected in the static stability curves (see also Figs 49, 51 and 52).*

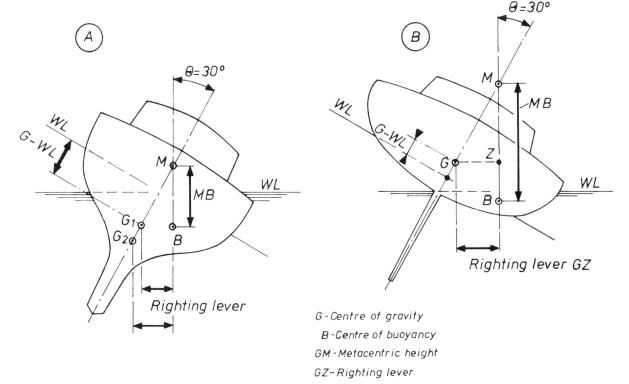

G - Centre of gravity

B - Centre of buoyancy

GM - Metacentric height

GZ - Righting lever

Distance MB - Form conditioned stability factor

Distance G-WL - Weight conditioned stability factor

be changed by the crew sitting out in an attempt to shift G to windward in order to increase the power of the boat to carry sails effectively. Ultimately, the magnitude of the righting lever (the distance GZ in Fig. 50B) can be determined if we know the metacentric height (GM) and the angle of heel (Θ):

$$\text{Righting lever (GZ)} = \text{GM sin } \Theta \qquad (14)$$

B. Stability due to form and due to ballast

'Every phenomenon affects and is affected by every other phenomenon. Any phenomenon which we choose to examine is to us conditioned by what we see and know. We exclude deliberately all other conditions. But Nature does not exclude them.'

T.A. Cook
'The Curves of Life', 1914

It is evident from Fig. 50A and B that the location of B depends exclusively on the shape of the hull section. For instance, by making the hull lighter and wider, the position of B can be shifted farther outwards from the centreline, thus increasing the distance BM, which can be regarded as a factor of *form stability*. With an upright hull, the righting lever is evidently zero. But at small inclinations of heel when the sailing conditions are not too severe, practically the only criterion of stability is the distance between M and B. This is shown in both sketches of Fig. 50 by thick vertical arrows.

It is also evident from Fig. 50A and B that boat stability largely depends on the location of the centre of gravity (G) in relation to the waterline level WL $-$ 0. With a greater proportion of weight concentrated below the waterline, the centre of gravity may be shifted from G_1 to G_2 (sketch A). Subsequently the righting lever (GZ), which is a direct measure of the boat's tendency to return to an upright position, is increased. Since the location of the centre of gravity (G) substantially affects the magnitude of the righting lever, the distance G $-$ WL can be regarded as a factor of *weight or ballast conditioned stability*, which may also be called the *pendulum stability*. Thus, the resulting hydrostatic stability of any boat is partly determined by *hull form*, and partly by *weight distribution* and boat's weight; however, one or another type of stability may predominate.

At relatively small angles of heel, up to about 25–30 degrees, form stability is the main factor which determines stiffness of the boat. Beyond 30 degrees of heel, weight-conditioned stability begins to play an increasingly dominant role. Figures 51 and 52 show qualitatively the effect of the cross-section of the hull, i.e. the influence of the beam to depth ratio (B/D), and the influence of the flare angle on initial stability. It is seen in Fig. 51 that the larger the B/D ratio, the higher is the metacentre (M) above the water surface, and the stiffer the boat within the range of small angles of heel. The flare angle effect (Fig. 52) is

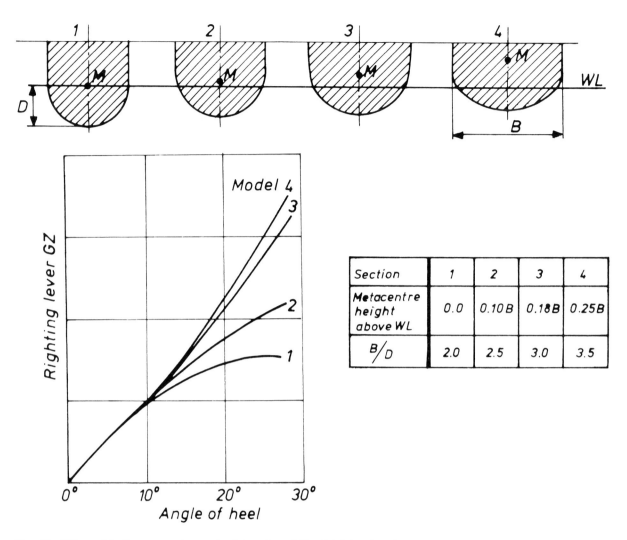

Fig. 51. *Effect of hull cross-section on initial static stability (righting lever).*

similar to that of the B/D ratio, i.e. the larger the flare angle the stiffer the boat. Thus, depending on the cross-sectional shape, beamy flat-bottom boats tend to be 'stiff as a church' (but only up to a certain angle of heel) and this may result in considerable rolling accelerations and hence discomfort in a seaway. While other boats with narrow, deep hulls of predominantly pendulum stability tend to be more sluggish in response to waves, and therefore more comfortable for the crew, particularly so in long run. This is just one aspect of the stability effect. There is also another aspect, more important from a safety point of view, namely: the stability range up to the upside down attitude (from 0 to 180 degrees of heel), much relevant to heavy weather conditions.

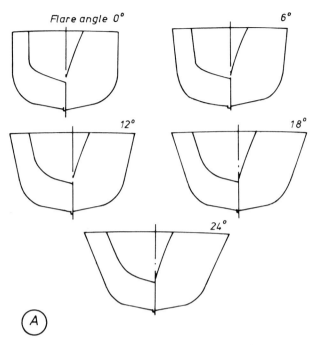

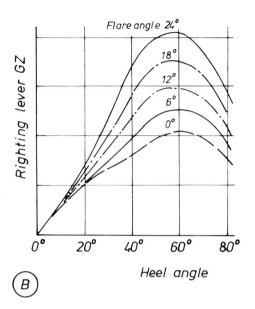

Fig. 52. *Effect of flare angle on initial hydrostatic stability of the hull, with five different cross-sections; sketch A shows hull forms with increasing flare. Position of the centre of gravity (G) was kept constant*

relative to the keel. *Although the hull form with greater flare angle has larger initial stability, it is likely to roll more heavily in rough seas than the wall-sided form.*

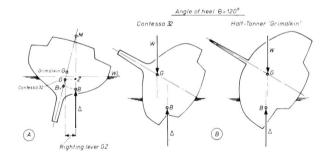

Fig. 53. *The effect of G position on the hydrostatic righting lever (GZ). Note that the centre of gravity of the* Contessa 32 *in sketch A is* below *waterline level, whereas that of* Grimalkin *is* above *(see also Fig. 54). Symbol B_v in sketch A stands for the position of the centre of buoyancy (B) vertically in the hull.*

As shown in Fig. 53A the metacentric height (GM) can be regarded as made up of two components: the distance between the vertical position of the centre of buoyancy (B) and the metacentre (M), and the distance between B and the centre of gravity (G). When considering whether a boat has a low or high position of G value, one must have some reference point to compare it with. The most useful reference is the centre of buoyancy (B), since it is the relative distance between B and G which provides the righting lever. Thus, the *Contessa 32* has a B − G value of 0.26 ft (which is below the water level WL);

whereas the Half Tonner *Grimalkin* has a B − G value of 1.32 ft (which is above the WL). Clearly, *Grimalkin* has a high G when compared with the *Contessa 32*. The consequence of opting for a high position of the centre of gravity may be seen in Figs 53B and 54A, in that as the angle of heel increases *Grimakin* has a lesser righting lever value (implying less stability) throughout its range up to 180 degrees.[43] This results in an early angle of maximum stability, an early capsize threshold (below 120 degrees) and an early departure into the region of negative stability (danger zone). In a similar situation (Fig. 53B) the *Contessa 32* still retains her positive stability. It is clearly better, from a safety standpoint, to have as low a practical G value as possible. Why then is quite the opposite fashionable nowadays?

Since the adoption of the International Offshore Rule there has been a steady trend towards making yachts beamier, with the centre of gravity (G) usually located above the waterline. Thus, their hydrostatic stability is mainly determined by the form stability of a wide, shallow hull section of type B in Fig. 50. In smaller, light displacement classes, where the ratio of crew weight to displacement is large, the resulting righting moment becomes sensitive to the position of the crew. The actual power to carry sails is greatly influenced by the number of docile bodies on the weather rail. For instance, with the whole crew sitting outboard the racing stability of a Quarter Tonner is boosted by about 30%. But for her bigger sister, the One Tonner, effective stability is increased only by about 15%; and for the yet bigger maxi-raters (Fig. 55), crew contribution to stability is a mere 3%–4%.

In the case of traditional, heavy displacement cruiser-racers, hydrostatic stability is largely conditioned by the weight (ballast) and position of G below the waterline. The IOR taxes low centre of gravity (stability due to weight). But the form stability, depending largely on the beam and volume of the hull above the water (not to mention the crew weight contribution to the righting moment shown in Figs 5 and 6) is not penalised by the rule. On the contrary, form stability has been encouraged by giving a rating allowance under the Centre of Gravity Factor (CGF) discussed in the next chapter.

Figures 54A, 55 and 56 demonstrate the hydrostatic stability curves of these two different types of boat. It can be seen that the *safe stability zone* of the contemporary type of yacht such as *Grimalkin* (Fig. 54A) ends when the angle of heel reaches about 115 to 118 degrees. Beyond this, the boat will capsize even in the absence of any external force, such as the effect of a wave, because her righting lever (GZ) becomes negative.

Another important point is that at about 60 degrees of heel, when the boat is rapidly losing her positive stability, the keel and rudder begin to emerge from the water, and the crew is losing control over subsequent events. Figure 57 illustrates such a situation and needs no further comment. Furthermore, when the keel is tilted over the rising water at the front of a wave, it will act as an additional lever to roll the boat.

Perhaps an even more alarming result of recent design trend is the broad range of the *danger zone*, the large range of negative stability (Fig. 54A) when, after capsize, the boat floats upside-down. The frightening aspect of this

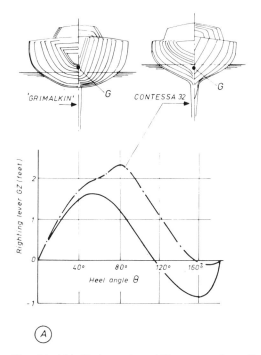

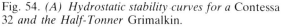

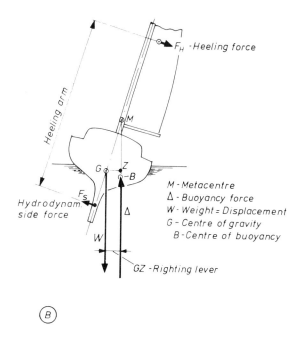

Fig. 54. *(A) Hydrostatic stability curves for a* Contessa 32 *and the Half-Tonner* Grimalkin.

(B) Forces operating in the heeled position, and symbols used (see also Figs 48–50).

situation is that, to regain positive stability, the boat must be heeled 63 degrees to either side, hopefully through the action of waves, before the positive righting lever begins to operate to bring her right side up.

The maxi-raters (i.e. the large, ultra-light displacement boats shown in Fig. 55) are no better in this respect. Some of them may reach the capsize threshold at smaller angles than given in Fig. 54A. The arc of their danger zone may be wider, and this makes maxi-raters potentially threatening craft, if it were not for their large size. Once capsized, such a vessel will behave like a catamaran, extremely difficult to recover from the point of no return.

Unfortunately, this contemporary trend in yacht design – the product of clauses in the IOR whose results were not foreseen – became fashionable and has affected many non-IOR designs as well. In contrast the traditional type of yacht shown in Fig. 56 produces a stability curve often without substantial unhindered recovery to the upright from total inversion if capsize occurs.

The question of questions is: if the large range of stability of the type shown by the stability curve in Fig. 56 is a Good Thing from the seaworthiness and safety standpoint, why then did our modern IOR designs depart so radically from such desirable stability characteristics, a common feature of the 'proper boat' before the new rule was introduced?

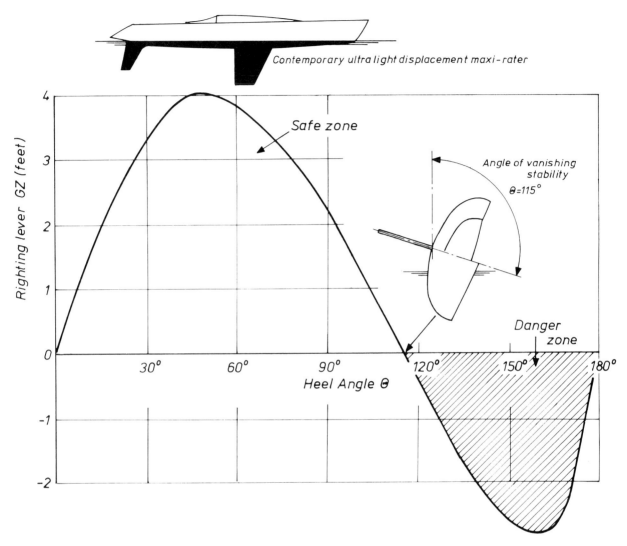

Fig. 55. *Hydrostatic stability curve of a maxi-rater built to the IOR. Quite apart from their dangerous stability characteristics in rough seas, these boats are vulnerable for a different reason. Their displacement/length ratio $(\Delta/(0.01 \times LWL)^3$ is not infrequently in the order of 100; hence they are not structurally strong and may disintegrate under heavy prolonged stresses inflicted by wind and waves.*

It was reported for instance that for some lightly built maxis made of exotic and composite hull materials (very expensive Kevlar/Nomex/Kevlar sandwich) the 1985 Whitbread Round the World Race became a demolition derby in the later stages of the first leg. Thus, for example, the Drum's *Nomex honeycomb core failed and the structural integrity of the hull was dramatically reduced.*

According to the 1984 Sydney–Hobart report the damage to some more modern hulls was 'hair raising',

and exotic and composite hull materials had shown very badly in comparison with conventional glass-reinforced polyester laminates (resinglass). The percentage of the 'exotic' hulls which failed was seven times *greater than that for resinglass.*

There are horses for courses. Application of expensive aerospace technology to marine craft in order to produce fast but fragile air-bubble operating on rough surface of comparatively dense water does not appear to make sense. And even if a light hull made of extraordinarily strong exotic materials may survive heavy sea impacts, the crew inside is likely to become incapacitated, bearing in mind, the large, neck-breaking accelerations which an exceptionally light boat must necessarily experience. Needless to say, catastrophic failures not caused by grounding or collision were rare in the case of heavier, strongly built traditional yachts.

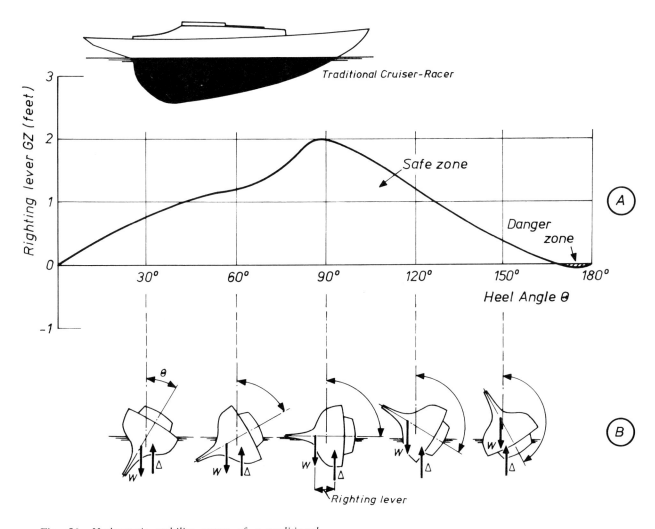

Fig. 56. *Hydrostatic stability curve of a traditional cruiser/racer built to the RORC rule. Note that the 'dangerous zone' is negligible as compared with the 'safe zone'. A boat with this kind of stability has a good chance of recovering quickly from inversion if a capsize occurs. Because of her large 'safe zone', and for other reasons which are discussed in later chapters, boats with a long keel and low G are much less susceptible to knockdown than contemporary cruise/racers.*

Fig. 57. *Crossbreeding of the ocean racer with the sailing dinghy, encouraged by the IOR and accepted by go-fast fanatics, does not appear to be particularly promising from the viewpoint of seaworthiness. Although strange parents (not to mention the anonymity of artificial insemination) may occasionally produce winners, the influence of heredity should not be ignored. As in the case of horse breeding, the most careful selection must be made of ancestral qualities.*

*'There will be some fundamental assumpions
which adherents of all the variant systems
within the epoch unconsciously presuppose.
Such assumptions appear so obvious that
people do not know what they are assuming
because no other way of putting things has ever
occurred to them.'*

Alfred Whitehead

6 Effect of the Rating Rule (IOR) on Hydrostatic Stability

To the naval architect (who intends to build a yacht to the rating rule and win the grand prix), as well as to the rulemakers (whose role is not to allow the former to achieve glory by cheating) the stability of a boat has one definite meaning: the magnitude of the righting moment, developed by the hull at a given angle of heel, determines the power to carry sail effectively. The greater this power for a given rating, the larger the sail area, and thus the higher the speed to be expected. Hence, stability is one of the most important speed performance factors. To quote from the *Yachtsman's Guide to the Rating Rule*: 'any measurement rule that omitted stability control could be properly accused of giving licence, if not outright encouragement, to owners and designers to build very lightly constructed and highly ballasted yachts.' Such a trend was not assumed to be good for the sport, and consequently the IOR pundits decided to tax stability due to ballast by introducing some measure of the hull tenderness (TR), which in turn is used in suitable form as the Centre of Gravity Factor (CGF) as a multiplier of the rating (see rule 12 on page 59).

For convenience, the IOR formula is rewritten below:

$$R = (0.13 \frac{L \times \sqrt{S}}{\sqrt{B \times D}} + 0.25\,L + 0.3\,\sqrt{S} + DC + FC) \times EPF \times CGF$$

The minimum CGF allowed by the rule is 0.968. This implies that it is advantageous to have CGF close to the minimum to make the boat appear slower (lower rating R) under the terms of the handicap formula than she really is. The formula for CGF is:

$$CGF = \frac{2.2}{TR - 5.1} + 0.8925 \tag{15}$$

and TR − tenderness ratio is given by:

$$TR = \frac{0.97 \, L \times (BWL)^3}{RM, \, 1°} \tag{16}$$

where L −   rated length of the boat
   BWL −   waterline beam (see Fig. 58A)
   RM, 1° − Righting moment at 1 degree of heel angle measured by an inclining test similar to that known to naval architects for stability testing of ships.

In an attempt to answer the question: Why is the centre of gravity factor (CGF) in the rule at all? *The Yachtsman's Guide* gives the following explanation: 'Stability is not a direct speed factor in a yacht, but the possession of stability enables the yacht to use is real speed potential expressed in its length and sail area.'

Olin Stephens, who headed the International Technical Committee responsible for the IOR, explicitly stated: 'it will be seen that the method by which the CGF is measured and applied should provide a good approximation of the effect of light or heavy ballast in a given hull, so that in effect it becomes a measure of ballast ratio. While the merits of this approach may, of course, be argued, it is the purpose of this section of the Rule to act partly as a *speed measuring device* and partly as a control of scantlings and accomodations and *not in any direct way is it intended to measure stability*' (the italics are mine).

In yet other words – the rule-makers' logic, or rather wishful thinking (behind the CGF concept) was to exclude the extremes – stability due to form only and stability due to ballast only – typified on the one hand by flat bottomed, skimming dishes or scows and on the other by plank-on-edge lead-mines in the form of late 19th century cutters, as discussed earlier (Figs 24B, 28, 29).

A. CGF effect on hull form and stability

The CGF is most ingenious and well protected by its great complexity against being proved wrong. To borrow a few words from Einstein, how does this *real witches* calculus work? And what are its implications? Have the rule makers achieved their objectives?

It can be seen in Fig. 54B that the yacht righting moment (RM) is given by:

$$RM = \Delta \, GM \sin \Theta \tag{17}$$

It is evident that the same initial stability moment can be produced by a heavy-displacement yacht with a small GM (Fig. 50) or a light-displacement yacht with a large GM.

It is instructive to express the original formula for the tenderness ratio, as defined by the rule, in a different way (see Note 46).

$$\text{TR} = \frac{0.97 \, \text{L} \, (\text{BWL})^3}{\text{RM, } 1°} = 22.3 \, \frac{\text{BM*}}{\text{GM}} \tag{18}$$

substituting this into the CGF formula 15 we have:

$$\text{CGF} = \frac{2.2}{22.3 \, \dfrac{\text{BM}}{\text{GM}} - 5.1} + 0.8925 \tag{19}$$

Let us now assume that, following the implications of the rule, the yacht designer wishes to take full advantage of the CGF minimum = 0.968 allowed by the IOR. It is apparent that the only quantity taxed by the rule is the $\dfrac{\text{BM}}{\text{GM}}$ ratio in the denominator of formula 19. All that remains is to calculate this $\dfrac{\text{BM}}{\text{GM}}$ ratio which results in a CGF value close to the minimum allowed, i.e.:

$$0.968 = \frac{2.2}{22.3 \, \dfrac{\text{BM}}{\text{GM}} - 5.1} + 0.8925 \tag{19A}$$

Taking a few simple arithmetical steps, we find that the $\dfrac{\text{BM}}{\text{GM}}$ ratio giving maximum CGF advantage is about 1.4, i.e. BM = 1.4 GM. This means that the centre of gravity G must be well above the centre of buoyancy B. The intention of the IOR was clearly to penalise a low centre of gravity. This was meant to encourage designers and builders to put more weight and strength into the hull superstructure, spars and rigging, instead of saving weight at these points so that it could be put into the keel for a high ballast/displacement ratio in order to achieve a large power to carry sail for a given size of boat.

Unfortunately, 'the wisest men who had not the gift of foresight' and who with good faith introduced the centre of gravity factor into the IOR (to replace the old scantling principle of the RORC rule or ballast/displacement ratio rule of the CCA) gave large credit for boats with extremely low hydrostatic stability. *Foresight* in the above quotation – after C.P. Snow – meant ability to appreciate properly the true character of wicked human nature as it is.

Over the years since the IOR was implemented, the designers have done whatever was possible to take advantage of the CGF through an increase of tenderness ratio. As a result, beamy boats with pinched ends, relying heavily on form stability, became a fad. Figure 58 demonstrates the effect of the

---

* BM is the distance between the centre of buoyancy B and the metacentre M (see Fig. 50).

tenderness ratio factor in the formula on ultimate hydrostatic stability. The four mid-sections of hulls A–D were derived from the parent form of a Three-Quarter Tonner.[47] To show the influence of the centre of gravity (G) and centre of buoyancy (B) positions relative to the metacentre (M), and also the effect of beam on hydrostatic stability, all models have the same weight and were given fairly the same righting moment (RM) at 30° of heel. With these constants, the centre of gravity of each model was calculated and is shown in Fig. 58A–D, together with the relevant centre of buoyancy and metacentre. Subsequently, the hydrostatic stability curves, over the range from 0 to 180 degree of heel, were established and plotted above each hull section. It is seen that, as the position of G rises relative to B with increasing beam, the maximum righting lever (GZ) and the angle of vanishing stability (Θ_0) (stability threshold) both decrease quite sharply, scoring minimum for model D, a representative of the shape fostered by the IOR.

B. Some statistics, measurement facts and conclusions

'When dealing with people, remember you are not dealing
with creatures of logic, but with creatures of emotions,
creatures bristling with prejudice and motivated by pride and
vanity.'

Dale Carnegie

'Too many apples from the tree of systemalised knowledge
lead to the fall of progress.'

Alfred N. Whitehead

To all seamen, sailing people included, boat stability has one vital meaning. That is, whether the boat will float safely in rough seas or will be susceptible to capsize; and there appears to be no confusion in this respect. From the viewpoint of cruising men a positive stability range from 0 to 180 degree, of type A in Fig. 58, is what the designer should strive for. A well constructed boat with such stability characteristics and watertight integrity, even if rolled completely upside down, would return from this embarrassing position within a relatively short time. On the contrary, the hull shape of type D, with its extremely unsafe stability features of low capsize threshold angle Θ_0 is dangerous to life and investment. Once capsized, such a boat is likely to remain in the turned turtle position for a sufficiently long time to drown her crew.

Referring again to Fig. 49, it could be added that the Half-Tonner *Grimalkin* with her integral ballast of 1100 lb of her 2890 lb total weight (which remained upside down for at least five minutes and subsequently drowned some of her crew), is not as extreme as many later level-raters. As reported in *Sail* magazine in 1980[48] two One-Tonners which disappeared in bad weather (presumed lost with all hands) had most of their ballast inside the hull. Large form stability gained from wide beam and high freeboard introduced in small

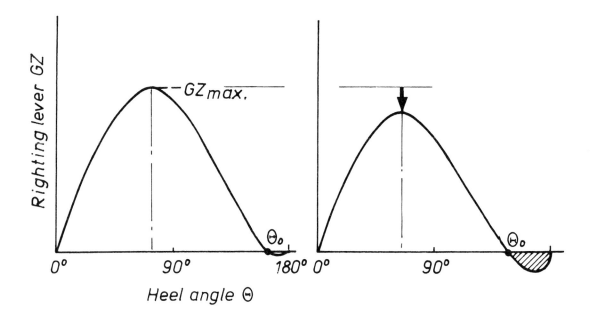

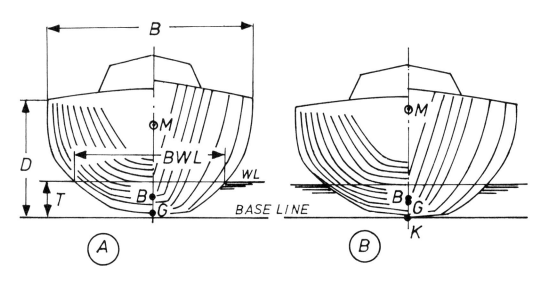

Fig. 58. *The effect of hull section and relative positions of centre of buoyancy (B) and centre of gravity (G) on hydrostatic stability. Sections A–D were derived from the parent form of a Threequarter-Tonner; basic dimensions are given below.*

LOA	*32.8 ft*	*(10 m)*
LWL	*27.25 ft*	*(8.3 m)*
Beam	*11.25 ft*	*(3.4 m)*
Draft	*4.9 ft*	*(1.5 m)*
Displacement (Δ)	*3.0 tons*	
Δ/(0.01 LWL)³	*148.3*	

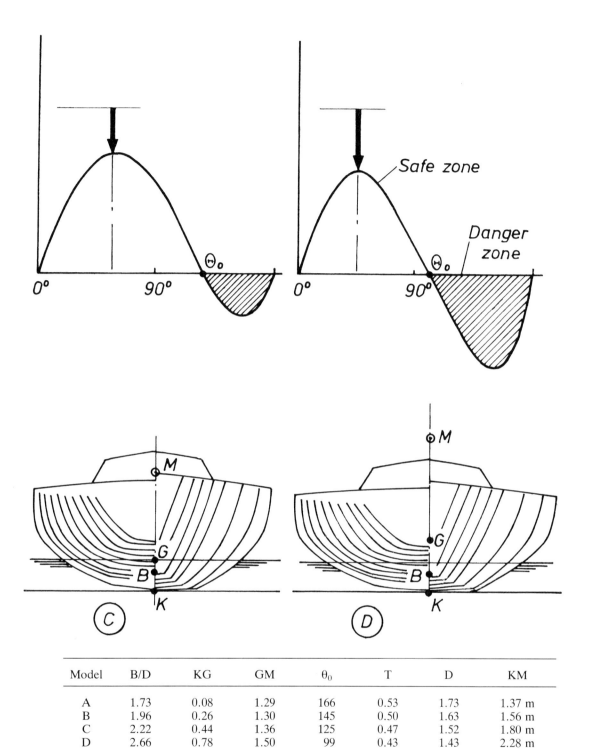

Model	B/D	KG	GM	θ_0	T	D	KM
A	1.73	0.08	1.29	166	0.53	1.73	1.37 m
B	1.96	0.26	1.30	145	0.50	1.63	1.56 m
C	2.22	0.44	1.36	125	0.47	1.52	1.80 m
D	2.66	0.78	1.50	99	0.43	1.43	2.28 m

where θ_0 = angle of vanishing stability
KG = distance from the baseline to G

Note: When calculating displacement/length ratio, $\Delta/(0.01\ \text{LWL})^3$ the displacement (Δ) should be expressed in tons and LWL in feet.

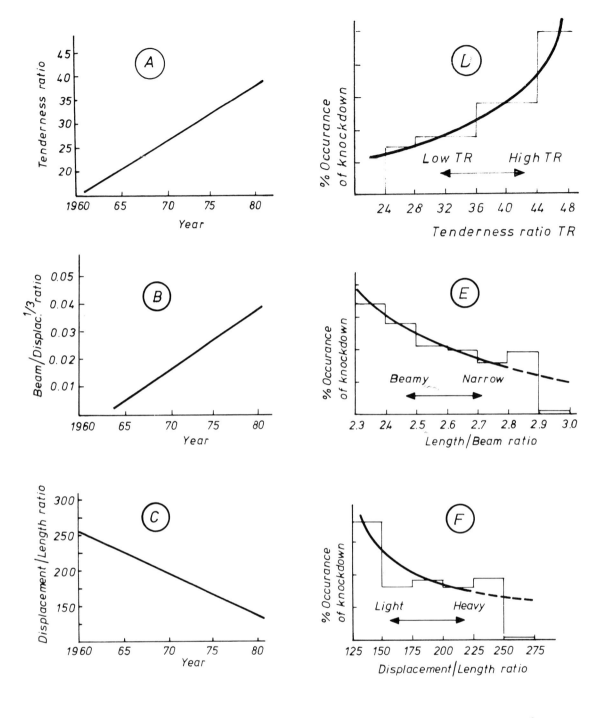

Fig. 59. *Effects of tenderness ratio, beam and displacement/length ratio on capsize probability. The centre of gravity factor (CGF) in the IOR formula was designed to give increasing penalty as the G position is lowered. It was originally believed that the effect of this would be to discourage lightly built yachts with a high ballast/displacement ratio.*

Tenderness ratio $= \dfrac{0.97\,L \times (BWL)^3}{RM(1°)} = 22.3\,\dfrac{BM}{GM}$

BWL = Beam waterline
RM(1°) = Righting moment at 1° heel
CGF = $\dfrac{2.2}{TR - 5.1} + 0.8925$

classes for the sake of headroom, has been shown to be no substitute for a low centre of gravity, achieved through external ballast.

Figure 59A–C show the trends in yacht proportions (since the inception of the IOR in 1968) towards higher tenderness ratios (larger $\dfrac{BM}{GM}$ ratio), wider beam in relation to displacement, and lower displacement/length ratios.[49] Figure 59D, E and F indicate a correlation of these design trends, with capsize occurrence based on the Fastnet Race Inquiry. The statistical data speak for themselves.

Fig. 60. *These two waterplanes have the same rated Beam Waterline Length (BWL) measurement. Hence the two hulls, despite their different waterplane areas, might be assumed to have the same stability as measured by the tenderness ratio (see Fig. 59 for formula). However, boat B with pinched ends, produces a smaller righting moment at a given angle of heel, than boat A with fuller ends (See Addendum page 121.)*

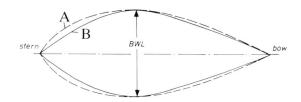

Quite apart from the influence of the tenderness factor on seaworthiness (Figs 58 and 59), there is yet another unseaworthy effect of the hull shape encouraged by the IOR measurements. Since the tenderness factor in formula 16 calls for only a single beam waterline measurement (Fig. 60), it has been rightly argued that the TR of the two waterline planforms A and B would be identical.[50] The yacht with the fuller stern A is, however, about 12% more stable for a given height of the centre of gravity than the yacht with the finer stern B. Thus, contrary to the intentions of IOR, the fuller-sterned boats of older type are penalised for their form-stability and will receive a higher CGF, as if their ballast ratio were higher than in fact it is. H. Barkla[51] has proved that 'pinching the ends and bulging the middle, increases the righting moment, but by increasing BWL^3 more, increases the tenderness ratio and so lowers the rating.'

In addition to the effect on the CGF, pinching of the ends reduces the rated length (L) of the boat. Independently, increased BWL makes the product B × D larger (in the denominator of the IOR rating given in formula 12), and therefore again favourably reduces the rating. Thanks to the triple bonus afforded by the rule, the rhomboidal water-line planform became 'fashionable' to the point that BWL was artificially increased by local distortions, such as the notorious 'beam bumps' shown in Fig. 6, because they offered considerable rating advantage.

Right from the inception of the IOR, it did not take designers long to realise that it would pay to increase the BWL measurement by all means. To quote one successful designer P. Norlin[52]: 'Even before I began carving the block of mahogany, I could see *Scampi's* form within it: a very beamy, sharp-ended, light displacement hull nine metres in overall length and three metres across the beam. By 1970, the year *Scampi* won the World Half-Ton Championship and her class in the Southern Ocean Racing Conference, the low length/beam ratio and light displacement concept was well established.'

A beamy boat with pinched bow and small buoyancy reserve may look advantageous as a legal rule cheater. But, as usual, something for nothing cannot be achieved – a penalty in terms of seaworthiness is bound to be paid. Such a boat hardly resists the temptation to gyrate in a circle when heeled. When pressed hard, the heeled hull tends to trim by the bow so lifting the stern, together with the rudder, out of the water (Fig. 39).

Some small displacement ocean-racers with high $\dfrac{BM}{GM}$ ratio, deliberately designed to benefit from a lower CGF, and also for another reason discussed in Appendix 1, may in some stronger wind conditions suffer a lack of sufficient stability to carry sail effectively. Then the crew-weight contribution becomes an important factor of speed performance and Fig. 61 indicates the approximate increase in stability with the crew outboard for boats of different LWL ranging from 20 to 60 feet.[53] In a letter written to the Editor of *Yachting World*, van de Stadt made a comment relevant to the Rule which allows the crew to be used as 'live ballast': 'I think it is ridiculous that for a race longer than 50 miles the crew is allowed to sit on the deck with legs outside the lifelines. There are skippers who allow the free watch to sleep on deck. You cannot expect a crew treated like that to be in good condition.'[54]

As we recall, the Centre of Gravity Factor was devised partly to compensate for the scantling rules and partly to eliminate the possibility of a return of the unhealthy, unseaworthy boats of the past such as skimming dishes and the so-called lead-mines. What has been achieved exactly opposes this desire – the present trend of yacht design shows a reversion to many ideas which were in practice some hundred years ago, but which were rejected until recently as dangerous or undesirable. Nowadays, the racing scene is dominated by a bastard: the skimming-dish and its ugly sister in the form of the sandbagger (Fig. 62). The only difference between the contemporary type of cruiser-racer and the sandbagger is that the task of the old professional crewmen was not only to shift their own body to windward, but also to carry heavy sandbags with them. Usually these boats carried 25–28 sandbags, each weighing 52 lb (24 kg). An interesting point is that the rule demanded that 'a yacht must bring home all the sandbags with which she started'. In a falling wind or when reaching the rule was easily circumvented by bags being 'lost' overboard from the weather rail when the boat suddenly righted from the heeled position, supposedly before the crew could prevent it.[22]

In this respect contemporary skippers are in a worse position than their predecessors – they can't dispose of live ballast overboard, no matter how much such a trick might improve their racing chances.

It eventually came to be realised that the possibilities for undetected bending of the rules about shifting ballast had a detrimental effect on the design and ethics of the sport, and around the 1880s sandbaggers vanished from the scene, giving room for deeper more seaworthy yachts with fixed ballast.

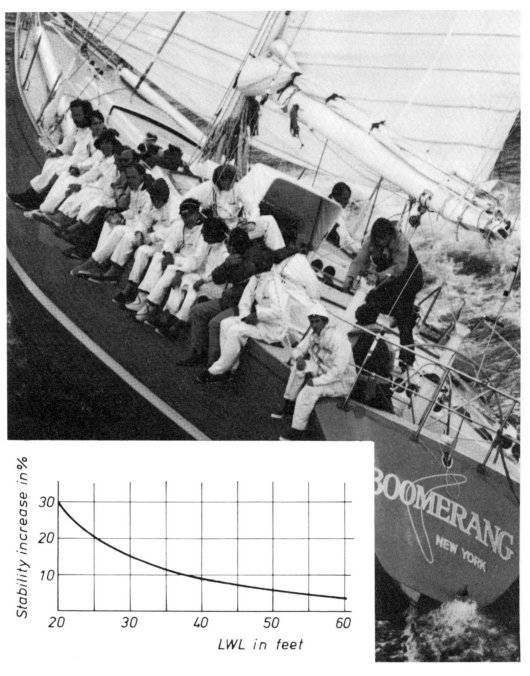

Fig. 61. *Estimated increase in stability (power to carry sails effectively) with crew sitting outboard, for IOR boats of different LWL. The question of crew fatigue was highlighted in an analysis of those One-Tonners which completed the 213-mile Channel Race in the 1985 Admiral's Cup series, with all hands on the weather rail – all the way, without rest, not even breaks for meals, when going to windward. The reason for this practice has been advanced (Daily Telegraph 16th August 1985) as being the loss of speed by as much as 1/10th knot when just one crewman left the rail. We are now faced with yachts which, if they do not have movable ballast in the form of crew weight, do not possess enough stability to carry the sail plans they need in order to win.*

According to recent opinion of the Offshore Racing Council: the current IOR fleet is beamier for its depth and displacement than is healthy; and also that topsides are too flared, rendering boats both too stable upside down, and too reliant on the stability provided by the crew. The latter depends on the number of crew and on the distance they are seated from the centreline of the hull.

A new formula called Crew Augmented Stability Factor (CASF) has been introduced after 1st January 1986. It will be applied to yachts measured for the first time. If CASF is greater than 1 it will be used as a multiplier on the rating in similar manner as the Centre of Gravity Factor (CGF) in formula 12 page 59.

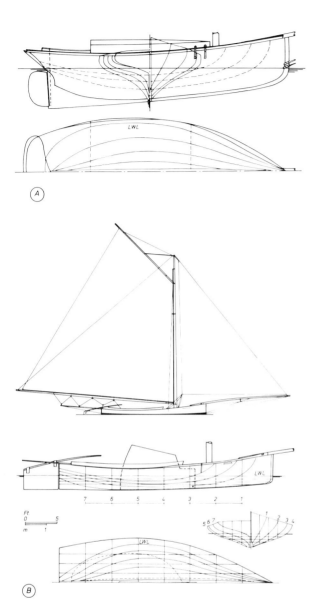

Fig. 62. *(A)* Shadow, *one of the most successful skimming dishes designed by Nat Herreschoff (in 1870); she gained 126 first prizes in 150 races. She had all her ballast inside, and a sail area of 1,342 sq ft on a waterline of 35 ft. Herreschoff expressed his concept as follows: 'My idea was to shape the hull so the ballast would be lower, have the bilges practically out of the water, so as to get easy lines when the vessel is upright, and great beam that would give stability when heeled in a breeze'. Shadow's most famous contest consisted of two races against the* Madge, *a narrow Scottish 'lead mine'. The result was indecisive, with* Shadow *coming first in light weather, while* Madge *won in a fresh breeze. Since that time (1881) we are told that there was 'a steady increase in the number of deeper, more seaworthy yachts – a direct result of the* Madge *races'. (B) The sandbagger* Susie S. *Although modern off-shore racers are not direct descendants of those smooth-water racing machines, in the sense that their hull lines are different, the basic speed concept of light displacement and crew contribution to stability (shifting ballast) is the same.*

LOA　　　　　　　*27.25 ft (8.3 m)*
Beam　　　　　　　*11.0　ft (3.34 m)*
Sail area about 1,500 sq ft (140 m²)

Our investigation has shown that the tail wags the dog, in other words the rating rules tend, willy-nilly, to 'design' the yacht. In some cases they may even operate as an assassin of the wholesome seaworthy boat, by eliminating all the qualities of hull shape which would otherwise be evolved by the demands of the sea if yachts were allowed to develop through a process of natural selection. The shadow of the rule, as a frame of reference, is always with the yacht designer influencing his way of thinking and thus the lines of the hull. The Art of yacht design is rooted in the rating formula. The Rule works like a system, and it has been verified over and over again that you can't beat the system. Indeed, the rule is where the problem of unseaworthiness largely lies, but not entirely.

In his closing chapter on yachts in the *History of American Sailing Ships*, Chapelle writes: 'When it is possible for yachtsmen and designers to obtain a more complete knowledge of past experiments in hull-design and rig than it is now available, an intelligent and natural development of yacht design, free of fads and the effects of badly constructed measurement rules, seems reasonable to expect. When that time comes, a great amount of "scientific" hocus-pocus will be thrown overboard.' What the author had in mind by *scientific hocus-pocus* was an indiscriminate abuse of science regardless of side-effects, to achieve a single objective: speed.

To our generation it became abundantly clear that science may greatly contribute to the improvement of the quality of life, or may be used to alleviate the undesirable effects of a vicious cycle set up by men without scruple or imagination. Unfortunately, what science has too frequently done in the past has had a result exactly opposite to what was intended. This observation is not a new one; it has been known from time immemorial, witness Adam and Eve in the Garden of Eden, and the tale of Pandora's Box. The perfection of the world is undermined by the introduction of knowledge. When Eve ate the apple from the Tree of Knowledge and Pandora lifted the lid of the box opening the secrets of Nature, it led to the unhappiness of Man (and Woman) from then on in an increasingly disordered and unholy world.

The art of yacht design, as any other kind of human activity, is not immune from this original scientific sin, committed deep in the past. The ultimate question of our time – and this applies to yachting too – is whether we can use existing knowledge and careful, discriminating logic within the allowable scope of Nature's law, to pull ourselves out of our predicament?

*'Men are so simple and yield so readily to the
wants of the moment that he who will trick will
always find another who will suffer himself to
be tricked.'*

Niccolo Machiavelli (XVI century)

*'Men are born ignorant, not stupid; they are
made stupid by education.'*

Bertrand Russell (XX century)

7 Stability in a Seaway – Part 1

More than two centuries ago Bouguer published (1746) his *Traité du Navire*, in which his original concept of the metacentric height (Fig. 50) was expounded. Since that time naval architects, including yacht designers, have been content to assume that positive hydrostatic stability of a certain degree can be adequate to take care of all situations experienced by ships in rough seas. Sailing yachts are normally designed in such a way that they are statically stable. The degree of transverse stability, which limits the boat's power to carry sail effectively and thus her speed performance, can practically be checked by the so-called Dellenbaugh Angle Method or the Wind Pressure Coefficient Method (Appendix 1). Either can be used to tell the designer whether the boat will be 'tender' or 'stiff' in response to the wind.

This rather empirical concept of stability verification may be justifiable, since the presence of some degree of static stability, with a liberal margin allowed for rough sea conditions, usually ensures that the sailing craft, after being disturbed (say by sail forces), will return towards the equilibrium or trimmed position in some oscillatory manner. We say 'usually' because, as we already know, it is not always so; a yacht which is statically stable may not necessarily be dynamically stable. There are aerodynamic as well as hydrodynamic reasons for dynamic instabilities in yacht behaviour. Nevertheless, the orthodox assumption accepted today is that the static stability of the boat, as expressed by her stability curve or metacentric height (GM) is a reasonable foundation on which seaworthiness criteria can be established. Both the International Maritime Organisation (IMO) criteria for fishing vessels and the International Offshore Rule (IOR) screening tests for offshore racing yachts are essentially based on the hydrostatic stability concept.[55] To illustrate the point further, yacht designers are prone to believe that 'stability curves are the only things not derived from the emotive interpretations and reports by yachtsmen . . . they give us a dispassionate, objective view of the mechanics of the problem.'[56]

Unfortunately such a view cannot be substantiated. It is an error which mistakes the abstract for the concrete, or an error which might be termed – after the famous mathematician and philosopher A.N. Whitehead – *a fallacy of misplaced concreteness*. Hydrostatic stability curves (Figs 54, 55 and 56) substitute a fraction of reality for the complete range of causes and facts relevant to boat behaviour in a seaway and her survival ability in heavy seas.

Although most seamen have an intuitive feeling as to what stability means, the concept of stability in relation to seaworthiness is rather confusing and almost intangible, even to the best experts in the field. The state of the art of offshore yacht design with respect to seaworthiness, as critically seen after the 1979 Fastnet Race tragedy, is not much worse than that relevant to fishing boats. Here too, a large number of foundering fishing vessels and fatal capsizing events are reported every year, in spite of the fact that the lost boats fulfilled the so-called IMO stability requirements.[55] Therefore a closer look at the stability concept and some definitions appears to be necessary to provide a deeper physical insight combined with theoretical simplicity.

A. Difference between static and dynamic stability

A basic assumption of the hydrostatic stability concept is that the sea surface is flat, undisturbed by waves, and that the hull has no forward motion. A sweeping simplification, justifiable only in conditions when a boat is, say, on moorings in a calm marina or sailing steadily in gentle winds, but indefensible and untenable in rough weather, when waves and other forces of various origin dominate. The crux of the stability problem is that the actual stability for static condition obtained by calculation, as shown for example in Figs 55 and 56, does not remain the same when the boat is in waves as when she is in calm water.

When the late Lloyd Woollard, an Honorary Vice-president of the Royal Institution of Naval Architects, assured his readers that: 'The stability of ships is the only branch of Naval Architecture for which the theory is exact. There is no danger of this theory being upset later by experimental evidence . . . A thousand years hence the theory of stability will be much the same as it is today, although, perhaps, the methods of its calculation will be improved; but the theory, by its very nature, cannot change.'[57]

He meant hydrostatic stability only, although the term 'stability' was used ambiguously. It might suggest a quantitative measure of the boat's ability to survive when exposed to severe weather, i.e. dynamic conditions which are distinctly different from the hydrostatic ones.

Capsizing is a dynamic event and so the static state of equilibrium does not arise among waves. Thus, the static stability concept, a beautifully simple theory which appears to be immune against being proved wrong, is unfortunately applicable only to calm harbour conditions. For most of their working life, however, yachts (and ships for that matter) do not experience this unrealistic physical condition of static stability. After all, boats are not built to be kept safe in harbours. This ties up with an apt remark expressed by Angus Primrose (who tragically lost his life in a yacht disaster): 'For every hard case boat that is built, one that is really comfortable in a blow, there are about ten that are jolly nice and lush in harbour but misery at sea.'[58]

Let us now make a clear distinction between static stability and dynamic stability in a seaway.

Definition of static stability

Static or metacentric stability can be defined as that property of a boat by which the action of the buoyancy and weight forces tends to restore the boat to her original position if her equilibrium has been disturbed. This occurs when the metacentre (M) lies above the centre of gravity (G) as in Fig. 47. Use of the word 'tends' underlines the tendency, not the certainty, that buoyancy and weight (gravity) forces will restore a vessel to her normal attitude when pitched or heeled in a seaway. A rolling boat with increasing angles of roll may well serve as an illustration of what is meant by the word tendency – she oscillates about the equilibrium condition without ever remaining in it. In such a case the boat, although statically stable, may become dynamically unstable and in the end capsize.

By definition, in the static stability consideration *motion is not taken into account at all*. A statically stable boat is regarded as a system *without input* of energy from external sources.

Definition of dynamic stability

Dynamic stability is that property of a vessel which causes her to maintain her steadiness or stability only *through reasons of motion*. It is a dynamic stability that we consider the motion of a boat (regarded as a system), taking into account all the forces which affect the boat's behaviour; that is to say, not only the forces considered under static stability above, i.e. buoyancy and weight, but also including inertia and damping forces and taking into account input from waves and wind.

B. Example of dynamic instability (aerodynamically induced rolling)

When running before a fresh wind and following sea, rhythmic rolling and even broaching tendencies become almost inevitable characteristics of all sailing craft. However, some types of boat (Figs 39 and 57) are more susceptible than others to this kind of instability. By contrast, when watching a large fleet of racing yachts on a *windward leg*, no matter whether they be modern or old fashioned, one is easily struck by the steadiness of all boats in maintaining a roughly constant angle of heel even in strong, gusty winds. No rolling tendency can be noticed, provided boats are sailed with speed.

Why does the same boat, sailing *in identical wind and sea conditions*, behave so differently? The aerodynamic forces developed on the sail can act in two dissimilar ways, entirely depending on the course sailed relative to the wind – in fact on whether or not the sail is set below or above the stall angle.

The author has shown elsewhere (see Appendix 2) that, when running in strong winds, wild rolling can be induced by sails for aerodynamic reasons alone (Fig. 36). A rig can extract energy from the wind in a self-excited manner by its own periodic motion in such a way that the sail can be regarded as a *rolling engine*, which operates even in steady (non-oscillating) winds. Consequently, the boat *may be knocked-down even in a condition where the size of waves is insignificant*. Of course, bigger waves can accelerate and aggravate the whole process of rolling build-up to the point that capsize may suddenly take place in just one or two oscillations. Here we have an example of dynamic instability in an otherwise statically stable boat.

Such a type of dynamic instability in yacht behaviour recorded on a model in the wind tunnel, and frequently observed in the full-scale, is presented in Fig. 63. Rolling builds up when the course sailed (β angle) is greater than 120 and less than about 195 degrees. Under these conditions once the boat is set in rolling motion, no matter how small, the alternating aerodynamic forces that amplify and sustain the oscillation are created and controlled by the rolling rig itself. Since the periodic aerodynamic force is automatically resonant with the natural rolling frequency of the boat, this kind of aerodynamically induced instability may be defined as *self-excitation*.

Referring to sketches A–D in Fig. 63, it is seen that the boat is statically stable since a certain tendency to return to an upright position is clearly maintained; nevertheless the amplitude of rolling grows more or less rapidly, which indicates dynamic instability. This is due to the lack of energy balance – energy lost due to the damping action of the hull, and energy taken from the wind by the sail action. Energy balance therefore determines whether or not, and to what extent, the boat will roll. The process of magnification of rolling will continue until the rate of wind energy input due to sail action is matched by the rate of energy dissipation in damping (mainly due to hull action).

C. Aerodynamic damping (dynamic stability)

An entirely different rolling response is recorded in sketch E of Fig. 63. Here the boat is both statically and dynamically stable; the amplitude of rolling has a clear tendency to diminish with time. Wind tunnel tests have indicated that aerodynamic damping is particularly effective in the close-hauled attitude (Fig. 64). The rig was tested at β = 30 degrees and α = 15 degrees. With the

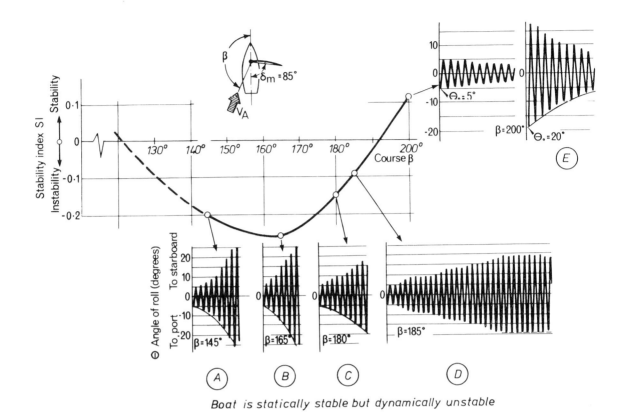

Boat is statically stable but dynamically unstable

Fig. 63. *Sketches A–E illustrate different roll angles recorded on various courses β relative to the apparent wind (V_A); the trim angle of the mainsail ($δ_m$) was kept constant during these tests. The degree of dynamic instability (A–D) or stability (E) in rolling is given by the stability index (SI). A positive stability index (+SI) indicates that the rig, when disturbed by heeling forces (say, due to wave action), will tend to* damp *any rolling motion. A negative stability index (−SI) indicates that the rig, when given a small rolling motion, will tend to* magnify *it. Note that, as distinct from the situations shown in sketches A–D, the boat sailing by the lee in sketch E is statically and dynamically stable.*

wind on, the average angle of heel Θ was about 8 degrees, and the model oscillated about this mean angle in a random way ± 2 degrees due to unsteadiness in the air stream. When the rig was deliberately displaced to 20 degrees of heel, and then left free, the return to the mean angle of heel was immediate without overshoot. The model responded in the same manner when the heel angle was reduced to zero and then released. The results recorded in Fig. 64 clearly show that positive damping generated by the sail is strong. In fact, the rolling model (regarded as a dynamic system incorporating three basic component qualities: inertia, stability, and damping) when subjected to energy input from the wind, behaved like an overdamped system; despite the fact that hydrodynamic damping due to hull and its appendages was deliberately made nil. This explains why sailing boats are so stiff on the windward leg. The boat

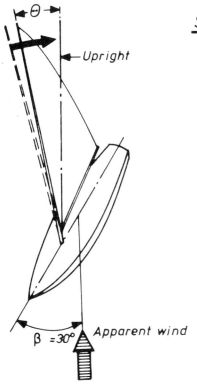

SAILING CLOSE-HAULED

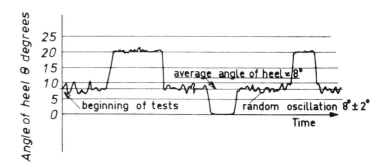

Fig. 64. *A triangular sail tested in the close-hauled condition (β = 30°) in a wind tunnel (left), produced the rolling response recorded in the graph at right. The tests demonstrated that lack of rolling when sailing to windward is largely due to heavy aerodynamic damping from the sail.*

sailing close-hauled can be looked upon as a dynamic system with two in-built damping devices, one aerodynamic and the other hydrodynamic, working in unison. On broad courses relative to the wind (Fig. 63) these two damping devices usually work against each other and this may and usually does lead to dynamic instability.

Thus the same aerodynamic forces and processes which may translate energy taken from the wind into incipient rolling can also act as roll suppressers (see Appendix 2). This fact was surely discovered through trial and error many years ago by fishermen who hoisted a sail on motor driven vessels when sailing to windward, not as a driving device but as a roll stabiliser.

The report on the 1979 Fastnet suggests that those who managed to carry trysails at the height of the storm and kept steering to the waves, in other words, *sailed through the storm*, fared better than those who battened down and went below. Indeed, a proper storm-sail forms a real contribution to seaworthiness by helping to maintain dynamic stability and so control the boat's heading. This tactic presupposes skill, experience and enough stamina on the part of the crew. There is, however, no such thing as an invulnerable crew under long term stress. The modern IOR type of boat needs a lot of human control to remain relatively safe, and may quickly become dangerous when left to her own devices to cope with the eternal vagaries of the sea.

Model of a rolling boat

A physical model of the rolling boat, considered as a system, can be represented in the form of a block diagram in which three fundamental components of the system (static stability, mass inertia and damping of the hull, plus sail and wind as a source of driving energy) are denoted simply by blocks as in Fig. 65. The mutual interaction or cause and effect are marked by arrows 1, 2, 3, 4, indicating the direction of action. As shown earlier, the sail as a means of energy transfer affects the amplitude of rolling in two different ways. It either increases rolling by *extracting energy* from the wind (marked by arrows 1 and 3), or it damps any rolling which may be originated by wave action, by *dissipating energy* into the air (arrows 2 and 4). Whether the rig does the former or the latter depends on a number of factors: sail area S_A, course sailed β, trim angle of the mainsail δ_m, wind speed V_A, sail configuration set (anti-rolling sail) etc.[59]

As indicated in Fig. 65, and this will become evident soon, there is a feedback between the hull and the sail. Thus, for instance, carrying more sail area than is prudent when running or broad reaching vastly increases the aerodynamic input of energy from the sail – a *rolling engine*. When coupled with low inertia of the hull (light displacement) and inefficient hydrodynamic damping (too small a lateral area of the hull underbody), such a combination of factors inevitably tends to stimulate wild, and occasionally disastrous, aerodynamically aggravated rolling which may end in a flat knock-down.

D. Problems to be considered

Referring again to Fig. 49, both yachts *Contessa 32* and *Grimalkin* appear to have ample reserves of positive stability beyond 90 degrees of heel. Both yachts would therefore pass the IOR stability test and would, on that basis, be deemed *seaworthy*. However, in the heavy weather conditions experienced in the 1979 Fastnet Race, both yachts suffered severe knock-downs although, it must be admitted, the *Contessa 32*, which may be thought to be more representative of the traditional long keeled cruising boat, suffered less. Three lives were lost when *Grimalkin*, a typical IOR racer-cruiser, went completely upside down, remaining in that position for at least five minutes. Where did the fault lie? Design? Seamanship? Severity of the weather conditions rather than any obvious defect in boat design? One thing is certain – reserve of positive stability (safe zone in Figs 54–56) is not the only factor that determines whether a boat will capsize in heavy seas. Nevertheless, a large reserve of static stability at big angles of heel (possibly well beyond 90 degrees) appears to be *necessary although not a sufficient criterion for safety*.

How do the three fundamental hull components indicated in Fig. 65 contribute to the dynamic personality of the boat and so to her seaworthiness? How can a statically stable yacht, even when no sails are carried, be knocked

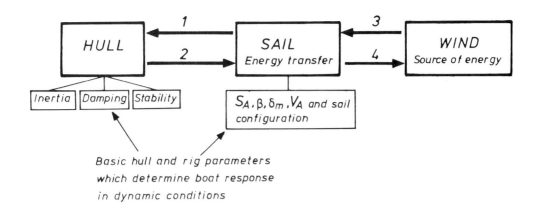

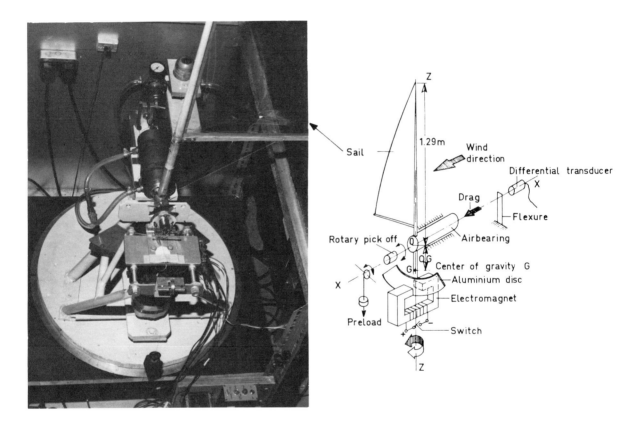

Fig. 65. Top, *a block diagram of a rolling boat considered as a dynamic system. As shown, the sail may either convert wind energy into rolling motion (and thus operate a rolling engine; arrows 3, 1) or dissipate energy coming from the waves into the air (and thus deliver positive damping; arrows 2, 4).*

Bottom, *an apparatus designed by the author for rolling tests in the wind tunnel. It is based on pendulum stability, and incorporates:*

(a) An air bearing support for the rig, permitting almost friction-free oscillation of the sail about its horizontal axis x − x.

(b) Variable and controllable magnetic damping, produced by an aluminium disc swinging between the poles of an electromagnet. This simulates the damping action of the hull and its appendages.

(c) Movable ballast, attached to the aluminium disc, which allows change of the CG position, and also of

the inertia of the rolling mass (hull).

(d) A rotary pick-off to measure and record rolling amplitude variation with time.

(e) A flexure combined with a differential transformer to measure the variation of the drag component (D) due to rolling.

When designing the oscillating part of the apparatus, including mast and sail, attention was given to the problem of dynamic similarity. From a physical point of view, it is essential that the two systems – model and full scale – must not only be geometrically similar in form (shape of the sail), but also in mass distribution (moment of inertia), in damping due to hull action, and in stability. Provision was also made for arbitrarily changing the attitude of the sail (trim) by rotating the whole apparatus around the vertical axis z − z. For further study of sail damping, including the anti-roll sail, consult Aero-Hydrodynamics of Sailing *(Ref. 59).*

down in waves and capsize? These questions bring us to the heart of the problem of dynamic stability and seaworthiness in a seaway.

Although a variety of possible reasons and situations may cause knockdown or capsize of a sailing boat, the observed modes of these events can be divided into three basic patterns – knockdown due to:

(a) rolling
(b) broaching
(c) impact of a single, catastrophic wave.

Apart from aerodynamic causes, heavy rolling may built up in a cumulative manner for three different hydrodynamic reasons, and so we may distinguish:

(1) rolling induced by waves
(2) rolling due to the combined effect of heaving motion and stability variation in waves
(3) rolling inflicted by rudder action (helmsman response)

Let us consider separately these hydrodynamic components of rolling which may ultimately lead to a fatal roll of no return – even in conditions when the boat is sailing under bare poles – a frequent cause of loss in heavy seas. Apart from this ultimate danger, heavy rolling creates problems in a number of ways:

Fig. 66. *The strain of rolling wildly (with a possible broach) like that shown on the left may prove too much, as demonstrated on the right, which shows* *Edward Heath with* Morning Cloud's *rudder stock, which broke during the 1979 Channel Race.*

for instance, a significant yawing may develop while rolling and this may lead to loss of directional control and ultimately to the broach; rolling can cause structural damage to the rig, fittings, steering gear and equipment (Fig. 66). Besides, as indicated earlier, it can seriously degrade the crew's ability to perform their work efficiently. Some seaworthiness criteria have laid down that the worst conjunction of wind and waves that can possibly be encountered should not cause the boat to roll beyond the safe range of heel angles. That ideal cannot, of course, be achieved in the case of small sailing craft. Nevertheless the probability of heavy rolling occurrence can be reduced by the designer. Available theoretical knowledge and the results of research should enable him to weigh the relevant factors and balance one against the other in the search for a reasonable or acceptable solution.

Addendum to Fig. 60 (page 107)

In the denominator of formula (18) there is a righting moment measured at 1 degree of heel (RM, 1°). By changing the amount of flare in the midship section, the measured RM, 1° can be affected to a large extent. Thus, in the range of the small angle of heel at which RM, 1° is measured, the centre of buoyancy B for section a moves outboard more quickly than in the case of a yacht with the midship section b.

Quite apart from the effect of the midship section shape on the righting moment, there is another way to change the RM, 1°. For instance, if the boat is too stiff for rating purposes, then trimming her by the bow will reduce the RM, 1°. Conversely, trimming down by the wide stern will increase the RM, 1°. As a result of these tricks properly used, two boats with different waterplane areas, as shown in Fig. 60, may have the same tenderness ratio and stability as measured for the rating purpose, but very different actual stability at the larger angles of heel at which yachts usually sail. Certainly boat B in Fig. 60 (with a pinched bow) produces a smaller righting moment at, say, 20–30 degrees of heel in a close hauled attitude when, for obvious reasons, the hull usually assumes trim by the bow.

The lower part of Fig. 60A shows the stability characteristics of the two hulls with the two midship sections, a and b, shown above. The midship sections at 5 degrees of heel and the relevant shifts of the centre of buoyancy (B) are also depicted. It will be seen that at small angles of heel B moves outboard more quickly for section a than for section b. This is reflected in the initial stability indicated by the continuous lines in the lower graph. Since, according to the IOR, the RM is measured at an average of 2 degrees of heel, the assessment of stability of those two boats indicated by the broken lines, is misleading. It is evident from this figure that the hull with midship section b (flared) has much more actual stability at larger, practical angles of heel than that estimated by the IOR measurements. At 15 degrees of heel the righting moment of hull b is about 50 per cent greater than predicted by the rule. Conversely, the actual stability of the boat with section a is substantially overestimated.

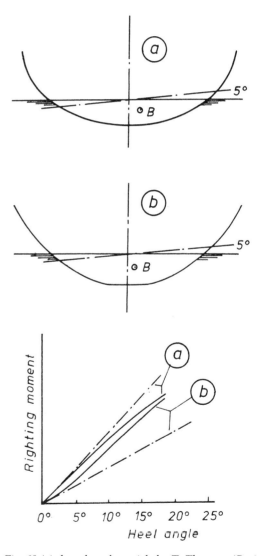

Fig. 60A is based on the article by T. Thornton 'Rating Inclinations' published in Seahorse *in November/December 1986.*

*'Forewarned and forearmed to be prepared is
half the victory'*

M. de Cervantes (1547–1616)
Don Quixote

8 Rolling Induced by Waves

Any boat among waves will roll. The degree of rolling, as measured by the increase in angle of roll with time, depends upon a number of factors, of which the most important are given in Table 4.

Table 4

1. The relation between the natural period of rolling of a given hull and the wave period.
2. The shape of the hull, its stability, weight and mass distribution.
3. The wave slope (steepness).
4. The damping efficiency of the underwater parts of the hull (mainly keel and rudder).
5. The speed of the boat and course sailed, relative to wave crests.

Perhaps the easiest approach to rolling is to picture the motion of a liferaft floating freely in waves. Assuming that the raft is light and small, as compared with the waves, it will passively follow the wave profile in a manner illustrated in Fig. 67A left. If there were a mast erected on the raft, its attitude would, at any given instant, be always perpendicular to the actual wave slope. The raft would have no rolling motion of its own but would conform to the shape of successive waves. So there would be virtually no lagging or overshoot of any kind in the liferaft attitude and motion in relation to the instantaneous wave slope. The fact that the liferaft follows the water surface so closely brings the risk of capsize in large breaking waves. As a wave grows so it curls over, as perfectly expressed by Hokusai Katsushika (1760–1849) in a passionate painting (Fig. 68); a liferaft may follow this curve and, with the added effect of the

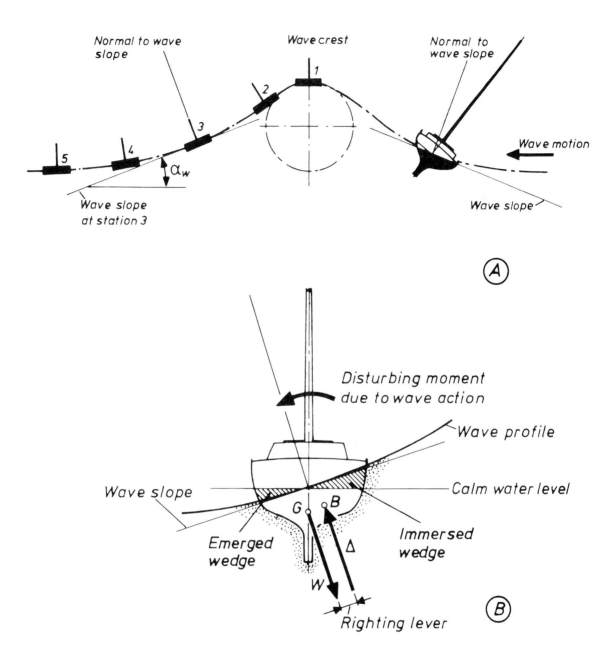

Fig. 67. *(A) Behaviour of a light raft and of a keelboat in waves.*
(B) Experiments conducted by Froude (and results published in 1861) confirmed in a striking manner that the water in waves, and also the floating hull for that matter, are acted upon by some force other than gravity alone. *As a result, the buoyancy force Δ as well as the weight force (W) acting on the hull in waves is normal to the variable slope of the wave. Boats roll in waves for the same reason that a stable boat, forcibly inclined in calm water, returns to her upright attitude when released.*

Fig. 68. *Waves off the coast of Japan, painted by Hokusai Katsushika (1760–1849).*

Fig. 69. *A circular life-raft flips due to the combined action of waves and wind (47 knots). Photograph taken in the wind and wave test tank of the National Maritime Institute at Teddington (NMI Report R 123 by L.R. Cole and J.A. Wills; courtesy NMI Ltd).*

wind, turn upside down. Figure 69 illustrates the point with a model circular raft tested in the National Maritime Institute. Indeed, a number of seafarers have lost their lives while attempting to save themselves by using inflatable rafts.

A. Rolling mechanism

As compared with a raft, a boat has an appreciable mass and therefore inertia, so that she enjoys a damping effect due to action of the hull and its appendages. She therefore responds to waves in a different manner. For example, the motion of a boat in a beam sea (Fig. 67A right) lags behind the disturbing force or moment set up by the wave. Her mast at a particular instant is not necessarily perpendicular to the wave slope. Due to inertia and damping she takes time to respond to the hydrodynamic forces.

Sketch B in Fig. 67 illustrates, on an enlarged scale, the mechanism of the disturbing water forces which act on the hull. With the wave surface rising from the right, wedges of immersion and emersion are formed, and the buoyant force Δ is shifted to the right of the gravity force W. The resulting disturbing moment, $\Delta \times$ 'Righting Lever', will tend to roll or tilt the hull until it floats with its mast at right angles to the wave slope, which is equivalent to a static equilibrium. Thus the rolling motion is initiated. But with the wave slope constantly ascending or descending, the boat's attitude does not conform with the wave configuration in the manner demonstrated for the raft in Fig. 67A (left). She is forced to roll. This fact is of great importance. It determines entirely different patterns in the behaviour between light displacement boats (rafts or open boats of ship's lifeboat form) and heavy displacement boats with hulls of wineglass section, penetrating relatively deeply into the lower water strata.

In his 1861 paper W. Froude, the father of modern ship hydrodynamics states that 'The effect of stability is the lever by which a wave forces a ship into motion – if a ship were destitute of this stability no wave that the ocean produces would serve to put her in motion. The consequence is that the ships are very easy rollers'.[60] Froude was perfectly aware that metacentric stability operates like a double-agent and, as such, cannot be trusted.

This situation is shown in sketch A of Fig. 70, where stability produces a rolling moment which is due to the action of the wave slope. The 'righting lever', deliberately put in inverted commas, now becomes the *rolling lever*. The hull is forced to roll by the wave, whose energy is transferred to the boat in the form of kinetic energy of rolling motion. On the other hand, sketch B in Fig. 70 illustrates the situation when stability operates in its more usually understood sense: it checks the roll at a certain angle and tends to push the boat back again. Kinetic energy, stored in the heeled position of the hull as potential energy, initiates a rolling motion in the opposite direction in the same manner as a pendulum.

In a real sea we are going to be subjected to a great deal of

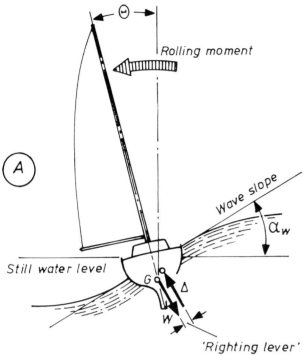

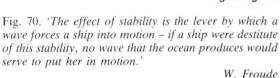

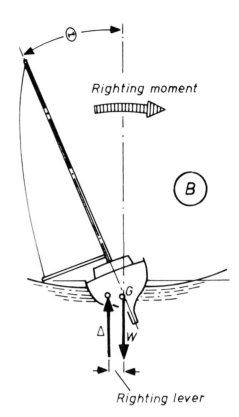

Fig. 70. *'The effect of stability is the lever by which a wave forces a ship into motion – if a ship were destitute of this stability, no wave that the ocean produces would serve to put her in motion.'*

W. Froude

hydrodynamically-induced rolling which may ultimately lead to a fatal roll of no return. That can happen even in conditions when the boat is sailing under bare poles, because it is an effect of waves not of wind pressure.

After a boat has been heeled by wave action, she begins to roll on her own. Thenceforward the development of rolling will largely depend on the period of successive waves encountered in the sequence. When the boat's natural period of rolling (T_n) is about the same as the period of wave encounter (T_e), the rolling angles can increse progressively by *resonant magnification*. That happens when the disturbing moment is applied in a regular and tuned manner, just as a child on a swing learns that by pumping in synchronism with a swing's motion, he can make the swing move with increasingly larger amplitude.

The sea is continuously applying energy to the boat, and she must dissipate this energy or suffer its damaging effects. Her metacentric stability will make her 'bounce back' just as the springs of a car will make her bounce on a bumpy road. A car needs shock absorbers, to slow and smooth the response of the springs – a boat needs hydrodynamic and, possibly, aerodynamic damping to slow and steady her rate of roll.

When a boat meets regular waves which are in tune with her natural rolling period, the energy in each wave adds to the pendulum energy of the boat, so she will roll with increasing angular velocity to ever greater angles. Such rolling, developed under synchronous conditions, is demonstrated in Fig. 71, where it is assumed that the damping effectiveness of the hull with its keel and rudder is small. In this example the energy added by the wave train exceeds the energy removed by damping, so that the boat rolls farther and farther and is heading for disaster. It should be added that this is an imagined example to illustrate a point: in reality a sufficient number of uniform waves rarely occurs. Nature does not pump the swing with perfect timing.

Fig. 71. *Synchronous or near-synchronous rolling pattern (see also Figs 67 and 70). The force of gravity is always trying to restore the boat to an even keel, but* *a synchronous application of the force of buoyancy (immersed wedge in Fig. 67) builds up an ever-increasing roll angle.*

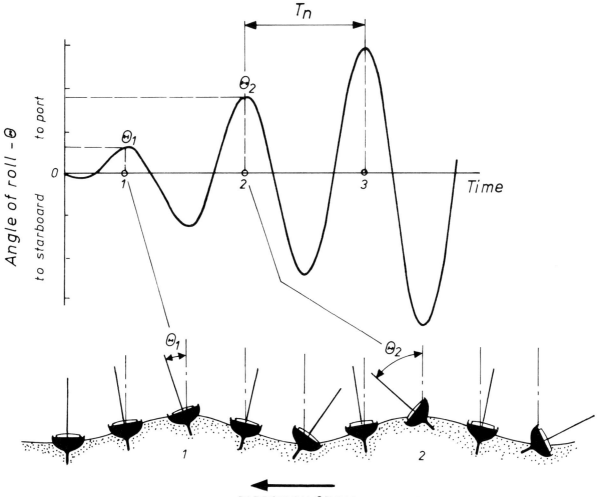

DIRECTION OF WAVE APPROACH

Fortunately, most waves encountered at sea are irregular in both frequency and direction, so that the boat rolls with an irregular period and amplitude. The rolling may build up to a maximum over a period of several rolls, when the boat and the wave train are in tune. Then they get out of tune and rolling diminishes. The successive maxima attained in rolling are not equal, nor are the number of rolls the same, in the successive cycles from maximum down to minimum and back to maximum. However, one cannot ignore the possibility that fairly uniform trains of waves can be met and resonant conditions may therefore occur. Then, if the waves are high or steep and so contain a great deal of energy, large roll amplitudes can build up in a few cycles giving little warning that matters are past remedy.

Dangerous synchronous conditions may arise at any time – in the middle of a wave train of otherwise insignificant and random size and shape, there often occurs a succession of a few high waves of approximate regularity. If the boat is already rolling to large angles of heel, perhaps for aerodynamic or other reasons (which will be discussed in later chapters) and the period of encounter T_e of these few waves synchronises with the natural rolling period of the boat (T_n), i.e. $T_e \simeq T_n$, then dangerous rolling will certainly arise with great rapidity during the passing of only two or three waves.

Natural period of rolling (T_n) is fairly constant for each boat. It might be about 2–3 sec for a small dinghy (for a Finn class boat $T_n = 2.1$ sec with centre-board up and rudder amidship, and $T_n = 2.4$ sec with centre-board down); for a heavy keelboat $T_n = 6$–8 sec.

Period of roll (T_n) can be found with sufficient accuracy, by simple experiment in still water with the help of a stopwatch. It is enough to force the boat to roll to a small angle of heel (by moving the crew from side to side) and then to measure the time it takes to roll from, say, port to port, i.e. from out-to-out and back again. A number of timings should be taken and averaged if T_n is to be reliably estimated.

The *Wasa* sank at Stockholm in 1628 on her maiden voyage due to heeling too much in a gust of wind, after Admiral Kleming had conducted just such a test with 30 seamen. He stopped the test half way, because there seemed to be a danger she might go over, yet he still allowed her to sail!

Natural period of rolling can also be calculated if the metacentric height (GM) and the so called roll moment of inertia (I_r) of a boat of given displacement (Δ) are known. It can be shown that the physical law which binds T_n with GM, I_r and Δ can be expressed by formula:

$$T_n = 2\pi \sqrt{\frac{I_r}{GM\,\Delta}} \simeq 6.3 \sqrt{\frac{I_r}{GM\,\Delta}} \qquad (20A)$$

We may take this to be a fact, because this equation, as well as others given in this book, have been tested by confronting them with real situations, over and over again. They stand for many experiments conducted in the past.

Moment of inertia*

The unknown term, the roll moment of inertia (I_r), in this equation calls for commentary. The problems we shall consider in connection with rolling motion, and ultimate capsize of the boat, are in some respects similar to those associated with rotating objects (masses). It is known from experience that the application of a force at some distance from the centre of rotation of a flywheel will cause the wheel to rotate in the direction of the torque. It can be demonstrated that the resistance of a flywheel forced into rotation depends on the mass of the wheel and the manner in which its mass is distributed in relation to the axis of rotation. The importance of the mass distribution can be illustrated as follows: two wheels have the same mass and the same outside diameter, but the mass of the first is concentrated mostly around the rim, whilst in the other it is close to the centre. No doubt, the first wheel will be more sluggish in responding to torques speeding it up or slowing it down. This sluggishness can be measured by taking into account combined effort of mass (m) and its location (k) relative to the axis of rotation. This particular combination of m and k is called the *moment of inertia* and is usually given the symbol I.

$$I = \text{mass (m)} \times \text{radius}^2 (k^2) = mk^2$$

where k, usually called gyradius, is an index of the mass location.

The greater the moment of inertia of an object, be it flywheel or rolling boat, the larger its sluggishness, i.e. the larger the torque needed to produce a change in its rotational (angular) velocity. As shown in the formula, the radial location of the mass is more important than the mass itself in determining the moment of inertia since I depends on the square of k.

Detailed calculations of the roll moment of inertia (I_r) of a boat is more laborious than that of a wheel with uniform distribution of its mass. It is based on the tacit assumption that the fore-and-aft axis of rolling of the boat goes through her centre of gravity CG. The boat usually rolls about this axis or close to it – somewhere between CG and the actual plane of flotation of the hull. A breakdown of the various components of the yacht, hull, rig, ballast etc, indicating both the weight and the distance of each component from the rolling axis, is required for I_r calculation. Each piece of the boat with individual mass has its own particular gyradius and contributes its own particular value, mk^2, to the total roll moment of inertia (I_r). The resulting inertia moment of the whole boat is simply the sum of all those contributing components.

From the foregoing one may expect that, for instance, the mast will substantially contribute to the total moment of inertia, because its centre of mass is a long distance from the rolling axis. It will be shown that, apart from the effect on the rolling period (T_n) the roll moment of inertia is of fundamental importance from the viewpoint of the capsize probability.

Since mass of the boat $\qquad m = \dfrac{\Delta}{g}$

* For an explanation of moment of inertia see page 153.

where Δ is the displacement (weight)
g = 32.2 ft/sec^2 (the acceleration due to gravity)

the expression for the moment of inertia (I_r) given earlier can be presented in a different way:

$$I_r = \frac{\Delta}{g} k^2$$

If we substitute this into Eq. 20A we find that the natural period of rolling:

$$T_n = 2\pi \sqrt{\frac{k^2}{g\,GM}} \tag{20B}$$

or

$$T_n = 6.28 \frac{k}{\sqrt{32.2\,GM}} = 1.108 \frac{k}{\sqrt{GM}} \tag{20C}$$

From inspection of Eq. 20C it will be seen that the larger the GM the shorter the rolling period (T_n); hence the higher, less bearable rolling acceleration and the greater the discomfort.

The other factor determining the rolling period is gyradius (k) (see the numerator of Eq. 20C). The larger the gyradius (k) the longer the rolling period (T_n). Desirable increase in T_n can therefore be achieved in two different ways: either by reducing GM or by increasing k by winging out the live ballast – the crew. The latter may of course, be applied if the weather condition allows the live ballast to be safely moved and kept along the gunwale.

Contemporary light displacement types of boat built to the IOR, as distinct from the old heavy displacement types, have relatively short rolling periods for two reasons:

(i)   their metacentric heights (GM) are, as a rule, large.
(ii) their roll moments of inertia (I_r), as well as gyradiuses (k), are small.

B. Effect of metacentric height

Since the magnitude of the righting lever is related directly to the metacentric height (Figs 47 and 50), it will be apparent that a stiff boat with a higher GM should roll more heavily in waves than a tender one with a lower GM.

The well known fact is that tender ships do not roll in high waves as heavily as stiff ships; and this may give the crew a feeling of security, which may not necessarily be justified for reasons discussed in the following chapters. 'This is the great paradox of naval architecture' states Barnaby[37], 'that the more stable (statically) the vessel really is the more unstable she appears to be in a seaway'. Such a paradox can exist only because all relevant factors have not been taken into account in developing an explanatory theory. Strictly speaking a paradox invalidates scientific theory only as does a fact stand contrary to the theory.

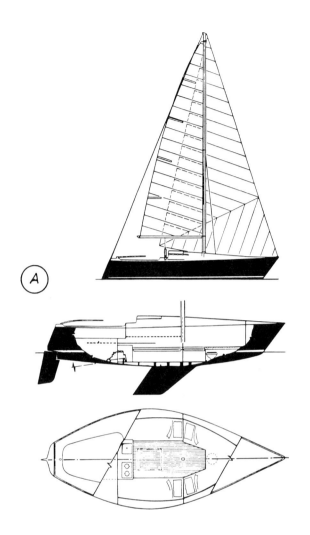

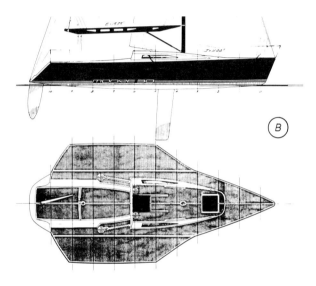

Fig. 72. *(A)* Eyghthene *designed by Ron Holland; a*
1973 Quarter-Ton Cup winner.

LOA	24 ft (7.32 m)
LWL	20.5 ft (6.25 m)
Beam	9.66 ft (2.95 m)
Displacement	4,300 lbs (1,955 kg)
Ballast	2,250 lbs (1,020 kg)
Sail area	270 sq ft (25 m²)

(B) Moore 30 *designed by Gary Mull; 1985.*

LOA	29.98 ft (9.14 m)
LWL	25.62 ft (7.81 m)
Beam	14.0 ft (4.27 m)
	8.3 ft (2.5 m)
Draft	6.5 ft (1.98 m)
Displacement	2,000 lbs (907 kg)
Sail area	465 sq ft (43.28 m²)

*The designer is on record (*Yachting World *Nov. 1985)*

*as saying: 'The sailing waterline length has been kept
very long and this has been matched with a relatively
narrow hull which displaces only a little more than
2,000 lbs (907 kg). The characteristic wings which
allow the crew to get their weight well outboard, hinge
up for trailing and are locked in the extended position
when the yacht is racing . . . Fairly generous (sail)
area ensures an impressive performance in light airs.
The keel is very high aspect ratio and has a wingleted
tip. The accommodation has been kept to a minimum
in the interests of low weight, but there is room for six
adults to sleep aboard. Initial sea trials have shown the
Moore 30 to be very fast in all conditions.' The roman
lettering is mine, and I calculate* $\Delta/(0.01L)^3 = 54!$
*Presumably the designer means that the boat is fast in
all conditions in which she can be sailed – it is unlikely
that these would include stormy seas.*

There is no room for the paradox in science. Nevertheless some of them are remarkably long lived, as for example the famous d'Alembert paradox about resistance of fluids against moving bodies which persisted in hydrodynamics for about 150 years until finally put down by L. Prandtl.

The well known paradox of stability which Barnaby referred to is glaring evidence that one cannot predict the conditions for rolling behaviour (or pitching, yawing or steering behaviour for that matter) in rough seas purely from static considerations. In other words, metacentric height alone is of limited validity as a criterion of safety or seaworthiness. Static methods cannot be used for the cure of dynamic ills.

What is the practical significance of Froude's statement (Fig. 70) in the context of IOR or IMO stability criteria? These safety criteria are directly or indirectly expressed in terms of minimum values for certain key features of static stability, such as metacentric height (GM), righting moment calculated from inclining tests, etc. The accepted principle says: find the static stability parameters of the vessels that have been lost, and establish new parameters that are higher than these as the minima to be used in evaluating safety or seaworthiness in the future. By implication one might expect – and the IOR and IMO criteria justify such an expectation – that if GM is increased, the vessel is safer. However, one might be surprised to learn that such a 'safer' vessel with greater GM could with a high degree of probability, be even more dangerous in rough seas than one with a lower GM.

Serat's experiments on the rolling of hull models among waves, published as long ago as 1933[61], showed that 'Increasing GM (without change in other hull characteristics) not only reduces the angular damping, thereby entailing heavier angles of roll, but actually reduces the energy damping, thus augmenting the angle of roll still more.' This finding, although it may strike one as somewhat paradoxical should, after some reflection, be regarded as a clear enough hint that sailing boats and fishing vessels cannot be made safer by sheer fudging of the metacentric stability parameters.

This is confirmed by practical observation, recorded in the *Theory of Naval Architecture*[62]: 'The avoidance of excessive metacentric height in order to minimise the probability of heavy rolling is not prompted only by concern for the comfort of passengers. Experience indicates that ships make their best passages when they are so loaded that they are not excessively stiff. There is the further consideration that heavy rolling may cause . . . damage to the cargo (due to high acceleration) sometimes even endangering the ship.'

With increasing metacentric height, a small, beamy boat (Fig. 72) is approaching the rolling conditions of a raft, and may easily capsize in breaking waves under the combined action of wave impact and/or the wind, as shown in

Fig. 73. *(A) An artist's reconstruction of* Livadia, *a 4,000 ton yacht designed by Admiral Popov (who also designed an unsuccessful completely circular battleship), and built in the Clyde in 1880 for Czar Alexander II. She was an unusual example of an attempt to diminish rolling by using an exaggerated beam (153 ft on a LWL of 235 ft) to increase stability. She survived over 45 years, to be broken up in 1926. INA Transactions Vol. XXIV.*
(B) Hull lines of the Foundation Cousteau's Alcyone, *an oceanographic, wind-assisted research vessel, driven by turbosails (aspirated foils shown in the photograph). The declared intention of the designers (A. Mauric and J.C. Nahoh) was 'to combine the advantages of* monohulls with those of catamarans'. *It is not an uncommon belief, even among naval architects, that – to quote – 'transverse stability acts to reduce rolling of the craft'. A large metacentric height, however, results in a short rolling period and high accelerations; these may lead to crew incapacity. Indeed, in 1985 on the last leg of an Atlantic crossing in Force 6 conditions, the crew of* Alcyone *experienced extremely uncomfortable heavy rolling, with a period of under two seconds! Evidently, the crew inside a flat bottomed hull, built on the dish principle, cannot easily tolerate the accelerations and forces released by waves generated by relatively modest 25-knot winds.*

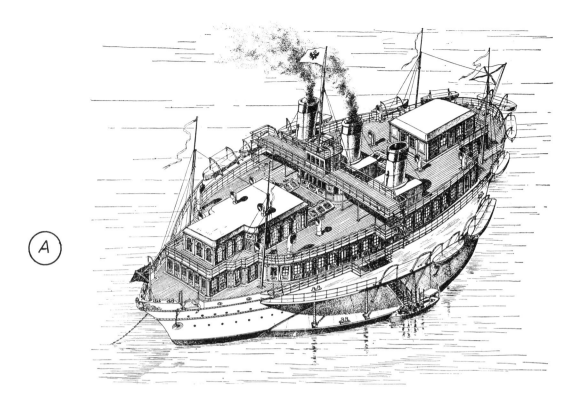

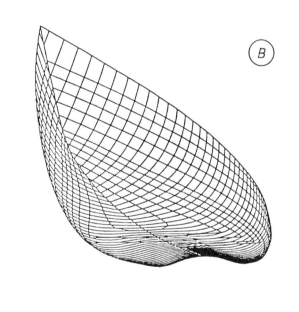

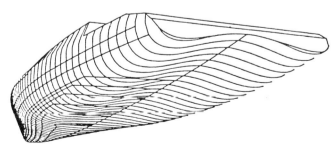

Figs 57 and 69. However, sufficiently big rafts have a good chance of surviving in large waves. Such a big raft – in fact a Russian Imperial yacht *Livadia* of unusual proportions – where only some of the desirable qualities of an ordinary ship have been attained in a degree never realised before is shown in Fig. 73. She was designed by Admiral Popoff and was built on the Clyde in 1880 for Czar Alexander II. It was decided to make all her qualities subordinate to the utmost safety and comfort through elimination of any rolling motion. With her length of 235 ft, beam 155 ft, draft 7 ft and displacement of about 4500 tons, it was intended to be satisfied with a speed of 14 knots (about 0.9 √LWL). It was reasoned that such an enormous raft, by following the surface of the waves, would be exempt from the tendency to accumulate the effect of a succession of waves. And, indeed, during the trials in the Bay of Biscay in rough weather the angle of roll in no case exceeded 4 degrees. It came out, however, that her form was a most disadvantageous one which had to be protected against the heavy blows and slamming shocks she received from short, steep waves in the underwater part of the bow. She suffered damage common to all shallow hull form driven against the sea. The *Livadia* reminds us that boats are not built to achieve any single aim. Every vessel is a compromise amongst a large number of qualities which, if carried to extremes, become incompatible with one another, and this may easily lead to unseaworthiness.

C. Conditions for rapid magnification of rolling

As already discussed earlier (Fig. 70), when wave forces or moments are applied to a boat approximately in phase with any type of oscillatory motion, be it rolling or pitching, the amplitude of this motion increases progressively by a process known as *resonant magnification*. Large angles of roll, or large accumulation of heel, which are occasionally reached are seldom due to the single impact of one big wave (except sporadic breakers) but are invariably the cumulative result of the action of successive waves *in tune with* the natural rolling motion of the boat characterised by her natural period of rolling (T_n); see Eq. 20. That is to say, at each successive wave crest or hollow, the range of rolling angles will be augmented (Fig. 71). It can be shown that if there were no damping (a theoretical assumption of unresisted rolling), the successive increment in roll ($\Delta\Theta$) of a boat placed broadside to waves which have her own periodic motion, i.e. $T_n = T$, at each wave crest, would be directly proportional to the maximum wave slope (α_w).

$$\Delta\Theta = \pi \cdot \alpha_w = 3.14\ \alpha_w \qquad (21)$$

Thus, in regular, relatively smooth waves as shown in Fig. 71 where the wave length (L_w) is about ten times its height and the maximum slope (α_w) is about 9 degrees, the roll increment at each successive crest $\Delta\Theta = \Theta_2 - \Theta_1$ would be $3.14 \cdot 9 = 28.3$ degrees. Therefore just three relatively gentle successive waves would be enough to knock down the boat almost to the horizontal. In theory, given enough time, a boat exposed to a series of uniformly recurring waves, must ultimately roll completely over, however small the waves may be. In view of the fact that, in the absence of damping the concurrence of wave period and boat period may produce such a formidable effect, it is evidently desirable to find out what factors limit the probability of capsize in real conditions, i.e. when water resistance against rolling is taken into account.

Continuous line curves in Fig. 74 illustrate the general consideration which, for the case of unresisted rolling, has been outlined above. Values of magnification ratio (Θ/α_w) – which is the ratio of the rolling angle accumulated (Θ) to the wave slope angle (α_w) – are plotted against the period ratio, i.e. the ratio of the natural period of the boat (T_n) to the wave period (T). It is seen that when $T_n/T = 1$ (i.e. $T_n = T$) the ratio Θ/α_w may grow indefinitely if, of course, disturbing rolling moment persists. Accordingly, there is no maximum value for the magnification ratio (Θ/α_w) and so there are two separate curves. It can also be shown that in regular waves there exists another case of synchronism in long waves when the boat period (T_n) is about half of the wave period (T), i.e. $\dfrac{T_n}{T} = 0.5$. This case of relatively little importance is shown in Fig. 74 to the left of the main branches of the curves relevant to $\dfrac{T_n}{T} = 1.0$.

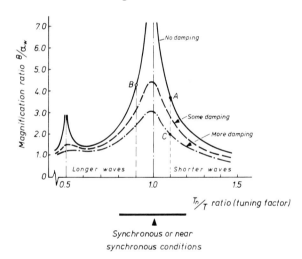

Fig. 74. *Primary factor affectors affecting the magnitude of objectionable boat motion (rolling, pitching, deck wetness, high accelerations, discomfort and even danger) are:*

(A) The tuning factor $(\dfrac{T_n}{T})$ ratio, where $T_n =$ the natural period of the boat's motion, and $T =$ the wave period. The significant values range from 0.8 to 1.2, with the peak usually near 1.0. This is indicated and labelled in the figure: 'synchronous or near-synchronous conditions'.
(B) The magnification ratio ($\theta/\alpha w$ ratio, where $\theta =$ angle of heel and $\alpha w =$ maximum wave slope angle. The greater the damping, the less the magnification of motion in the vicinity of synchronism (see points A, B and C). Instability leading even to catastrophe may occur by complete convergence of the two periods (boat motion T_n and wave period T), i.e. where
$T_n = T$ *or*
$T_n = T_e$ *(where T_e is the period of encounter).*
Two distinct solutions may be tried in order to reduce resonant oscillation to an acceptable level. Either detune the system so that the natural frequency (T_n) is shifted away from the exciting frequency (T); alternatively, increase damping efficiency. As a general rule, rolling may be expected to reach large angles only when the natural period (T_n) of the boat and the period of encounter with waves (T_e) differ by less than 10 per cent.

When the water resistance against rolling i.e. damping begins to play its role, the maximum angle of heel can be dramatically reduced; the angle of roll, or magnification ratio (Θ/α_w) then decreased inversely as the intensity of damping. This effect is shown in Fig. 74 by two broken line curves. It is seen that, even in synchronous conditions ($\frac{T_n}{T} = 1.0$), damping imposes a definite limit on the maximum angle of roll inflicted by waves.

In the example of a boat rolling amongst waves (Fig. 71) it was assumed that she is placed broadside to waves which have the same periodic motion $T_n = T$. In such a situation, the period of time separating the meeting of successive waves by the boat is the actual period of the waves in seconds, i.e.:

$$T = 0.442 \ \sqrt{L_w} \ (ft) \tag{22}$$

When a boat is sailing with the waves overtaking on the quarter (sketch A in Fig. 75) the waves' velocity (c) relative to the running boat is reduced, and accordingly the frequency with which the waves meet the boat is reduced. In other words, *the period of encounter* (T_e) is increased as compared with the wave period given by Eq. 22. Since the character of rolling motion depends critically on the *timing* of the waves meeting the boat, an extended period of encounter will inevitably lead to synchronous conditions, when the boat is amongst waves of period T smaller than her own period T_n. Thus, in addition to the period of the boat (T_n), there are three quantities which determine whether or not synchronous rolling will occur, namely the length (and thus the period) of waves, the course sailed relative to the wave crests and the boat's speed. The period of encounter (T_e in seconds) for the boat travelling with the waves overtaking on the quarter is given by the following formula:

$$T_e = \frac{\text{Wave length}}{\text{Relative speed of approach}} = \frac{L_w}{c - V_s \cos \beta} \tag{23}$$

where L_w – length of waves in ft
c – wave velocity (celerity) in ft/sec
V_s – boat speed in ft/sec
β – angle of encounter measured from the stern.

Fig. 75. *Nomogram for determining resonant or near-resonant conditions for rolling and pitching. For example: to find resonant conditions in rolling when the boat sails down wind in overtaking seas at $\beta = 165°$ (15° off the stern), assuming that her natural period of rolling (T_n) = 5 sec. The solution is given by the thin broken line marked X, which intersects the two diagonal lines relevant to wave lengths 80 ft and 100 ft, at points marked (a) and (b) respectively. In the first case, resonant rolling will occur when boat speed (V_s) is about 2.4 knots; in the second, when V_s is about 1.5 knots. This indicates that when the boat is sailing in* overtaking seas it is unlikely that resonant rolling will occur in long waves, but it may in shorter ones. Another thin broken line, marked Y, gives the solution to the situation where the same boat is close-hauled, i.e. advancing towards the waves at $\beta = 45°$. This time, resonant rolling will occur in waves about 200 ft long if boat speed (V_s) is 7.0 knots (point c), or in waves about 150 ft long if V_s is 2.0 knots (point d). Lengthening the natural period T_n of the boat produces resonance in longer waves, and this may be advantageous because the critical resonant conditions are shifted towards longer and usually less steep waves (Ref. 63).*

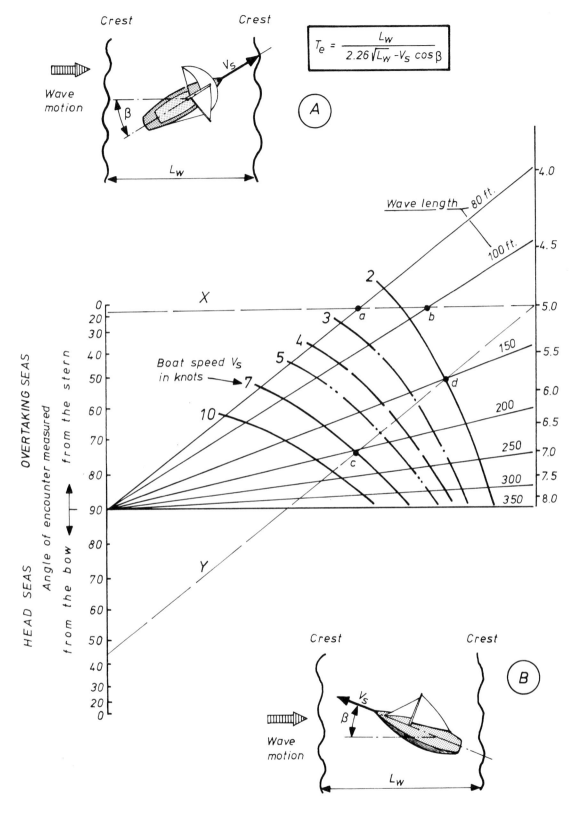

$$T_e = \frac{L_W}{2.26\sqrt{L_W} - V_s \cos\beta}$$

A

Crest   Crest

Wave
motion

β

L_W

Wave length   80 ft.

100 ft.

Natural period of oscillation T_n in seconds

X

Boat speed V_s
in knots

OVERTAKING SEAS

Angle of encounter measured   from the stern

HEAD SEAS

from the bow

Y

Crest   Crest

B

Wave
motion

β V_s

L_W

For example: If the boat's course is parallel to the wave crest, i.e. $\beta = 90°$ (Fig. 75) then $\cos 90° = 0$ and hence the period of encounter will be $T_e = \dfrac{L_w}{c}$ which is the true period of the waves. If the boat's course is relative to the direction of wave motion $\beta = 60°$ and her speed (V_s) equals the wave celerity (c) i.e. $V_s = c$, the period of encounter will be:

$$T_e = \frac{L_w}{c - V_s \times \cos 60°} = \frac{L_w}{c - V_s \times 0.5} = \frac{L_w}{0.5\,c}$$

that is, the period of encounter (T_e) will be twice the wave period (T).

It is convenient to express wave velocity (c) in terms of L_w which is $c = 2.26 \sqrt{L_w}$, in ft/sec if L_w is in ft.

Then

$$T_e = \frac{L_w}{2.26 \sqrt{L_w} - V_s \cos \beta} \tag{23A}$$

This formula together with an explanatory sketch A is repeated in Fig. 75 (upper part).

If boat speed (V_s) is given in knots (1 knot = 1.69 ft/sec) the above formula reads:

$$T_e = \frac{L_w}{2.26 \sqrt{L_w} - 1.69 \, V_s \cos \beta} \tag{24}$$

It is useful to distinguish between a *following sea* and an *overtaking sea*. A *following sea* is one in which the boat speed V_s exceeds the wave velocity (celerity) of the dominant wave train, so that the waves follow the boat and she advances relative to the wave train. An *overtaking sea* is one in which the velocity, c, of the dominant wave system exceeds the speed V_s of the boat, so that the waves, travelling faster than the boat actually overtake her. In the first case speed of encounter $V_e = V_s \cos \beta - c$, in the second $V_e = c - V_s \cos \beta$; the period of wave encounter $T_e = \dfrac{L_w}{V_e}$ for both cases. Since wave velocities (see Table 5) are usually greater than the average speed of sailing boats (which are relatively small in relation to wave lengths) in most cases the boats heading downwind sail in overtaking seas.

The nomogram in Fig. 75 may be used as a ready means of determining whether or not resonant rolling (as well as pitching) is likely to occur with a given combination of boat speed (V_s), wave length (L_w), angle of encounter (β) and period of boat oscillation either roll or pitch (T_n). Two examples described in the caption of Fig. 75 illustrate how the diagram can be interpreted in practical terms. It can be deduced, for instance, that in overtaking seas a boat will tend to develop synchronous rolling in shorter waves than when sailing in head seas. The reason is straightforward. The period of encounter (T_e) will be longer with waves on the quarter, than when the boat meets the same waves on

Table 5

Length, L_w, in feet	Velocity, c,	
	knots	ft/sec
30	7.34	12.4
35	7.93	13.4
40	8.47	14.3
45	8.99	15.2
50	9.47	16.0
60	10.38	17.5
70	11.20	18.9
80	12.00	20.2
90	12.70	21.5
100	13.40	22.6

the bow; and chances of synchronism between T_n and T_e will also be greater. Short waves are more common than long ones – these are the ones which built up more quickly. It follows that for less violent rolling the best course for the boat will be to meet the sea on her bow. In addition, bearing in mind that in closehauled conditions and usually concomitant head seas, sails normally operate as a damping agent so that the probability of knockdown is relatively low; provided, of course, sails can be carried effectively (no flutter).

In overtaking seas, however, the probability of heavy rolling and even capsize in the same waves is much higher. Sails do not provide aerodynamic damping (steady effect) on broad courses relative to the wind. To the contrary, once triggered by the waves, rolling becomes self-perpetuating unless a special anti-rolling sail is hoisted; provided, of course, that the weather allows any canvas to be carried at all. For these reasons, it became a matter of common experience that boats usually roll most heavily when waves are overtaking on the quarter. Both theory and experience indicate that the most practical way to ease rolling, if synchronism has occurred, is to change course radically. To quote an expert opinion – 'Nine times out of ten this will do the trick'.[64]

Next to changing course, the best way to moderate rolling is to reduce speed, in an attempt to *detune* the period of encounter with roll producing waves. 'Finally when all else fails, the shipmaster can still do two things: pray or swear. Few can do the first, most are artistically letter perfect with the second and, indeed, it is a wonderful comfort in moments of frustration'.[64]

It has been noted in the caption to Fig. 75 that a longer natural rolling period (T_n) is advantageous; and one of the reasons is that it shifts the probability of resonant conditions towards the sea with longer waves which usually are less steep. In other words, the longer a boat's period is, the more rarely will she experience the conditions of synchronism – Fig. 76 illustrates the point. It shows the relationship between the size of storm waves and their steepness (surface slope) under the worst conditions for three different localities.[65] Scientific observations of the maximum dimensions of storm waves are not numerous, nor are the published data to be taken at their face value. Those

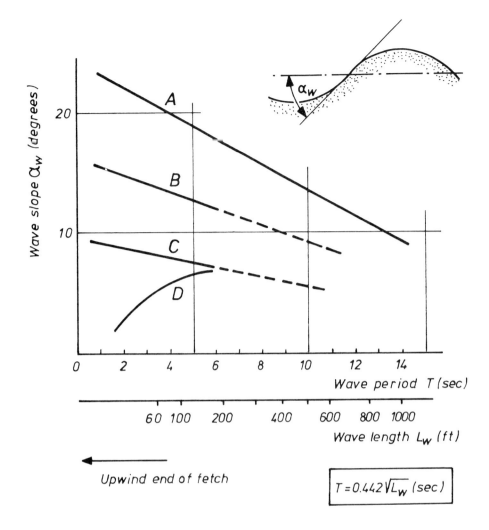

$$T = 0.442\sqrt{L_W} \ (sec)$$

Fig. 76. *The surface slope of storm waves plotted on a base of wave period (T) and wave length (L_W).*
(A)   Open sea.
(B)   English Channel.
(C)   Estuaries and sheltered waters.
(D)   The meaning of this curve is explained in the following chapter.

At the upwind end of the fetch, shorter and steeper waves build up more quickly, while down wind, the longer, less steep waves predominate. The shorter waves are multi-directional – often angled to the wind – but the longer waves are more aligned to each other and to the wind. As long ago as the early 1860s Froude wrote in his classic paper On the Rolling of Ships *(INA 1881)*: '. . . it is a matter of experience that small waves are steeper and more abrupt than large ones, where generated by winds of the same force'. In a more modern reference, D.W. Taylor (SNAME, 1922, Vol.

30) stated '. . . as regards ocean waves, the shorter they are, the steeper they are . . . waves formed as a storm sets in and begins to develop, are always shorter and steeper on the ocean as well as on the (Great) Lakes than the long, low waves after a storm has passed'.

K.F. Bowden appears to have been the first to offer a rational explanation of this observed fact. His formula indicates a rapid increase of energy dissipation with increase of wave height and length. On the other hand, the accepted formula for transfer of energy from wind to wave depends upon the wave form (profile, steepness) but is independent of wave height. Thus the balance between energy delivered to the wave, and energy dissipated by it, can only be achieved in larger (longer) waves at lower values of the steepness ratio (The Effect of Eddy Viscosity on Ocean Waves; Phil Magazine Sep 1950 Vol 41).

given in Fig. 76 should be regarded as a reasonable approximation taking into account the following facts: apart from the regularity of the wind and its duration, the maximum size of storm waves in any locality is determined by two main factors: *the fetch*, i.e. sea-room to windward and the *wind velocity*.

At the beginning of a storm, short waves which build-up swiftly reach a high steepness gradient and then the point of instability so that they break. Although they break – thus dissipating wind energy – part of their energy is fed into longer waves; while residues of these shorter waves are rebuilt to the breaking point over and over again. Thus, within any storm zone the sea surface is dominated by *steep* and *short-period waves*. Lines A, B and C in Fig. 76 which relate the slope of waves to their period clearly indicate this close correlation.

The true picture of the sea surface is far removed from what might be called a two-dimensional corrugated-iron like case, in which the waves are long and long-crested, and wave follows wave like a sort of wave-train. In reality, particularly in the area of wave generation (fetch) by the storm-wind, the sea surface undulation consists of many waves of different height, length and direction of propagation.

Waves arriving some distance downwind of the fetch are more closely aligned to each other, i.e. they become longer crested than inside the fetch and with increasingly longer period. These longer waves will be of rather modest steepness (Fig. 76) and, in general, will be less dangerous because their longer period is well outside the resonant rolling conditions for smaller craft such as yachts or fishing boats. This, of course, does not flatly exclude the possibility of meeting an abnormally high, steep, freak wave, caused by coincidental interference of several waves, possibly of different origins, crossing just at the wrong time and place for the unfortunate crew. In such episodic, aberrational waves, no yacht can ride out or heave-to safely. Fortunately, there are some living eye witnesses who have survived to testify to the existence and power of freak waves.

Let us quote from *Once is Enough* by Miles Smeeton referring to *Tzu Hang* which was almost swamped by a freak wave but happily recovered albeit with both masts and the dog-house torn away. 'Close behind a great wall of water was towering above her, so wide that she (Beryl at the helm) couldn't see its flanks, so high and so steep that she knew *Tzu Hang* could not ride over it. It didn't seem to be breaking as the other waves had broken, but water was cascading down its front, like a waterfall . . . To us it seemed that in one tremendous movement she was stood on end and plunged bow first down into the sea, falling over on her side at the same time.'

Figure 77 gives an artist's impression of how much a freak wave may look in character; note the size, as compared with the yacht in front of the overtaking wave, when she may travel across the sea with a velocity in the order of 30–40 knots. A boat engulfed by such a single overtaking wave may be driven completely under, with such a suddenness and catastrophic ferocity that neither the hull nor the crew will ever rise to the surface again.

Admiralty Pilot books have traditionally pointed out where freak waves

Fig. 77. Top. *An artist's impression of a boat riding the near vertical slope of an overtaking breaker (Michael Pocock,* Yachts and Yachting, *Feb 1980).*
Bottom. *Two consecutive pictures illustrating a real, rapidly developing plunging breaker of over 40 ft (13 m) height, recorded at Hawaii on 27th February 1984; further waves up to 65 ft (20 m) high were also noted. If a boat is knocked down, or even broaches, in such seas, the period of breaking waves may be so short that the next plunging breaker may be upon her before she can recover from the first impact.*

might occur and in what conditions. Thus, to some degree, they lead and safeguard prudent navigators by telling them not to be in known danger areas at given times of the year.

These episodic waves of exceptional steepness which can roll over a boat in one go – the bane of all mariners – are not indicated in Fig. 76. The important factor of wave motion and shape that requires notice in dealing with synchronous rolling is the prevalence of the maximum wave slope associated with wave period which makes synchronism possible. The other wave characteristics such as length or height are, in this respect, irrelevant. Waves may be high, very high, but at the same time of gentle steepness because of their length; and what makes the boat roll heavily is, according to Eq. 21, the maximum slope although this is not the only factor which matters.

D. Light versus heavy displacement controversy

'Things and actions are what they are, and the consequences
of them will be what they will be: why then should we desire
to be deceived?'

Bishop Butler's Sermons
(1692–1752)

Let us consider the two types of hull, the cross-sections of which are shown in Fig. 78. Sections marked A are those of old fashioned cruiser-racer hulls, while section B is that of a fashionable, contemporary type hull. The question is, will the rolling motion of these two types of hull be the same in similar waves? One

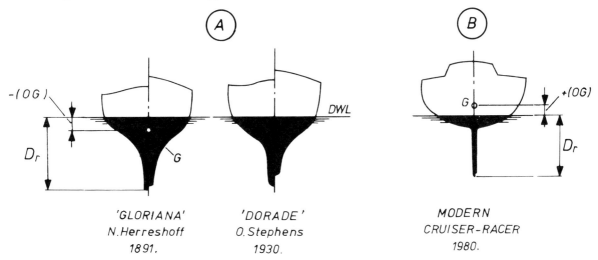

'GLORIANA'
N.Herreshoff
1891.

'DORADE'
O.Stephens
1930.

MODERN
CRUISER-RACER
1980.

Fig. 78. *Cross sections of old-fashioned (A) and contemporary (B) hulls. Will these two different types of hull behave differently in heavy seas? If so, why? The significance of the position of the Centre of Gravity*

(G) in relation to the LWL taken as a base 0, i.e. the distance ±0 G (positive being upward) is discussed in the next chapter.

does not need to be a prominent yacht designer or a very experienced seaman to guess, without any hesitation, that these boats will behave differently in rough seas. However, if we are to ask the question – which of these two boats is safer and *why*, we may expect much confusion and arguments. This is inevitable whenever there is no reliable information which might eliminate ill-reasoned theories (read the view expressed by prominent designers on page 8).

As compared with the older heavy displacement type of cruiser-racers (A), contemporary light displacement racers (B) have a shorter natural period of rolling; about half of that of the older type boat, i.e. 3–4 seconds depending on the size of the hull.

Remembering that it is not the absolute size of the waves but their steepness which governs the magnification of rolling, it becomes evident from Fig. 76 that contemporary IOR cruiser-racers (type B in Fig. 78) will roll through larger angles when synchronising with comparatively small waves than with comparatively large ones. By the same token, an old-fashioned type of boat (A in Fig. 78) will, on the account of her larger period, be less susceptible of heavy rolling in similar seas. The working out of these circumstances may be put in more general form on the basis of Eqs 20, 21 and Fig. 76, namely: the maximum range of roll which any given boat will attain when exposed to a series of synchronising waves will be proportional to the maximum wave slope, her stability (!) as expressed by her metacentric height (GM is in the denominator of Eq. 20A), and inversely proportional to her displacement (transverse moment of inertia I_r which is in the numerator of Eq. 20A). Other things being equal, energy communicated to the boat by each wave impulse is enlarged by the ratio in which her stability (GM) is increased (Figs 50 and 70).

Advice given by W. Froude in his classic paper *On the Rolling of Ships* (1861) may sound, to some ears, blasphemous; nevertheless it is scientifically correct. It reads: 'The surest and readiest method of giving a ship a long periodic time, is by lessening her stability under canvas. The effort of stability is the lever by which a wave forces a ship into motion – if a ship were destitute of this stability, no wave that the ocean produces would serve to put her in motion.'

When talking about stability, W. Froude had in mind the metacentric height (GM) or inertial hydrostatic stability and this, according to him, is frequently mistakenly given in excess for safety's sake. In this context Scott Russell, one-time lecturer in geometry at the University of Edinburgh and a successful yacht and ship designer in those days, expressed the following axiomatic view: 'I should not regard it as expedient to design a ship with high metacentric height attended by a high centre of gravity . . . I should endeavour to diminish the violence and the extent of rolling motion in the design of a new ship, by diminishing the metacentric height above the axis of rotation or the water-line. I should by this seek to diminish the forces by which the water acts to cause rolling . . . the dangers of the sea to a ship having already a high metacentre, would be greatly aggravated by giving to her also, a high centre of gravity. *I believe in a low metacentre and a low centre of gravity for a wholesome ship.*' (The italics are mine.) It might be added that research made since has not detected blemishes in these intuitive maxims.

Reverting to Froude again, he rightly argued that the boat which has the longest periodic time will fare best. This claim can be justified as follows: on the approach of a gale, the growth of waves is undoubtedly gradual. If the period of the boat is long, not only will the condition of synchronism be longer deferred but, when it does occur, its effects will be of a more moderate scale (Fig. 76). As the storm continues, fresh waves continue to be generated and to grow in steepness till they break. Their growth, however, being but little modified by the existence of developing longer waves; the surface of the latter being interlaced with smaller waves of almost every intermediate stage of growth. Hence, as argued by Froude, it cannot be hoped that during the continuation of the storm a time will come when the waves have outgrown the period of a quickly rolling boat. Relevant to this is one more conclusion which can be derived from Fig. 74, namely: of the two boats, one of which (A) has a periodic time (T_n) longer than that of the prevalent waves (T) in a ratio, say, $\frac{T_n}{T} = \frac{11}{10} \simeq 1.1$; the other boat (B) has T_n shorter than that of the waves in reversed ratio, i.e. $\frac{T_n}{T} = \frac{10}{11} \simeq 0.9$; boat B with the shorter period will accumulate the larger rolling angles. Points A and B marked in Fig. 74 indicate the corresponding magnification ratios for these two boats.

Thus, referring to two types of boat shown in Fig. 78, the contemporary beamy, light-displacement, IOR cruiser-racer with its short period of oscillation will be more susceptible of excessive rolling and associated misbehaviour than the more traditional heavy-displacement boat of type A.

Now, let us assume for the sake of argument, that the light-displacement boat of type B is given (by means of trickery with her metacentre and transverse moment of inertia, Eq. 20) the same period of rolling as the boat of type A. Will, then, these two type of boats behave in the same manner in stormy waves? One can do no better than to read Froude's argument in his own language quoted here from his paper[66]: 'Taken in the most naked form . . . if two ships, having the same natural period of rolling in still water, were exposed under the same circumstances to the same series of waves, their behaviour would be approximately the same, *whatever their size or whatever their peculiarity of form.*' (italics are mine.)

That was Froude's prompt but rather too dogmatic reply to Scott Russell's INA paper: *On the Rolling of Ships as influenced by their Forms and by the Disposition of their Weights* published in 1863 which, in turn, was a part of a 'hot potato' discussion between these two eminent scientists of those days. In essence, this discussion on the effect of hull form and its displacement on seaworthiness still persists unresolved – at least amongst yacht designers – as reflected by the already quoted opinions. It should be added that later on W. Froude substantially modified his view in this respect and he came to the conclusion that two vessels of identical periods may have materially different rolling behaviour, depending entirely on their hull shapes and, thus, on their damping characteristics.

Concept of wave anatomy

Scott Russell did not believe that two ships of identical metacentric height or identical periods, but substantially different in form, would behave in the same manner as alleged by Froude. On the contrary, he believed that what really matters in troubled waters is how the stability of a given boat is achieved. That is, Scott wanted to differentiate between what is called stability due to form and stability due to ballast. His attractive theory, illustrated in Fig. 79, was based on the anatomy of the trochoidal wave, the wave concept which has, in naval architecture, facilitated the study of boat behaviour in actual sea states for more than a century.

A wave may be considered to be formed by a series of layers (S, 1, 2, 3, and so on) marked by the thin lines in Fig. 79, which were horizontal (parallel) while the water was at rest. In waves however, these layers are distorted in such a way that they are no longer parallel but their thickness is increased under the wave crest and correspondingly decreased under the wave trough. Thick longitudinal lines show the curvature and direction of the deflected layers. Alternatively, we may conceive the water, when at rest, to be divided into a number of slender columns between vertical, thin lines. When the water

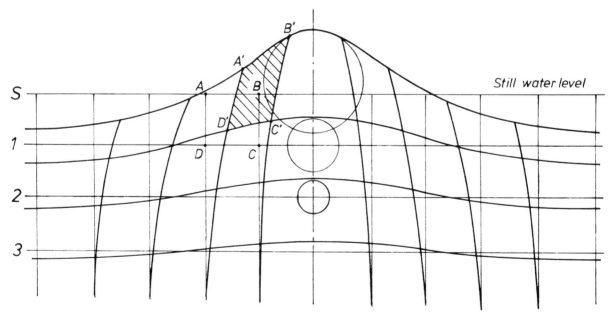

Fig. 79. *Mechanism of a sea wave as presented in 1844 by John Scott Russell in the Transactions of the British Association. The hatched area marked A', B', C' and D' shows how the initial parallelogram formed in still water changes its shape and place due to wave motion.*

Diminishing radii of successive orbits at successive depths, as we proceed down the vertical line, determine the decreasing effective slope of the water strata, marked S (surface) 1, 2, 3 and so forth.

is agitated by waves, those originally vertical columns bend and sway to and fro – to use M. Rankine's expression – 'like the stalks in a wind-swept field of corn'. And they do so in such a manner that an originally vertical column ABCD sways in the opposite direction to that in which its longitudinal layer S slopes, as indicated by the shaded column A′, B′, C′, D′, or thick lines which assume a peculiar deflection different along the wave length and depth of water. This mechanism of water motion is governed by the differences between orbital velocities of the water particles describing respective circles of decreasing radii as we proceed down the vertical line from the surface. These circles (orbits) are drawn for comparison in Fig. 79 below the wave crest. As a result, the slope of sublayers 1, 2, 3 and so on, below the surface layer S, must diminish quite rapidly. An approximate rule is that the so-called effective slope is diminished to one half for each ninth part of a wave length of depth below the surface.

Scott Russell referred his theory to this dynamical behaviour of water within the wave. For the sake of distinction, he considered the quality of rolling of two diametrically different forms: a raft-like plank floating flat on the wave surface, and a thin plank so ballasted as to float vertically edgewise in still water; these two extreme cases are illustrated in Fig. 80A and B. His argument was based on a fundamental premise that these two forms are bound to behave in waves in a similar manner as the mass of water in which they temporarily float. Or to put it differently, these forms are subject to dynamic forces which are responsible for the peculiar deflections of originally horizontal and vertical columns of water (Fig. 79). Thus, a raft-like craft with large beam/draft ratio floating in waves that are large with respect to its size, would predominantly be influenced by the slope of the surface layer of the wave and would carry its mast always *inclined from the advancing wave* (Fig. 80A). On the other hand, the plank which floats edgewise would partake of the motion of the originally vertical columns of water and would conform itself to the deviation of deflected vertical lines (imaginary membrane drawn in Fig. 80 top) so that its mast would be always *inclined towards the advancing wave* (Fig. 80B). Scott Russell argued that these two floating planks can be regarded as prototypes of two contrary kinds of boat, and their movement as two contrary kinds of behaviour in waves. Each sort of plank is part of the water it occupies and it moves with the water. If it could change its shape as readily as the water, without changing its bulk, it would really be part of the sea.

A vessel is usually an intermediate between these extreme forms. However, depending on the degree of predominance of one form or the other in the hull shape, their behaviour in waves will be dissimilar. Thus, in the case of a light-displacement, broad and shallow type of boat, her response to waves will be of the character shown in sketch A. To continue with Scott Russell – 'Such a vessel will be able to carry plenty of sail, will be very stiff under canvas, as well as extremely lively; she will take every motion of the sea as if she were part of it . . . I now come to the faults of this vessel. The great danger of a ship which is all shoulder, and has no underwater body, is that across a sharp and breaking sea she is liable to capsize. When the sea breaks, the front of the wave becomes

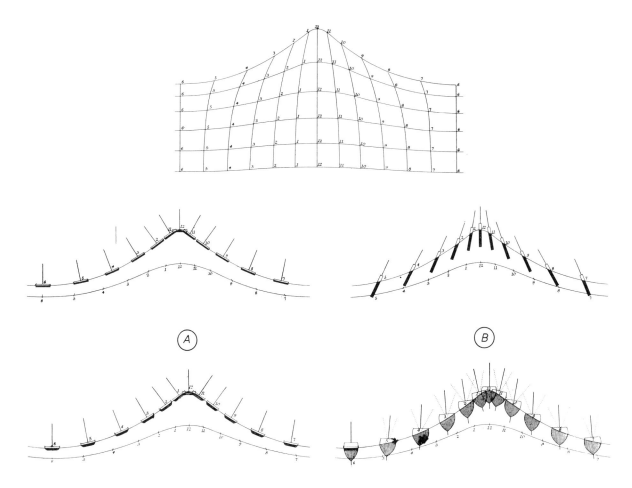

Fig. 80. *Behaviour of two different types of boat in waves, as suggested by Scott Russell's theory, and based on original illustrations.*
(A) A flat-bottomed, raft-like vessel with appreciable metacentric height (GM).
(B) A deeply immersed vessel, with narrow mid-ships sections and low metacentric height (GM).

While in case (A) the heeling action of the wave is predominantly hydrostatic, in case (B) hydrodynamic action is derived principally from the orbital motion of the water particles in the waves. Here the heeling and righting moments due to buoyancy forces are relatively small, but the area of hull exposed to orbital flow is large. As a consequence, the deeply immersed hull tends to assume a position parallel to the vertical 'membranes' shown in the top sketch, and therefore opposite to the inclinations of the raft-like hull of sketch (A).

nearly perpendicular. The shallow vessel takes of course the position of the surface of the water. Having taken it on the face of the wave, she retains it on the back of the wave . . . in other words, she turns over'.

The other extreme sort of boat (Fig. 80B) will also be part of the water which she occupies. She too, therefore, takes the motion of the surrounding water. And, although, her motion is a more complicated one than the former, nevertheless, 'the evils arising from surface oscillation may be remedied by using the pecularities of deep-water oscillation.'

In short, a narrow sailing boat with deep keel (Figs 10, 13 and 16C) may, by judicious choice of form, behave in rough seas in much the same fashion as the deep edge-wise floating plank; and, on account of its tendency to lean towards the advancing breaker, be deemed much safer than a broad and shallow type of boat.

One cannot deny that Scott Russell's theory is elegant and captivating although, alas, somewhat delusive – but not in all respects, the geometrical basis of the theory being unassailable. Froude forcibly attempted to refute the theory, but he himself had over-simplified the problem by setting up the periodic time of rolling as the major criterion of a ship's behaviour in waves. From further investigations still unfinished – after all no branch of science is self-terminating – it came out that there are four basic parameters which determine a boat's response to waves:

(1) her natural periodic time which decides to what sort of waves the boat might tune in a storm,
(2) the shape of the hull, distribution of displacement, i.e. draft in relation to the effective wave slope and position of the centre of gravity relative to the water surface,
(3) damping, and finally
(4) size of the boat (on statistical evidence it is clear that smaller vessels are more liable to loss).

Hull shape

Referring more specifically to the second parameter: the influence of hull shape, the fact that narrow, deep hulls tend to lean towards the advancing wave crest or breaker and are safer in storm, can be explained more comprehensively in a different way from that given by Scott Russell; but still on the basis of his concept of wave anatomy shown in Fig. 79, which holds good. An apt remark expressed by A. Einstein appears to be appropriate here: 'Every theory is killed sooner or later by a fact. But if the theory has good in it, that good is embodied and continued in the next theory.'

It is seen (Fig. 79) that the subsurfaces 1, 2, 3 . . . are gradually more flat and their steepness diminishes quite rapidly as we trace them below the surface layer S. In due time it became evident that the hydrodynamic heeling (rolling) forces acting on the hull do not entirely depend on the shape of the sea surface but also on the slope of sublayers which are penetrated by the hull. The deeper the draft of the hull the less will be the so called *effective wave slope*, and hence less will be the heeling (rolling) moment imparted by the waves at any instant (Eq. 21). After making a number of simplifying assumptions, it has been found that the proper effective wave slope to choose is that which traverses the calm-water centre of buoyancy of the immersed volume of the hull. A corollary of this is that, considering buoyancy effect only (leaving aside the effect of centre of gravity position for a moment), a wide shallow hull follows a steep wave slope near the surface, while a narrow deep hull seeks its equilibrium position about a lesser slope at a greater depth. On this basis alone, the latter shape could be expected to develop smaller angles of roll, and to lean towards the crest of the wave as compared with a shallow hull. Thus, although Scott Russell was wrong in part of his theory he was right in his intuition. It has happened not for the first time in the history of science.

Curve D in Fig. 76, derived from C, gives the expected effective wave slope for a craft of 11 ft draft, with the distance of the centre of buoyancy being assumed at 0.45 of the draft below the waterline. It has also been shown that the tendency to lean away from or towards the wave crest depends on the ratio of the natural period (T_n) of the boat to the wave period (T), or period of encounter (T_e). If $\dfrac{T_n}{T}$ is less than one (the wave period longer than that of the boat), the boat will heel away from the crest (Fig. 81A); if $\dfrac{T_n}{T}$ is greater than one, the boat will lean towards the crest (Fig. 81B). Light-displacement boats usually have a small T_n, and therefore will more frequently heel away from the advancing breaker.

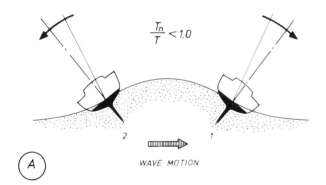

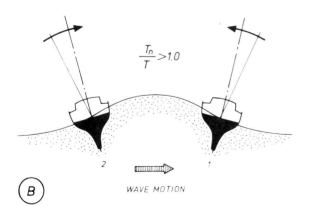

Fig. 81. *Depending on their natural periods of rolling (T_n), the light displacement boat of the upper sketch will roll differently from the heavy boat in waves of the same or similar length (L_w) and period (T). The ratio $\dfrac{T_n}{T}$ determines which boat will heel away or towards the wave crest. As indicated earlier in Fig. 80, boat behaviour is modified depending whether the hull is wide and shallow or deep and narrow. Wide hull rolling is primarily affected by the wave surface, while the rolling of deep hulls largely depends on the motion of water particles below the wave surface.*

After further study in making estimates of the probable maxima for rolling waves, the following equation for synchronism condition has been worked out, as applied to vessels in beam seas:

$$\Theta_{max} \simeq \frac{0.5\pi\,\alpha_{max}\,\zeta}{2\delta} \simeq \frac{0.78\,\alpha_{max}\,\zeta}{\delta} \qquad (25)$$

where: $\simeq$ designates 'is proportional' to . . .

α_{max} the maximum wave slope

δ roll decrement coefficient when the resistance to rolling is assumed to be proportional to angular velocity of rolling for a stationary ship in still water (Fig. 82). For definition read Note 70.

ζ effective wave slope coefficient given in Ref 67 is

$$\zeta = 0.73 + 0.6\ \left(\frac{OG}{D_r}\right) \qquad (26)$$

where: OG – vertical distance from DWL to the centre of gravity G, positive upward (Fig. 78)

D_r – draft of the hull

Although this formula holds good for a ship shape forms, and for that reason it may underestimate the effective wave slope relevant to the surface skimming forms such as contemporary IOR type of boats, it clearly reflects the significance of the centre of gravity position. The table in the caption to Fig. 49 shows that, for the Half-Tonner *Grimalkin* the centre of gravity is above the DWL, i.e. OG = +0.65 ft, while for the rather older type *Contessa 32*, the centre of gravity is below DWL, so OG = −0.75. This, evidently, makes the effective slope coefficient ζ greater for *Grimalkin* and, according to Eq. 25, inflicts larger maximum heeling angles even if the damping efficiencies of the two boats were identical; which is not the case, as shown in the following chapter dealing with damping. From the view point of seaworthiness another strong argument can therefore be presented in favour of a heavy hull with deep mid-section of wine glass shape rather than a light dinghy-type section as shown in Fig. 78B.

The closing remark given below and taken from A.O. Lovejoy's book *The Great Chain of Being*, reflects so accurately the author's own feelings while attempting to trace the origins and causes of the controversy which has been the subject of this chapter, that he could not resist sharing them with the reader. 'The adequate record or even the confusions of our forebears may help, not only to clarify those confusions, but to engender a salutary doubt whether we are wholly immune from different but equally great confusions. For though we have more empirical information at our disposal, we have not different or better minds; and it is, after all, the action of mind upon facts that makes both philosophy and science, indeed, largely makes the "facts"'.

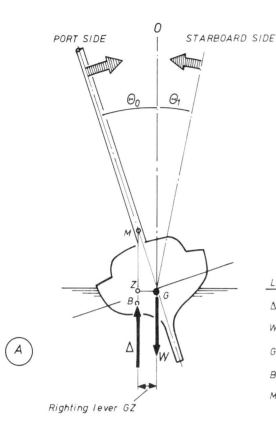

PORT SIDE   0   STARBOARD SIDE

Θ_0 Θ_1

M

Z   G
B

Δ W

Righting lever GZ

A

Fig. 82. *Recorded rolling of a statically stable boat (which has a degree of damping) in calm water (sketch B). Since consecutive angles of roll θ_0, θ_1, θ_2 etc. diminish with time, the boat is both statically and dynamically stable.*

LIST OF SYMBOLS

Δ - Buoyancy force = Displacement

W - Weight = Displacement Δ

G - Centre of gravity

B - Centre of buoyancy

M - Metacentre

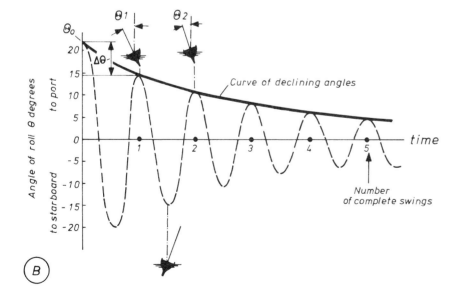

B

Addendum to page 129 (moment of inertia)

The explanatory comment below is taken from the author's article published in *Practical Boat Owner*, November 1986.

Those who are familiar with the idea of moment of inertia, *or* radius of gyration *will not wish to read this note. Others may find it helpful.*

Similarly, those who are familiar with the distinction between mass *and* weight *will need no explanation. On the other hand, those who are not so familiar will come to no harm if they treat mass and weight as one and the same. In real life, if you want to add mass half way up a mast you will finish up by adding weight: and the numbers will be the same if you want to add 30 lb of mass – you will add 30 lb of weight.*

Moment of inertia *is the resistance of a mass to any attempt to make it move in a circular path, or for that matter to stop it moving when it is already doing so. One way to get the 'feel' of it is to fit a pair of woodworking clamps to a suitable stick, and to rotate the assembly by holding it in the centre.*

equal to two feet, say, and then at four feet, it is evident that when you turn the stick through any given angle, the mass at the greater radius will have to move twice as far. And because it moves twice as far in exactly the same time as the inner mass it will have to have double the acceleration. That in turn calls for double the force.

Thus we have double the force acting with double the leverage, so the moment of inertia turns out to be proportional to the square of the radius.

In the imaginary case of the woodworking clamps, the radius from its centre of gravity to the centre of your hand would be the radius of gyration (if the weight of the stick is negligible for argument's sake). But where the stick is replaced by a boat's mast and rigging, and your hand by the hull, one has a whole range of masses at various distances from the rolling axis. These spread-out weights have a centre of gravity of their own, a point through which they can be considered to act. The radius of gyration, or gyradius, is then the length from the roll axis to that CG point.

Of course this 'centre of gravity' is not the CG of the complete boat which is actually very close to the rolling

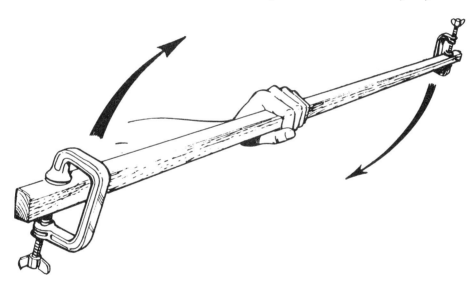

Set the clamps as near the middle of the stick as will clear your hand, and rotate (like a drum majorette). Then set the clamps well out toward the ends of the stick and try it again. The increased resistance to turning is self-evident, and is the moment of inertia. Moment *is really another word for* leverage, *and the* inertia, *or* resistance to acceleration of the two masses, *is now working against your hand with the benefit of longer leverage.*

The longer the radius, the greater the leverage, but the effect is greater than might at first be expected. Comparing two cases, where the same mass is placed first at a radius

axis. Moreover, what I have called the CG of mast, rigging and upper hull, is complemented by another one below the roll axis, formed by the lower hull, ballast and so forth. This too gives rise to a moment of inertia, but its lever arm is much shorter and its effect much less.

In real life one always has to take account of moments on each side of the rotational axis, and radius of gyration does so. It is a number such that if you square it, and then multiply by the mass of the whole assembly, you get the moment of inertia of the whole object – that's to say, its resistance to rotational accelerations.

'What is good is not new;
What is new is not good.'

German statesman of
the Third Reich

9 Damping – Protection Against Rough Sea

Extreme angles of heel in waves, and so the knockdown probability, can also be reduced by increasing the boat's resistance to rolling (damping). It is seen from formula 25 that the roll decrement coefficient (δ) is in the denominator – therefore the larger the damping the less the rate of accumulation of the maximum heel angle. Boats are different in shape, according to whether they have a keel or no keel, much or little gripe and deadwood, a round or flat or a sharp bottom, may have widely different damping characteristics and this will produce a marked effect in the boat's behaviour in similar waves. Keel action in this respect is far from immaterial. This fact, according to Froude, became only too evident during the period of transition from sails to steam, which rendered the abandonment of keels in shipbuilding both convenient and common. Gradually, small vessels – fishing boats and sailing yachts among them – were given less and less built-in damping capability. So much effort over the years has been put into the quest for speed and profitability of the fishing fleet, and so little into seaworthiness, that some penalty has become inevitable. As reported, the Royal Navy found out many years ago that there is little merit in designing the fastest vessel in the world if it can operate only in limited weather conditions.*

A. The *Gaul* case – need for reassessment

In an attempt to elicit what was wrong with modern fishing vessels (where the incidence of capsizing has increased alarmingly during the last two decades), some scientists have claimed 'that the main reason for the limited effort in

---

* That is, any kind of military vessel that cannot be used because of its vulnerability in heavy weather which may suit an enemy.

solving the whole issue of seaworthiness and safety criteria is due to lack of suitable mathematical tools to tackle the problem.' A somewhat ridiculous explanation, bearing in mind the enormous variety of most sophisticated equations of dynamics and computing techniques which are available. Moreover, it ignores the fact that safe fishing and pilot boats, able to stand up to severe gales, were built some hundred years ago without much mathematics and fished the stormy waters of the coast of Britain all year round.*

During an interesting discussion of the RINA paper: *Capsizing of Small Trawlers* by A. Morrall (1979), a critical voice reminded the audience that an acknowledged, forthright top skipper of the Scottish fishing fleet prophesied a sequence of disasters, saying that too many new fishing boats were being designed by inexperienced naval architects and built by yards without the background knowledge that existed in the traditional wooden shipbuilding yards. This observation has been perhaps unexpectedly, although differently, confirmed in a deliberately provocative statement made by the late Sir Rowland Baker: 'Mathematics was introduced into Design (rightly) but one of the side effects was the idea still alive that Mathematics and Calculation could "get it right"'. This view appears to refer to Bertrand Russell's favourite definition of mathematics: 'the subject in which we never know what we are talking about nor whether what we are saying is right.'

What Bertrand Russell and Sir Rowland Baker both had in mind was that from a couple of arbitrarily selected premises or assumptions, which may or may not correspond to reality, any conclusion can be derived and proved to be mathematically correct. Many propositions of yacht design science (as well as ship science), and particularly those related to seaworthiness and boat motion in rough weather, have not been logically and rigorously derived. Consequently when making engineering calculations some problems are in practice resolved on the basis of more or less arbitrary assumptions; and, sadly enough, sheer faith in Providence. Thus, the problem of vulnerability or survivability of the boat does not lie principally in mathematics or calculations which eventually supplement the design project but, broadly speaking, in understanding which design features primarily contribute to safety at sea, and why.

Boat designers usually start to develop a full scale craft concept from, at first, an imaginary model which may begin its existence as a sketch made on the proverbial back of an envelope, thereafter gradually taking shape on the drawing board and ultimately coming to reality in the boatyard. Obviously the design model, physical and mathematical, should include all important characteristics of the system components. The decision about which characteristics (design features) are important and which are of secondary significance – the kernel of the design process – requires good physical insight, experience and intuition. If the designers happen to be not only rational but also nonrational and irrational, as human beings are; if their assumptions do not correspond to the physical environment in which the boat will operate (i.e. they make errors in physical reasoning or in mathematical models of system components such as, for instance, the effect of stability or damping on boat motion); if they do not have an equal access to information, or are mislead by

---

* Although the builders of those craft did not enjoy the benefit of applied mathematics they seemed to suffer very little in their professional skill.

illusory safety standards (such as those set by the IMO or IOR); if they do not always conform to good standards of professional conduct – then the design model is bound to become empirically erroneous. Moreover, the whole design concept may become misleadingly precise – a 'rigorous fallacy parading in the guise of exact knowledge'.

Yet another RINA paper: *The Gaul Disaster: An Investigation into the Loss of a Large Stern Trawler* by A. Morrall (1980) may serve as a revealing illustration of what has been said above. In the conclusion to the paper we read: 'the vessel appears to have had an adequate reserve of (intact) stability, especially compared with minimum criteria recommended by IMO, and that this stability was sufficient to prevent capsize in the sea states expected in service for a Deep Sea Trawler.' This, perhaps the most important statement in the whole paper, is well documented by seventeen graphs (relevant to the metacentric stability in various sea conditions) to prove that the *Gaul* was safe from the mathematical point of view assumed by the IMO legislators. There is in this paper only one rather unrelated graph which demonstrates an attempt to estimate, through model tests, the roll damping characteristics of the *Arab* – the sister boat of the *Gaul*. During discussion about damping effects initiated from the audience, it was admitted that: 'From measurements it is clear that the *Arab* and the *Gaul* model are indeed fairly lightly damped by most standards; this gave rise to some large roll amplitudes . . .' Strangely enough this acknowledged damping deficiency of the *Gaul* does not seem to have been considered as a possible cause of disaster, neither in the paper itself nor in the Court of Inquiry. 'The findings of the investigation are consistent with the view that the *Gaul* was not lost as a result of inadequate intact stability or poor seakeeping qualities.'

How then did the *Gaul* founder with her crew of 36 so quickly that no distress signal was sent? Could larger damping have saved her? We shall never know; disasters at sea usually have many contributing factors, quite apart from stability consideration there is possible human error, flooding through openings, freak waves, etc. However, we may rely to some degree on an educated guess and say that the low damping efficiency of the *Gaul* certainly increased her rolling motion and thus the probability of capsize. It will be shown that boats with the same static stability but with increasing roll damping efficiency can have remarkably different and much safer roll performances. And this makes sufficient damping an important safety factor. Thus, until new safety criteria stipulate minimum roll damping, and relate the probability of capsize to design features such as the size and shape of hull appendages, smaller vessels will be sailed at unnecessarily high risk.

So far, the significance of damping is neither sufficiently appreciated nor so well understood as it deserves. An analogy may perhaps help to recognise the importance of damping. As already mentioned, one of the most familiar examples of damping action is the automobile shock absorber. It dissipates energy resulting from up and down oscillations of the car mass and suspension system (passengers included) caused by riding over bumps in the road. No sane car designer could possibly discard the shock absorber as a part of the suspension system. He knows full well that one cannot drive a car with speed on a bumpy road without shock absorbers – it would be dangerous, the car might bounce away from the road. And, for that reason, the authorities responsible for road safety would not licence such a car. If we compare a boat with a motorcar as a mechanical, physical or mathematical system, we find that the action of boat stability is analogous to the action of springs in the car; boat damping is equivalent to the action of shock absorbers; and weight or mass inertia plays the same role in both systems. If we agree that the design of a motorcar without shock absorbers is an unreasonable, if not nonsensical, exercise we should also agree that disregarding proper damping in boat design is equally unreasonable. Sufficient damping is much needed in rough seas.

B. Damping effect

Preliminary to considering the steadying action of the keel and hull underbody, it is instructive just to discuss briefly their effect in retarding and diminishing rolling in still water. Let us assume that the boat is forcibly heeled over to port (Fig. 82A) and then set free. If the heeling force is suddenly removed when the mast has reached an angle of heel (Θ_0), the stability forces will generate a righting moment (W × GZ) tending to return the hull to her upright position 0. In other words, when the yacht is released from the inclined position the *stability moment produces rotation of the hull* in the opposite direction to its initial heel. One must begin to think of energy, for a boat at sea is a dynamic system. The energy initially expended to heel the boat (and stored as the potential energy in the inclined hull), is converted into the kinetic energy of rolling motion. When the mast swinging to starboard reaches the upright position and the swing velocity is at a maximum, the kinetic energy or momentum of the rotating boat is also at a maximum. The hull and the mast, therefore, continue their rotation beyond upright to the starboard side. But not all the kinetic energy will be converted to potential energy of the inclined hull for, as the yacht rolls from one side to the other, some energy is dissipated into the surrounding water. The hull therefore comes momentarily to rest at a smaller angle of heel (Θ_1) than that from which the rolling was started. Subsequently, the boat will perform a series of successive rolls to port and back to starboard, decreasing in angle because of the damping action of the hull underbody, until it finally comes to rest in an upright position.

This action seems quite obvious, but its effect on seaworthiness does not appear to be properly appreciated. Such a damped rolling can be recorded and presented as in Fig. 82B. The broken sinuous line is the record of consecutive rolling angles reached in a number of swings to port and starboard. The initial heel angle is 22 degrees and after five complete swings diminishes, as a result of damping, to 5 degrees. The rate at which rolling extinguishes with time, as reflected by the thick continuous line, called the *curve of declining angles*, is of primary importance. Broadly speaking, it reflects the effectiveness of the hull underbody in dissipating rolling energy by stirring up the mass of water surrounding the boat.

Thus, we have dealt with two classes of mechanical system components: those which store energy (stability and mass inertia) and one which dissipates energy. The damping effect is therefore fundamentally different from that of stability or mass elements which store and may give back the energy supplied to them. This fact cannot be overemphasized, and we shall return to the point later. A little reflection will suffice to show that damping action does exist whenever disturbing, exciting, or restoring action is going on.

For instance, it is mainly to overcome the damping action of the air that the pendulum of a clock is made as flat as possible (streamlined) in the plane of oscillation. So inevitably every hull dissipates energy into water (damping) whenever the boat is forced to roll by waves and wind. But, as might be expected, certain hull forms are more effective in this respect than others. To illustrate this, consider a number of hulls (Figs 83 and 84). In Fig. 83 are shown the hull lines of two seaworthy English pilot boats of the past and one well known sailing yacht bearing close family resemblance. Figure 84 depicts the changing shape of the modern 40 ft hull underbody of some IOR racers, which have gained publicity for their racing performance and/or design features.

If we ask the question: which type of hull underbody shown in Figs 83 and 84 produces higher damping we might expect much controversy. Thus, for example, in a recent article *Evolution of the Modern Cruising Boat* one of the most prominent American designers writes: 'At the risk of being declared a heretic by some, I will state for the record that a *full-length keel does have its place in the overall scheme of things in yachting – in history books or museums.*[68] (The italics are mine.)

Can this statement, written in ardent defence of the present fad of resurrecting the separate keel-rudder configuration combined with light-displacement (a discovery made long ago – Fig. 28), be justified? Might it be that such a belief simply reflects an obsessive discoverer's complex which persecutes some contemporary yacht designers, or perhaps it is a syndrome of a sort of amnesia concerning the previous history, discoveries and achievements of boat architecture? After all, if one visits the Greenwich Museum, where hundreds (if not thousands) of boat models from all over the world are to be found, one can see both the long keel and the short keel with separate rudder designs side by side; some of the latter have been in the museum for more than one hundred years. So, there is no need to send any of these configurations in question to a museum – they are already there; and many other ideas waiting for new Columbuses.

This somewhat ties up with an observation made by F. Dostojewski on Russian society, where original creativeness is lacking or has been arrested for centuries: 'Give to a Russian pupil, ignorant in astronomy, the map of the heavenly bodies and next day he will bring it corrected.'

A big shift in speed-producing factors of IOR racers over the past decade has been particularly evident in increasingly higher aspect ratios of hull appendages (Fig. 84). As depicted in Figs 16 and 85, a definite trend towards more efficient foils (sails and keels) has been observed much earlier due to advances made in

Fig. 83. *Hull lines of some seaworthy English pilot boats of the past, and those of* Wanderer III, *the yacht designed in 1951 by Laurent Giles for Eric Hiscock and his wife. They sailed the seven seas for three years and experienced every kind of weather, and* Wanderer *showed that one of the principal objects of the Royal Ocean Racing Club can be realised: 'Design, building, navigation and sailing of vessels in which speed and seaworthiness are combined'.*

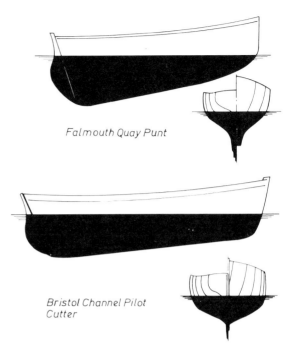

Falmouth Quay Punt

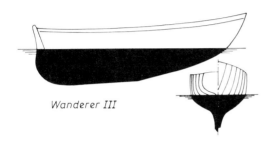

Wanderer III

Bristol Channel Pilot Cutter

Fig. 84. *Some recent evolutions in hull appendages on the IOR type of boat, inclining towards higher aspect ratio. This has been followed by a tendency towards hull lightness, and an increase in Sail Area/Displacement ratio; see table below.*

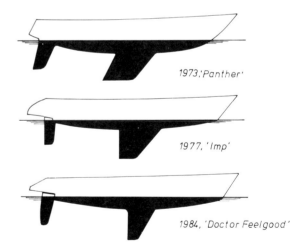

1973, 'Panther'

1977, 'Imp'

1984, 'Doctor Feelgood'

	Panther	Imp	Doctor Feelgood
LOA	40.0 ft	40.0 ft	39.8 ft
LWL	33.0 ft	33.2 ft	31.3 ft
Beam	13.7 ft	12.3 ft	13.3 ft
Draft	7.42 ft	6.75 ft	7.6 ft
Displacement	Δ 20,900 lbs	15,000lbs	13,900 lbs
Ballast	8,800 lbs	7,700 lbs	7,100 lbs
SA	760 sq ft	747 sq ft	739 sq ft
Δ/(0.01 LWL)	260	185	202
SA/$\nabla^{\frac{2}{3}}$	16.00	19.26	20.6

Such development, however, incurs a certain penalty in terms of damping efficiency and directional stability in rough seas.

Note: *Symbols Δ and ∇ in the two ratios given above indicate: displacement in tons, Δ (one ton = 2240 lb) and displacement in cubic feet, ∇ (one cubic foot of salt water = 64.0 lb).*

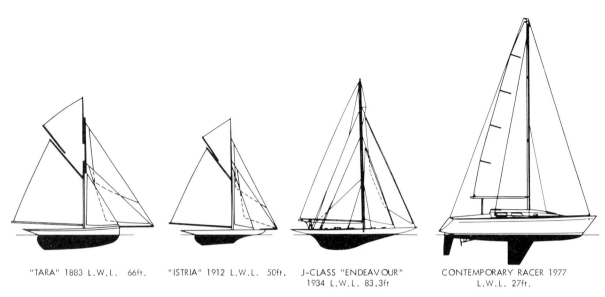

"TARA" 1883 L.W.L. 66ft.   "ISTRIA" 1912 L.W.L. 50ft.   J-CLASS "ENDEAVOUR"   CONTEMPORARY RACER 1977
1934 L.W.L. 83.3ft   L.W.L. 27ft.

Fig. 85. *Evolution of sail planform and underwater profile, towards higher aspect ratio foils. Advances in hydrodynamics and spar technology have made possible this kind of progress towards higher speed. These go-fast shapes are not, however, without some undesirable effects.*

aerohydrodynamics and spar technology; however, it was tempered by other considerations than, say, speed performance on the windward leg alone. The advantages and disadvantages of high aspect ratio foils have, to some extent, been discussed in the author's previous book[59] so there is no need to repeat them here. Relevant to the current subject is the fact that the higher the aspect ratio of hull appendages the more readily do they stall. And that, as we shall see, is one of the characteristics which makes contemporary boats unseaworthy.

Nowadays, an immediate concern of IOR yacht designers is not to produce well behaved craft which can look after themselves and the crew in most conditions, and forgive them their mistakes. Colin Mudie put this point rather mildly this way: 'in very bad conditions, some of these boats suddenly seem to go wrong and require very skilled seamanship for survival. In some cases designers and builders seem to leave this part of the performance envelope somewhere between Acts of God and the Chance that somebody on board will have read a good book on the subject. Unfortunately, this latter information may not help, since the action required depends on the type of boat.'[69] The problem is that, no matter what action can possibly be taken, even the best crew in the world, familiar with the best books written on the subject, cannot turn a basically unseaworthy boat into a safe one.

Why then do certain boats, notably those built to the IOR requirements, suddenly go wrong in survival situations? Are perhaps, these boats poorly damped?

Stabilisation of rolling

What is it you want to find in the behaviour of your boat due to damping? How much do the shape of the hull underbody and the keel area contribute to damping effectiveness and seaworthiness?

To answer the first question, the author made some wind tunnel tests on the rig shown earlier in Fig. 64.[71] The model under test simulated a sailing boat in still water without wind action, was given an initial heel angle of 20 degrees and then left free. The rate of decay of the rolling motion was recorded in order to establish the curve of declining angles, and hence the decrement coefficient (δ) for different damping intensities. Test results shown in Fig. 86A–D demonstrate how quickly the rolling motion extinguishes, when damping is gradually increased. Sketch D indicates the correspondence between damping, marked in arbitrary units of intensity 1.0–3.0, and relevant decrement coefficients (δ). Although the decrement coefficient does not directly determine the magnitude of damping (which in this particular test was proportional to the angular rolling velocity) it may conveniently be used as an index of damping effectiveness.

When comparing the damping produced by various hull forms it soon becomes evident that they are two different concepts of the term. One idea of damping is the loss of heel angle per swing when rolling from a given angle of heel. This might be called *angular damping*. The other is the loss of energy per swing which might be called *energy damping*. The loss of energy is due to the action of the hull underbody on the water; and the decrease in angle of heel is due to loss of energy. As indicated in Note 70, the energy lost (ΔE) during the swing from Φ_0 to Φ_1 (Figs 82 and 86), is the energy drained away by the work done against the water resistance:

$$\Delta E = 1/2 \ \Delta GM \ (\Theta_0^2 - \Theta_1^2) \tag{27}$$

The energy lost per swing can also be expressed in terms of the decrement coefficient (δ) as a fraction of the total potential energy (E_{tot}) stored in the heeled position at Θ_0. Thus, the fraction of energy lost per cycle is approximately equal to twice the decrement coefficient:

$$\frac{\Delta E}{E_{tot}} = 2\delta \tag{28}$$

A second series of tests, this time with the wind blowing, is presented in Fig. 87A–F. The same model with a single sail was set in the down wind attitude at which a large rolling amplitude is usually induced by aerodynamic reasons alone (see Appendix 2). The model (sail) was initially heeled to the angle $\Theta = -5$ degrees after which it was left to its own resources. As expected, the combination of resisted rolling, due to the action of damping, and aerodynamic self-excitation must produce different responses depending on the amount of positive damping introduced to the system. Other things being equal, the higher the degree of damping the less rapidly the rolling amplitude builds up and the lower is the final amplitude reached in limiting steady state motion, as

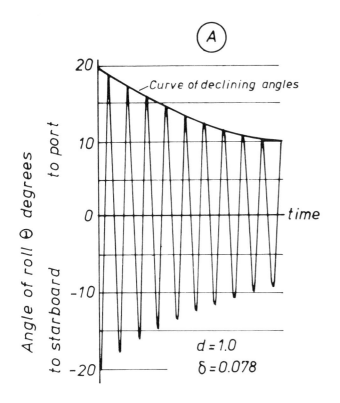

Curve of declining angles

A

Angle of roll Θ degrees

to port

0 — time

to starboard

d = 1.0
δ = 0.078

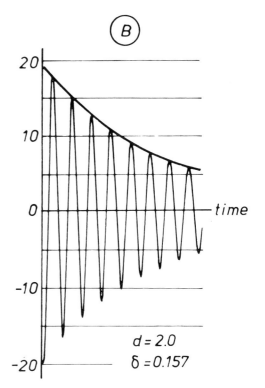

B

10 — time

d = 2.0
δ = 0.157

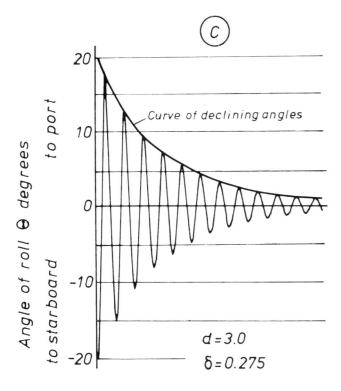

C

Angle of roll Θ degrees

to port

Curve of declining angles

to starboard

d = 3.0
δ = 0.275

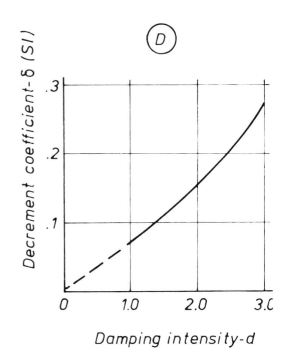

D

Decrement coefficient - δ (SI)

Damping intensity - d

revealed in sketches A–E. There is a certain critical damping (Fig. 87E) which makes the boat dynamically stable; that is to say, the oscillations are convergent, tending to reduce the initial heel angle which might be inflicted for whatever reason – for instance, due to the combined action of sail and waves.

The negative stability index SI (top graph in Fig. 87) indicates that the destabilising action of sail forces predominates over the damping forces while, conversely, positive SI points to greater contribution of damping in exchange of energy coming to (from the wind) and dissipated away from the rolling model. It can be shown that the quantity:

$$\frac{-(b_R)}{2\,I_r} \qquad (29)$$

determines the character of the rolling motion, namely, whether the boat will be dynamically stable or unstable in rolling. Factor $(-b_R)$ in this expression is the resulting damping coefficient (not the decrement coefficient δ to which b_R is proportional) and I_r is the transverse moment of inertia which largely depends on the displacement of the boat; the larger the displacement the greater the moment of inertia (Appendix 3). The resultant damping coefficient (b_R) is the sum of two parts: the hydrodynamic damping coefficient (b_H) related to the action of the hull underbody (usually positive, but not always), and an aerodynamic coefficient (b_A) which designates the aerodynamic contribution to damping. Coefficient b_A can either be positive (in the close hauled position) or negative (in the down wind condition, unless a special anti-rolling sail is used). Its magnitude depends on a number of factors investigated by the author (see Chapter 7), amongst them the sail area (Fig. 65).

Thus, $$b_R = b_H \pm b_A \qquad (30)$$

Depending on the relative magnitudes of b_H and b_A the resultant coefficient (b_R) can be positive or negative. With positive resulting damping $(+b_R)$, which indicates that hydrodynamic damping predominates, i.e.:

$$b_R = (b_H \pm b_A) > 0 \qquad (31A)$$

(even if b_A is negative but numerically smaller than b_H, say in down wind conditions) boat motion will be dynamically stable. Positive resulting coefficient (b_R) when substituted into expression 29 makes it negative, and this will produce oscillation in which each successive rolling has less amplitude (Θ) and

Fig. 86. *Graphs of the roll-rate of the model shown earlier (Fig. 65) for various degrees of hydrodynamic damping intensity (d); which was controlled magnetically; the initial angle of heel (θ_0) being 20°. This simulated roll damping produced by the hull in a calm without influence from the sails. Roll oscillations diminish evenly with time, as recorded in diagrams A–C so the boat is dynamically stable. Sketch D shows* the roll decrement coefficient (δ) plotted for various degrees of 'd'. The coefficient δ can be regarded as a stability index (SI) in the dynamic condition (SI is a measure of how quickly succeeding angles of roll diminish with time). The higher the damping intensity (d), the larger the decrement coefficient (δ) and hence the SI (see also Fig. 63).

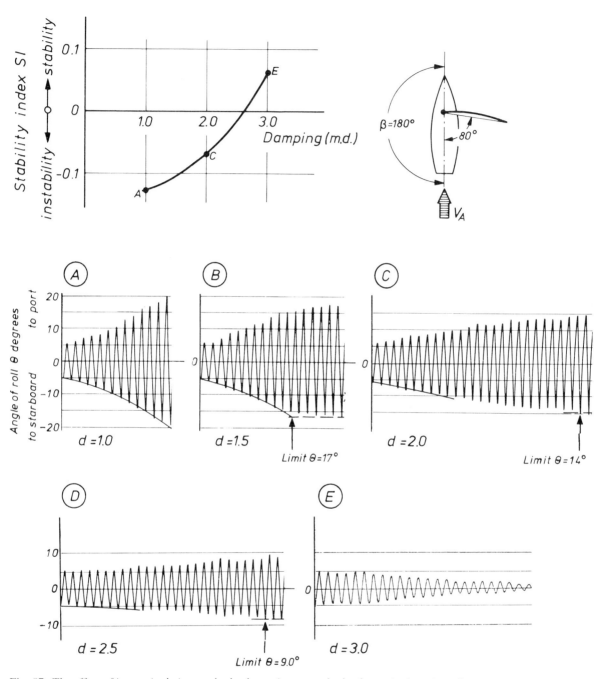

Fig. 87. *The effect of increasingly intense hydrodynamic damping (d varied from 1.0 to 3.0) on rolling in down wind conditions ($\beta = 180°\pm$) measured in a wind tunnel. It will be seen that there is a certain critical hydrodynamic damping, due to action of the hull and its appendages, which makes a boat dynamically stable despite the existence of destabilising aerodynamic forces.*

so less accumulated energy. This is recorded in graph E of Fig. 87 and can obviously be interpreted that, on the whole, more energy is dissipated through damping than is absorbed from the wind through the sail. The lack of rolling motion when going to windward has been shown by the author (see Chapter 7) to be due to heavy positive aerodynamic and hydrodynamic damping from sails and keel operating in unison in these circumstances.

Conversely, the lack of positive damping (and indeed the existence of a large destabilising aerodynamic moment) off the wind contributes both to wild rolling and to broaching behaviour. In other words, if the resultant coefficient (b_R) is negative, i.e.:

$$b_R = (b_H \pm b_A) < 0 \qquad (30B)$$

which means that, in terms of energy balance, the aerodynamic excitation predominates, then the b_A coefficient must be negative and numerically greater than the b_H coefficient. Negative b_R, when substituted into the expression 29, makes it positive and this will produce divergent, unstable oscillations of type A in Fig. 87.

Obviously, such a response of the boat without proper damping built in, with amplitude of rolling growing exponentially as shown in sketch A, is dangerous. Exponential growth in which the rate of change of the heeling angle to port and starboard accelerates is both treacherous and misleading. A boat can continue to roll through a number of swings to and fro without seeming to reach a significant angle of heel. But then, in just one more swing, she may become completely overwhelmed giving the helmsman no warning signal and no time for the crew to take any action to prevent capsize. (*Marques* the training square rigger foundered this way in 1984.) Figure 88 demonstrates the record of capsize for a model of a modern fishing vessel rolling in waves without sails; and also her stability curve. It was admitted that the model capsized frequently in breaking waves of modest severity, of height and length which the vessel could conceivably encounter in service[72]; and the sequence of events during capsize occurred rapidly. The elapsed time for each capsize was only 10 to 20 seconds (full scale) or about 2 to 3 roll cycles (or shorter if the boat is stationary in beam seas).

Moreover, as shown in Fig. 88, the full scale vessel (and the model) had their static stability (at rest) close to the IMO minimum and for that reason might be deemed seaworthy. However, in confrontation with reality the model tests and full scale experience told something different: with static stability criteria of the IMO type (or IOR for that matter) one cannot combat the danger of capsize effectively if one ignores the effect of the resistance against rolling offered by the water.

A remark expressed by W. Froude in this context in 1872[73] deserves to be written in every textbook on boat architecture, and to be kept in mind all the time by those whose business is to study, investigate, or make inquiries or recommendations to ensure better safety for offshore-going vessels: 'its modifying effects (damping against rolling) are under almost any circumstances considerably the greatest; under the circumstances which produce the

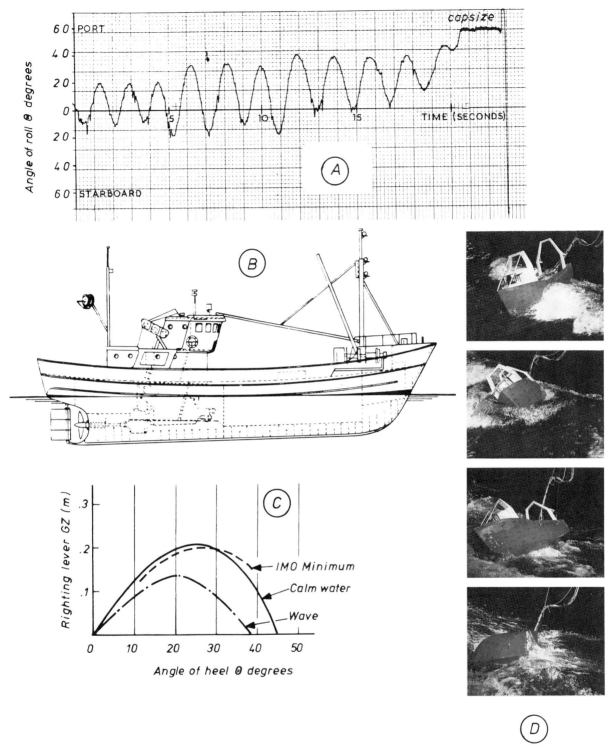

Fig. 88. (A) Sequence of capsize for a 1/15th scale model of a modern fishing vessel, rolling in beam seas and subsequently overwhelmed by a breaking wave; the experiments were carried out at the National Maritime Institute (Ref. 72). One of the most interesting findings of these tests was that, in breaking waves, the model broached and ended up beam-on to the waves despite all rudder action.
(B) Side view of the vessel, of full scale length about 85 ft (26 m).
(C) Stability curves of the vessel tested. The calm water stability curve was established by computation, based on hull lines; stability in waves was calculated assuming a wave height of 13 ft (4 m) and length 230 ft (70 m), and with crest amidships.
(D) Illustrates the capsize sequence for a free running model of a fishing vessel, tested in steep waves by the National Research Council of Canada. These tests were conducted as the result of public concern over the safety of fishermen caused through recent, not infrequent major trawler disasters, whole vessels and their crews having been lost.

maximum rolling in any given ship, *it is to the resistance alone that she owes her safety* . . . For it is unquestionable that if the oscillation were performed independently of resistance, a ship of any ordinary form if by chance exposed to waves the period of which is the same or nearly the same as her own, would inevitably be rolled over to a fatal angle in the transit of a few waves of ordinary steepness . . . But for the inherent powers of resistance which the ship possesses she would always be in the strictest sense 'at the mercy' of waves, and with waves of even approximate co-periodicity the mercy would be inexorably destructive, and no skill in the disposition of the weights, no excellence of nautical properties in the ship herself, would be a protection . . . The ship's 'resistance' being then, in truth, her *only real protection* under circumstances (to which she may be possibly exposed), which were in wanting, would be fatal to her, *a thorough investigation of the conditions on which it depends and of modes of giving the greatest effect to it*, appears to present writer, at least: the one point to which *attention should be most eagerly and persistently directed*.' (The italics are mine.)

Yet, this damping effect regarded by Froude as the 'only true protection' of the vessel in rough seas has been stubbornly ignored in almost all papers written more recently on the subject of survivalibility and seaworthiness. Instead, for example, in conclusion to the paper: '*Capsizing of Small Trawlers*'[72] much relevant to similar situations in offshore yachting, we read that lack of sufficient static stability (roll stiffness) was considered 'as the main cause contributing to capsize . . . The effects of this were clearly visible in the model where roll, even in a modest sea state, was excessive.' This conclusion sounds as if Froude's findings about the illusory nature of metacentric stability and his remarks about damping effect on rolling, just quoted, had never been heard of.[74]

An attempt to exempt a boat from deep rolling by simply increasing her metacentric height implies some basic misconception of the real principles and forces in action, particularly when viewed in the light of what was written on the subject more than a century ago. Nevertheless, following the conclusion of the above quoted paper[72] that the IMO stability criteria are insufficient to prevent capsize in certain probable sea conditions, a recommendation has been made for: 'an addition of 20 per cent to the IMO righting lever, to allow for inferior design, bad workmanship and human failure at sea'.[75]

Without denying that the character of the metacentric stability curve at rest matters much in survival situations (as already indicated in Chapter 5) the author of this book tends to regard the whole set of IMO stability criteria as a kind of conscience-money device rather than a scientifically acceptable measure of seaworthiness or safety. It is, as a matter of fact, the most expedient error of naval architecture. Consequently, the recommendation to modify it along the lines suggested in Ref. 75, i.e. by increasing GZ, is nothing more than an attempt to rationalise errors and omissions already existing in this respect.

Contradictions will arise – the surest sign of fiction. But let us assume, for the sake of argument, that the righting lever of the boat, as given in Fig. 88, has

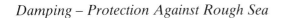
been increased by 20 per cent to compensate 'for human failure at sea or inferior design'. Would that sort of correction radically change the vessel's safety in rough seas? Answers to this and some other related questions are discussed in subsequent chapters.

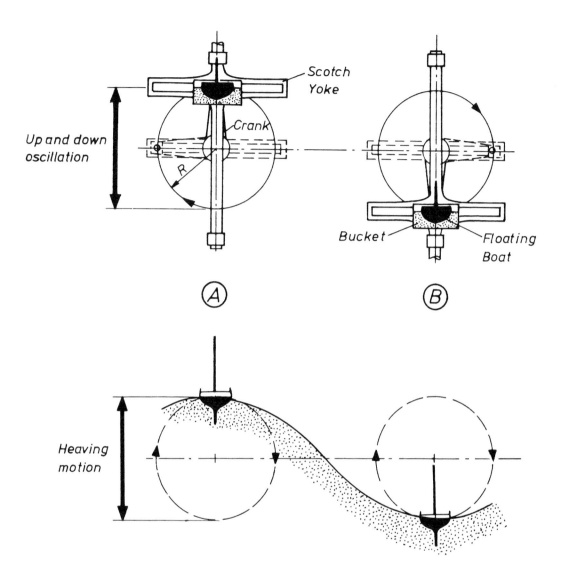

Fig. 89. *Sketches A and B show W. Froude's original bucket machine – the wave action analogy. The bucket, water and the boat floating on it, oscillate up and down by means of a Scotch yoke (driven by a crank) to simulate the heaving motion of a boat in waves.*

> *'The behaviour of ships on stormy seas is so hard to be understood and so important to be predicted, that it is worth any amount of hard thinking, and painstaking observation, and subtle reasoning we can expend on it.'*
>
> J. Scott Russell

10 Stability in a Seaway – Part 2

Referring to Figs 54–56 we have discussed the effect of hydrostatic stability on a boat's recovery from an inverted attitude. Although the stability characteristic of a boat is a feature of primordial importance, its meaning in the context of seaworthiness is still ambiguous. W. Froude expressly stated that the metacentric height (GM), i.e. the righting lever of the vessel, is the handle by which the waves roll the vessel and as such cannot be used as the safety criterion. Nevertheless, it can be accepted as an axiom that an ample range of hydrostatic stability as measured by the angle of vanishing stability (Figs 55 and 56) appears to be a necessary, although not a sufficient, safety criterion.

Perhaps it has not been set out clearly enough to boat designers that metacentric stability for a static condition, obtained by calculation and possibly checked by an inclining test, does not remain the same, with the same magnitudes, when the boat is in waves as when she is in calm water alongside the fitting-out pier at the boatyard.

The comments of Sir George Greenhill expressed in discussion on a paper[76] read at the meeting of the Institution of Naval Architects, London in 1920, are pertinent here: 'I should like him (the author) to come to our assistance and give some explanation, which we have not seen yet, of a *phenomenon well known to sea fishermen of the liability of a sailing boat to capsize on the crest of a wave. What is the reason for that well-known danger in a small vessel?* It is not often met with on a large scale, although we read that in the operation of laying the first Atlantic cable the *Agamemnon*, a large wooden battleship of the day, met a very large solitary wave, rose to it, and fell over on her side as the wave passed underneath. Here was a case of a very large vessel capsizing on the crest of a wave, and I am sure we should all give him our thanks if the author would direct his attention to giving us some explanation of the reason for that effect. The cause of it cannot lie very deep.'

Although, indeed, the cause of this strange pattern in boat behaviour does not lie deep, as Sir George Greenhill rightly believed, no explanation was forthcoming either from the author concerned or from learned societies for many years to come; in spite of the fact that a substantial knowledge of physical phenomena involved already existed as incorporated in W. Froude's papers. And, it has been known for many years that the distribution of forces around a hull when under way in waves is much different from that when in rest. Apparently knowledge distils slowly into human minds, and this perhaps explains why the hazards and loss in lives are readily accepted as the inevitable result of natural forces. To quote the late Harold Saunders, Captain US Navy and the author of excellent volumes on *Hydrodynamics in Ship Design*: 'one may wonder whether it ever occurred to many naval architects that the transverse metacentric stability of the ships they designed was different in certain wave conditions than in calm water, even when the ship was upright or nearly so!'[63]

A. Froude's approach to stability in waves

As long ago as 1861 W. Froude, being aware that a vessel's capsize is basically a dynamic phenomenon, gave the physical explanation of periodic changes of stability when the boat heaves up and down in waves. Since the effect of wave motion on stability is apparently too complex for intuitive understanding, Froude introduced an interesting analogy – the imaginary bucket-machine shown in Fig. 89. A 'bucket' containing water with the model of a boat floating in it, oscillates up and down in simple harmonic motion. The stroke of this device equals the wave height.

Froude argued that this situation 'so far as vertical motion is concerned, would represent fairly the circumstances of a similar volume of water when undergoing wave motion; in such a case, by varying the speed of the reciprocations, we might easily arrive at a velocity such that, at the summit of each stroke, the bucket should be actually drawn away from its contents faster than they could follow it in virtue of gravitation; or we might select exactly such a speed that the contents of the bucket would just, and only just, keep company with it at the summit of the stroke. On this (latter) supposition it is plain that the particles of water would at the moment (top of the stroke) absolutely fail to press at all, either against the bottom or sides of the bucket, or against each other, or finally against any immersed floating body; though at the same time, such a body would not acquire any increased immersion for want of support, since itself would be divested of its powers of pressing against the particles of water, exactly in the same way as these had, by the same cause, been incapacitated from pressing against each other and against it (the floating body).

'Similarly at the end of the down and the commencement of the up-stroke, if the same speed were maintained, the mutual pressure of the particles of water against each other, and their pressure against the sides and bottom of the bucket, or against any floating body, would be precisely doubled and the (absolute) stability of the floating body would here be doubled. The model boat would stand up under twice as great pressure of wind as she would bear if in still water.'

The floating boat in Froude's machine, and the water for that matter, experience the same kind of variation in forces acting upon them as that experienced by a child using a swing. We can all remember that fearful but exciting feeling of lightness when the swing accelerated up toward the top of the arc, followed a few seconds later by a hard pressing against the seat at the bottom of the downward motion.

Before we return to Froude's analogy and its practical implications for real wave conditions, let us remind ourselves of the basic principles of wave motion. These are presented in Fig. 90A and B. Text books on Naval Architecture often assume such shape of waves (sinusoidal or trochoidal) for introductory analytical purposes, although neither of them fits Nature; and, as observed, some pretty wild departure from the shape roughly sketched in Fig. 90 takes place in real seas. We shall subsequently consider the effects of steep-fronted seas at a later stage, after the interim concept of long-crested waves of Fig. 90A has served its purpose as a simple approximation to wave mechanics.

The concept of a long-crested (not breaking) wave is based upon an assumption, reasonably well supported by observation, that the water particles describe nearly circular orbits as a wave passes. While the water particles are executing one orbit about the centre of their rotation which moves only slightly forward, the crest of the wave will shift from position 1 to position 2 by full wavelength (L_w, Fig. 90A). The period during which the wave traverses one wavelength, in other words the period of passing of two successive wave crests through one fixed point, is called the wave period (T). If the height of the wave (H_w), which is equal to the diameter of the orbits (2R), and the period (T) are known, the orbital velocity at the wave surface (U_o) can be found from the simple expression:

$$U_o = \pi \, H_w/T = 3.14 \, H_w/T$$

or
$$U_o = \frac{7.11 \, H_w}{\sqrt{L_w}} \tag{32}$$

where U_o is in feet per second when H_w and L_w are in feet. Hence, the higher the wave (H_w) and shorter the period (T) or the wave length (L_w), the faster is the orbital rotation of water particles on the wave surface.

In still water conditions (sketch A in Fig. 91) the boat, partly immersed in water, is buoyed up by a force (Δ) equal to the weight of the boat (W), which is often expressed in terms of the weight of water it displaces. If the volume of water displaced by the hull is known then the buoyancy force can be calculated:

$$\Delta = W = m \times g \times \nabla$$

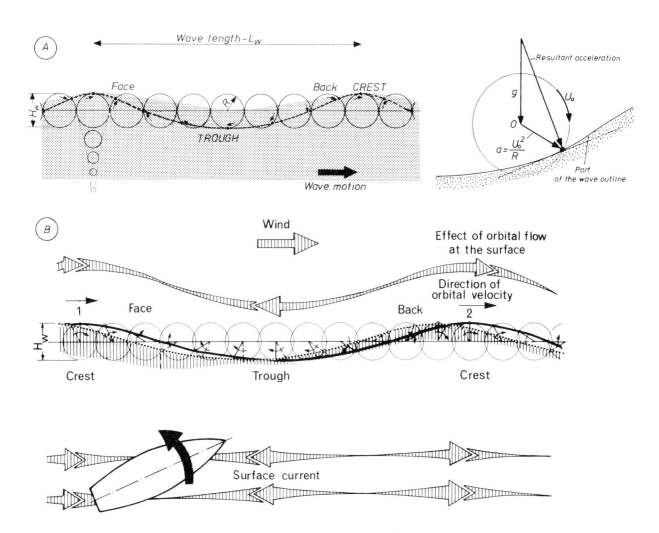

Fig. 90. *(A) The profile of a sinusoidal wave in deep water, showing circular orbits of water particles, with arrow-heads indicating the direction of water movement at various locations. The rapid decrease of the orbital radii with depth is shown beneath the crest. It illustrates the fact that orbital velocities and effective wave slope diminish below the surface. The enlarged sketch (right) shows that at each instant any water particle is under the influence of two component accelerations: 'g' due to gravity and 'a' due to centrifugal acceleration. The resultant acceleration, and hence the resultant force, is always normal to the water surface.*

(B) This diagram illustrates the intensity of orbital flow (current) at the surface. Orbital velocities in large waves can exercise a strong influence on the local flow round the hull and its appendages – the keel and rudder principally. As a result, alternating forces will be generated, tending to roll the boat and also periodically to change her prescribed compass course. With increasing size of waves (particularly their steepness), yawing and broaching tendencies become more acute, until directional stability is seriously impaired and even lost.

where m – mass density of salt water $1.99\dfrac{\text{slugs}}{\text{ft}^3}$

g – acceleration due to gravity $32.2\dfrac{\text{ft}}{\text{sec}^2}$

∇ – volume of displaced water in ft^3

Since the mass density of water (m) is constant and acceleration due to gravity (g) is for practical purposes constant, so is their product:

$$m \times g = 1.99 \times 32.2 = 64.0 \text{ lb/ft}^3$$

i.e. the weight density of water. Thus, the weight of unit volume of water ($\nabla = 1 \text{ ft}^3$) is:

$$m \times g \times \nabla = 64.0 \text{ lb}$$

However, this is no longer true of a mass of water in wave motion. When water

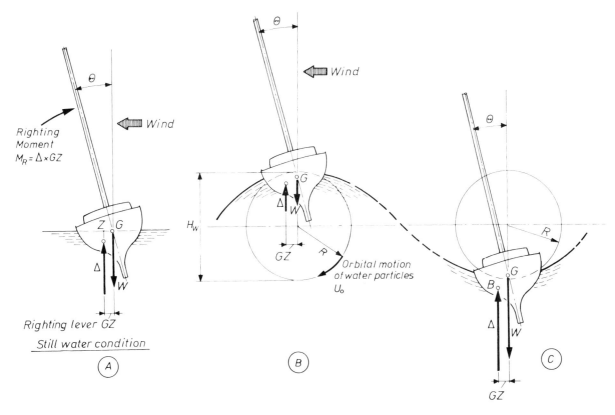

Fig. 91. Stability Variation in Waves. *For the sake of clarity, the hull size in relation to wave profile has been exaggerated. Only one dynamic effect of wave action is considered here; another will be looked at later. The* *wave action and its consequences are too complex for intuitive understanding; the components must be sorted out and dealt with one at a time.*

particles describe a circular orbit as shown in Fig. 90A, the weight density of water is no longer constant although the mass density (m) does not change. For our immediate purpose, it is enough to say that the water particles in waves acquire an acceleration acting radially outward from the centre of their circular orbit. According to a well-established principle of mechanics, the magnitude of this centrifugal acceleration (see Appendix 4) shown by an arrow in an enlarged part of Fig. 90A, is:

$$a = \frac{U_o^2}{R} \tag{33}$$

Since the orbital velocity of the water particles in a wave surface is related to the wave geometry, i.e. $U_o = \pi H_w/T$, the centrifugal acceleration can also be expressed in terms of wave characteristics such as height (H_w) and period (T):

$$a = 20\frac{H_w}{T^2} \tag{34}$$

Because the vector of centrifugal acceleration (a), relevant to orbiting water particles, rotates (Fig. 90, enlargement sketch), the resultant virtual acceleration, which is the combined effect of gravity acceleration (g) and centrifugal acceleration (a), will be g − a near the crest, i.e. less than the gravity acceleration (g). In other words, acceleration due to gravity acting always downward is partly reduced by the centrifugal acceleration acting, at that instant, upwards. Conversely, near the trough the resulting virtual acceleration will be (g + a), i.e. greater than g because the centrifugal acceleration is added to that of gravity. As a result, the virtual weight density (the apparent weight) of water, reckoned as the product of mass density and effective acceleration, decreases or increases in proportion to the effective acceleration:

$$\begin{aligned} m \times (g - a) \quad &\text{at the wave crest, and} \\ m \times (g + a) \quad &\text{at the wave bottom} \end{aligned}$$

The idea that virtual weight may change depending on acceleration is already quite familiar to most people of the space age; the force of gravity acting aboard a rocket accelerating upward at, say, 5 g has moved from the physics lab and entered day-to-day jargon – schoolboys know that the crew inside will experience an additional downward inertia force equal to five times their earth weight. In that case the masses, whether of the craft itself or its occupants, in accelerating motion remain the same, but their virtual weights become five-fold greater than those measured in static condition before the rocket was fired.

The fact that a boat heaves up and down in waves, following a rhythm imposed by the orbital motion, is of enormous consequence when considering stability variation along the lines suggested by Froude. The reason is that what has been shown to hold good for a water particle must also hold good for a boat which accompanies a wave motion. The extent to which the passage of waves will produce heaving motion must obviously depend upon the relative size of the waves and the boat. If the boat floating at or near the surface (like a raft) is small enough so that she partakes of the orbital motion of big waves, *she too will have her apparent weight (W) changed* in a manner closely approaching that of the surrounding water. This means that according to Archimedes' Law the buoyancy force generated by unit volume of displaced water in the wave crest is less than that in still water, while the buoyancy generated by unit volume in the trough is greater.

Since the virtual weight of the boat in question is diminished or increased in the same proportion as the buoyancy force, the boat may float at the same mean waterline whether on the crest or in the trough. But the stability moment, which is the product of weight and righting lever, will be reduced in the crest and increased in the trough, as shown in Fig. 91B and C. That is to say, the presence of a wave crest near amidships results in a *decreased* righting moment, while a wave trough amidships results in *increased* righting moment as compared with that in the calm water situation. The actual or effective righting moment of the boat at any instant is determined by the equation:

$$\text{Righting moment} = \text{Apparent weight } W \times GZ$$

where GZ is the righting lever corresponding to the angle of heel of the mast to the instantaneous position of normal to the wave slope. For the occasional very steep 'rogue' wave this difference in stability can be several times as large, particularly so when the boat is rapidly lifted up the almost vertical front of the wave before breaking of the crest takes place.

This ties up well with Froude's admirable exposition in his bucket machine analogy: 'the vertically moving volume of water, corresponds exactly with that of the vertical component of the motion in the particles forming respectively the crest and hollow of a wave; and the absence of mutual pressure in the particles at the crest of the wave corresponds with the circumstances that such a wave is on the verge of breaking; so . . . it is not a paradox to say her ultimate stability would absolutely vanish as she floated over the crest.'

B. Transverse stability in waves

The well known phenómena of sailing boats capsizing on the crests of even smooth-topped waves formed, for example, on the bars of harbours such as at Tynemouth, may be cited here in support of the necessity for considering the effect of heaving in waves on the boat's roll stability. The variation of the apparent weight of the vessel labouring up and down in a seaway was observed by Captain Mottez of the French Navy aboard a frigate and the results (reported in 1881) are of some interest. In waves about 26 ft high the apparent weight of objects on board was found by experiment to be about 20 per cent less on the wave crests, and about 20 per cent greater in the trough.[77] Little reflection will suffice to apprehend (see Eq. 34) that the higher (steeper) the waves and the shorter the period, the greater are the variations in acceleration (a) and, consequently, the bigger is the reduction of actual stability on the wave crest as compared with static stability in the calm water condition.

Referring to Fig. 91B which illustrates the boat in the most precarious situation, one can see that, although the righting lever (GZ) is the same as that in still water, her ability to hold an upright or nearly upright position is greatly reduced. At this moment the boat may capsize due to a wind heeling moment which would be safely resisted in calm water (compare sketches A and B in Fig. 91).

As an example, the Half-Tonner *Grimalkin* to which we referred earlier (Fig. 54) would resist, in smooth sea (hydrostatic) conditions a maximum heeling moment which is equal to her available righting moment, that is:

$$M_R = \text{displacement} \times \text{righting lever (GZ)}$$
$$= 8320 \text{ lb} \times 1.6 \text{ ft} = 13312 \text{ lb ft.}$$

This is shown in Fig. 92 where the continuous line curve illustrates the variation of the righting moment (M_R) is still water. It will be seen that this curve is symmetrical in the sense that the righting moment is identical, no matter whether the boat heels to starboard or to port, provided that the angle of heel (Θ) is the same. Note that the curve being below the horizontal axis does not in this case indicate that the craft is upside down. By contrast, the broken line curve illustrates the variation of the righting moment in sinusoidal waves, assuming that:

$$H_w = 40 \text{ ft} \qquad \text{and} \qquad T = 9 \text{ sec}$$

Thus the curve of righting moment in waves is no longer symmetrical in the sense mentioned earlier, i.e. *at the same angle of heel (Θ) the righting moment depends entirely on the position of the boat in relation to the water profile*, i.e. the righting moment in the crest is reduced, and in the trough is increased as compared with still water conditions.

Search and rescue aircraft operating in the Fastnet race area on 14th August 1979 reported a wave height $H_w = 50$ to 60 ft. Assuming $L_w = 50$ ft, the table below gives possible stability reduction in percentage of still water value for three different wave periods:

Period (T) sec	10	9	8
Stability reduction %	31	38	48

A stability reduction approaching even 50 per cent, although quite dramatic, does not entirely explain the disastrous effects of waves and wind experienced in that Fastnet race; it should be stressed that our calculation of stability reduction assumes that the shape of waves (Figs 90 and 91) was sinusoidal. As already mentioned, text books often assume such a shape because that makes it easier to grasp the mechanics of the wave motion and its effect on boat behaviour. Besides, surprisingly little is known about accelerations within unsteady, asymmetric waves such as a plunging breaker. Only quite recently are we beginning to understand why waves break and what happens during the process.

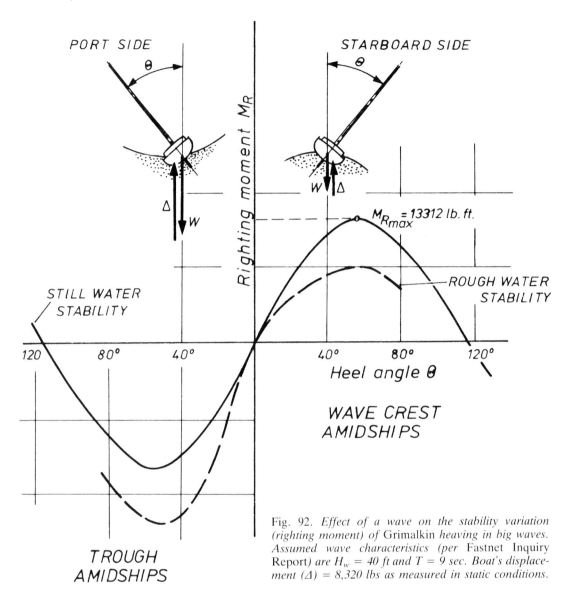

Fig. 92. *Effect of a wave on the stability variation (righting moment) of* Grimalkin *heaving in big waves. Assumed wave characteristics (per* Fastnet Inquiry Report) *are* H_w = 40 ft and T = 9 sec. *Boat's displacement* (Δ) = 8,320 lbs *as measured in static conditions.*

Figure 93 illustrates the development of a plunging breaker from the initial sinusoidal wave. It is seen that, as the wave moves to the right, the front face quickly steepens (1, 2) and at 3, 4, 5, the crest is overhanging. As might be expected, the acceleration distribution in such a plunging breaker will be different from that in a smooth-topped sinusoidal wave. In extreme waves, with great height and steep crest front, the resulting acceleration on the wave crest may, as indicated in Fig. 94, be only a small fraction of gravity acceleration (g). Comparison of the magnitude and direction of resulting acceleration recorded on the wave top with gravity acceleration given by the vertical vector marked g

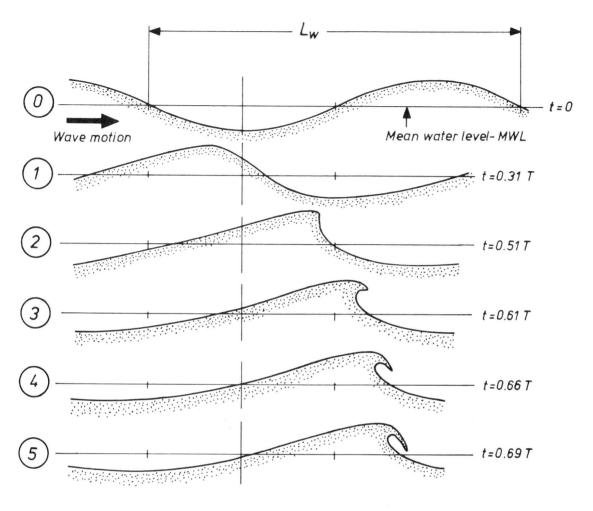

Wave motion

Mean water level- MWL

$t = 0$

$t = 0.31\ T$

$t = 0.51\ T$

$t = 0.61\ T$

$t = 0.66\ T$

$t = 0.69\ T$

DEEP-WATER BREAKER

Fig. 93. *Close-up of a plunging breaker at successive time 't' (expressed in terms of wave period T) developing from an initial sinusoidal wave (sketch marked 0 at the top) in deep water conditions (see also Figs 112 and 113).*

Wave period (approx):
$$T = \sqrt{2\pi L_w / g}$$
$T = 0.8\sqrt{L_w}$ *in sec, when* L_w *is in m*
$T = 0.44\sqrt{L_w}$ *in sec, when* L_w *is in ft.*
Drawing based on the report Kinematics of Deep Water Breaking Waves *by S.P.K. Kjeldsen, D. Myrhaug and P. Brevig, Offshore Technology Conference 1980.*

drawn to the corresponding scale, helps to appreciate Froude's early remark. Indeed, it is not a paradox that in such circumstances boat stability '*would absolutely vanish as she floated over the crest*'. The boat is virtually in freefall and consequently weightless in relation to the surrounding water and is thus destitute of the stability power to stand up against the wind.

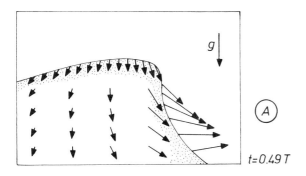

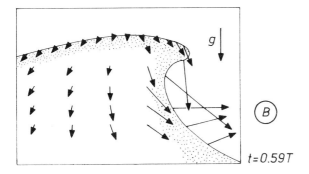

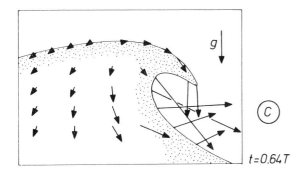

Fig. 94. *Acceleration field (distribution) within a plunging breaker (deep water). 'A' marks when the wave front (face) becomes vertical. 'B' and 'C' are some time after 'A', when the crest is overhanging. The arrow marked 'g' (top right) gives the magnitude of the acceleration of gravity ($g = 9.81$ m/sec^2 or 32.2 ft/sec^2) and may serve as a reference.*

C. No stability condition – weightlessness

A simple armchair experiment may be of some help in appreciating what is meant by saying that a boat can become weightless in relation to the surrounding water. Place a book on the palm of your hand. You will feel that the hand supports the book and prevents it from falling: the book is pressing down your hand with a force (weight) $F = m \times g$; where m is the mass of the book and g is the acceleration due to gravity. If you now suddenly drop your hand downward with the acceleration of free descent (g), the pressure due to

weight of the book on the hand ceases and the book falls freely following the
hand. If you lower your hand slowly, the book stays on it but feels lighter. You
will thus find that the pressure on your hand is determined by the relative
acceleration of the book and your hand. Thus the book may become virtually
(apparently) *weightless* in free fall, with no initial velocity relative to the hand.

Similarly, if you were in an elevator accelerating downward in free fall, i.e.
at the rate equal to g (because its supporting cable had broken), not only would
the book in your hand be weightless but your body would exert no force on the
floor of the elevator. You might float freely suspended and your body would
appear weightless relative to the walls of elevator. And if you were in such a
circumstance attached to a spring scale it would register *zero weight*. Of course,
hopefully, a descending elevator accelerates downward at a lesser rate than g,
say a, and for only a short time before reaching its operating speed. During this
short time interval your apparent weight, which is proportional to the relative
acceleration (g − a), would be reduced and you would certainly feel it. You
would experience a peculiar sensation, which must be due to the discontinuance
of the gravitational pressure on the parts of your body on one another – the
blood, the muscles and so forth. We might experience a similar sensation
during an earthquake if the ground supporting our bodies were sinking beneath
us, and again a spring scale would register a momentary reduction of weight
m (g − a).

We have all seen the pictures of astronauts floating effortlessly within the
capsule on the way to and returning from their space missions – they were
virtually weightless in relation to the capsule walls.*

One remarkable consequence of the gravitational force law is the fact that a
pendulum clock could not possibly work within a freely falling space capsule. A
pendulum of length ℓ with time of oscillation $T = 2\pi \sqrt{\dfrac{\ell}{g}}$ would acquire,
if its axis received a downward acceleration (a), a period of oscillation
$T = 2\pi \sqrt{\dfrac{\ell}{g - a}}$; and if allowed to fall freely would acquire
$T = 2\pi \sqrt{\dfrac{\ell}{g - g}} = 2\pi \sqrt{\dfrac{\ell}{o}}$ i.e. an infinite time of oscillation, which
means it would cease to oscillate. There would be no force which could swing
the bob to and fro.

Referring to the weightless boat conditions, the reader may recollect that the
formula 20B for the period of rolling oscillation also contains the factor g in the
denominator:

$$T_n = 2\pi \frac{k}{\sqrt{g\, GM}} \qquad \text{(20B)(repeated)}$$

If in free fall conditions the relative acceleration of the boat with respect to the
surrounding water becomes zero, then the formula 20B would read:

* In other words they were not gravityless but they were effectively weightless – i.e. freely falling.

$$T_n = 2\pi \frac{k}{\sqrt{(g - g)\,GM}} = 2\pi \frac{k}{\sqrt{0}}$$

If that happened the boat, like the pendulum, would lose the restoring moment and so her metacentric stability could no longer be maintained, because the surrounding water would offer no support for the hull.

It should be stressed that the term *weightless* used in all examples given above, is *relative* in the sense that it is applicable only to a body – be it an astronaut or a boat – *in relation to the surrounding container falling freely* considered as a frame of reference. Thus, although the astronauts returning from the moon are virtually weightless with respect to the capsule regarded as the frame of reference, they are not gravityless with respect to the Earth considered as another frame of reference. That is to say, the *true weight* (force due to gravity) of the space capsule and astronauts inside it would be mg if measured in relation to the earth, so that gravity brings astronauts back to Earth.

Similar reasoning applies to a boat heaving in waves, and periodically experiencing variation in effective vertical acceleration and resulting virtual weight, and hence variation in her stability with respect to the surrounding water.

Some practical observations recorded in one of the early INA papers[79] are relevant here to gain an insight into the dynamics of capsize in waves '. . . when towing a model boat from the bank of the ornamental water of Regent's Park or the Serpentine (Hyde Park, London) it is a great mortification for a boy to see the boat capsize on the top of a wave of its own creation. That is an experiment on a small scale not requiring the elaborate appliances of Mr. Froude . . . On a larger scale the waterman in his wherry experiences the same thing when he gets a cast from a steamer on the river . . . The length of a rope is a most important question. It can be so arranged that the boat is towed a little behind the crest of the wave, all the crew being in the stern and no one allowed to move. Great care has to be observed in casting off . . . one of the earliest experiences I had as a boy was seeing a boatload of passengers sitting in the stern of a wherry towed by a tug in the orthodox way. The tow rope was evidently too short for the wave formation corresponding to the speed of the tug and the depth of water and, when the rope was let go by a man on board the tug, the wherry and all the people in her went under water. Fortunately they were all saved.'

D. Effect of longitudinal trim

With regard to changes of stability of sailing boats in waves, little has been published so far and no tests have been conducted to show *How Much* and *How*. However, notable theoretical and experimental work has been done in this respect in relation to fishing vessels, and published in the comprehensive Volume 2 of the *Fishing Boats of the World*.[80]

Admittedly, yachtsmen interested in small cruisers liable to be caught occasionally in what is, for the size of the boat, very rough weather have two things in common with fishermen: the need for reasonable comfort (seakindliness) and the hope of expectation of getting there and back in safety (seaworthiness). For these reasons, research results into the safety of fishing boats are of some relevance to sailing non-professionals too; and although research will not automatically lead to the design of more seaworthy and safer boats, the results will certainly enable the designer to weigh the factors on a more rational basis. What follows illustrates the point.

The tuna clippers of the US Pacific Coast are characterised by extreme dissimilarity in the shape of the fore- and after-body of the hull. Distinguishing features of such a hull type are somewhat V-shaped sections forward and a high freeboard combined with broad, flat sections in the afterbody and little freeboard. In some hull designs to the IOR, similar features can be observed. As a result of this difference, the tuna clippers 'have been plagued with transverse stability problems, perhaps more severe than those encountered in most other types of fishing vessels'.[80] That such a hull shape is not desirable may be inferred from the fact that some 75 of these vessels were lost in a three-year period, with the implication that a significant number of these losses is attributable to inadequate transverse stability.

It has been shown that those boats trim by the stern as they heel, thus violating the basic assumption employed in conventional computation of hydrostatic stability curves, namely that no difference in trim should occur when the hull heels[80] i.e. the hull rotates about a fixed longitudinal amidship axis which *always remains parallel to the water surface*. This assumption stems from the generally agreed principle (duly respected by naval architects but not necessarily by contemporary yacht designers), that the hull should not too severely alter her fore and aft trim in the process of heeling. For seagoing vessels of normal merchant ship form, the fore and after bodies are sufficiently similar to satisfy the above requirement.

This does not mean that ultimately the two bodies must be identical, but a certain compatible relationship must exist between the bow sections and stern sections. Early yachts, as well as most old fishing and pilot vessels, were essentially well-balanced in this respect.

The Vikings' boats (Fig. 19) or their successors (Fig. 18), yachts of the Colin Archer type (Fig. 17), old pilot cutters (Figs 12 and 13), or the schooner yacht *America* (Fig. 22) would, on this similarity principle, pass the test of retaining the amidship axis reasonably parallel to the water surface when heeled; thus, no radical change in longitudinal trim should be expected.

In his *Notes on Yachts* published in 1869, Edwin Brett speaks about the necessity of both sides of a hull being alike because 'a serious feature is when the axis of the new shape that is immersed when heeled becomes out of parallel with the original amidship line' (when upright).[81] As a result of fore and aft asymmetry in the hull shape such as that incorporated, for example, in an extremely exaggerated form in the *Mach 1* project (Fig. 8B), these requirements cannot be satisfied. Boats with narrow V-shaped bow sections and full afterbody will tend to trim by the bow when heeled. Such a behaviour is typical for small, beamy cruisers with a LWL/beam ratio below 3 (Fig. 95A). These boats, like any other displacement type of boat, must have relatively fine fore-bodies, if an acceptably slender (from the resistance viewpoint) angle of entrance is to be drawn from the breadth amidships. But, if spacious accommodation is to be achieved in the quarters, it is impossible to draw a fine after-body properly to match the geometry of the bow sections. Besides, fairly flat buttock lines are needed for an easy delivery of water displaced at the wide mid-section.

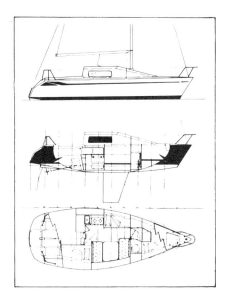

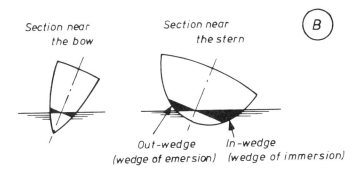

Fig. 95. *Sketch (B) explains the underlying cause of heel-induced bow-down trim of a wide, flat-stern contemporary boat as shown in sketch (A). In the heeled position there is a surplus of immersed volume in the afterbody, as compared with the forebody of the hull. As a consequence, the centre of buoyancy will be shifted aft, and this will result in a change of longitudinal trim towards the bow. To some extent this tendency is aggravated by sail pressure forcing the bow downward, as illustrated in photograph (C).**

* If the distribution of volume over the fore and aft body of the hull remains relatively even as the boat heels, there will be little tendency for the bow to depress and the stern to rise with increasing angle of heel. This keeps the whole rudder immersed and so its efficiency is not impaired. Finer hull forms of lower beam/length ratio tend to be more stable directionally than – to use Herreshoff's expression – 'pot-bellied rule cheating wind bags'.

Figure 95 illustrates the effect of heel on the longitudinal trim for such a type of boat. When a hull heels it immerses its topsides to leeward and emerges them to windward. Suppose for an instant that the boat does not change her trim. It will be seen that the areas of *in-wedges* for the fore- and after-body of the hull are generally greater than the areas of *out-wedges*. More importantly, the area of the in-wedge near the wide stern is much larger than that near the bow. An instantaneous difference in displacement between the fore and after-bodies of the hull occurs. It is obvious that in order to equalise this difference in buoyancy the stern must be uplifted and the bow must fall. Thus, every time the boat rolls or heels to one side or the other she dips her head. Such a situation is shown in Fig. 39. The longitudinal symmetry axis of the hull is no longer parallel to the water surface, therefore the conventionally obtained hydrostatic stability curves, based on fixed longitudinal trim assumptions, become unrealistic. One may expect that, in general, the departure from this assumption becomes greater the larger the dissimilarity between the fore- and after-bodies of the hull. Consequently, the actual transverse stability of an inadequately balanced hull may bear little resemblance to the transverse stability of the same vessel conventionally estimated on the designer's drawing board. And, indeed, it has been demonstrated by Pauling and others[80] that the heel-induced trim nearly always results in transverse stability appreciably less than that predicted by the conventional method of computation.

Figure 96 shows the magnitude of this trim-induced error in conventional stability calculations for a typical, broad-square stern form. The large disparity between the results with and without allowance for longitudinal trim over the range of heel angle beyond 10 degrees, may be attributed to the rather pronounced difference in the shape of sections fore and aft – in particular, the lack of sufficient freeboard at the wide, flat sections of the after-body. The low freeboard/beam ratio results in early submergence of the deck edge, with concomitant radically altered shape of the immersed volume of the hull in the quarters at relatively small angles of heel. Consequently, the metacentric stability of hulls with the shape peculiarities indicated is even less valid as a criterion of seaworthiness than in the case of vessels without such a pronounced fore-and-aft asymmetry.

So far we have distinguished two factors which may cause the actual, *seagoing stability* of a boat to differ by a broad margin from that predicted by conventionally applied calculations of hydrostatic stability. These are:

(i)   the wave motion which alters the stability by changing the virtual weight (displacement) of the vessel as described earlier
(ii) variation in longitudinal trim which occurs during heeling, as a result of fore-and-aft asymmetry of the hull form.

Figure 97 together with Fig. 96 illustrate the combined effect of these two factors on the magnitude of the righting lever. The continuous line curve in Fig. 97A represents the calm water stability of the same vessel as in Fig. 96, but taking into account large, trim-induced errors in traditional stability evaluation. The two other broken line curves, upper and lower, illustrate the wave-induced

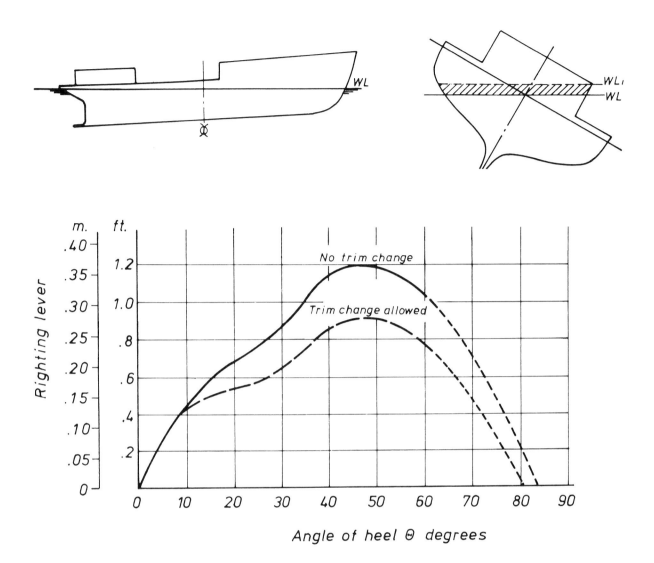

Fig. 96. *Transverse stability curves of a tuna clipper in calm water, with and without longitudinal trim change. Such hydrostatic stability curves can be established by the traditional, so-called* cross curves *method, at fixed longitudinal trim. Alternatively, the hull is allowed freedom to change its trim until equilibrium of hydrostatic forces is reached for each angle of heel. In the latter case, the tedious and time-consuming calculation can be performed rapidly by microcomputers, using currently available software. The heel-induced trim nearly always results in a transverse stability appreciably less than that predicted by the cross curves method of computation.*

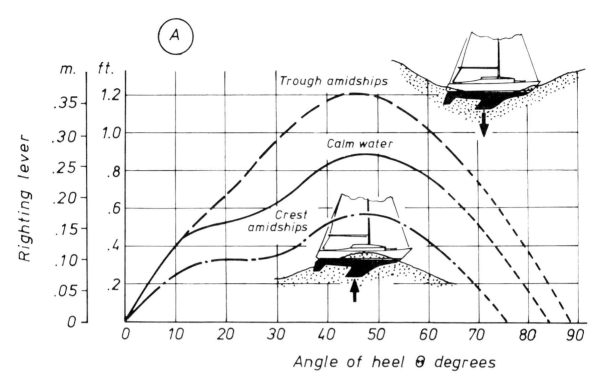

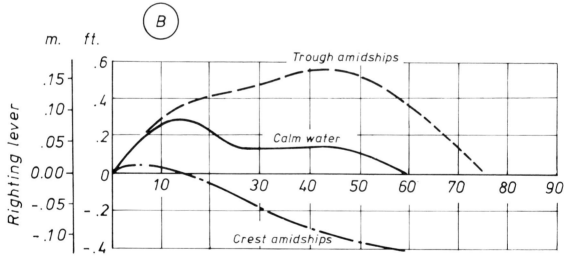

Fig. 97. *Transverse stability curves of two tuna clippers of different hull shapes and metacentric heights (GM) in following seas.*
   GM for boat A was 3.3 ft (1.0 m)
   GM for boat B was 2.07 ft (0.63 m)
Loss of stability in waves appears to be greater than one might expect; it is certainly great in the case of small craft labouring among short and relatively high, steep waves. Stability reduction on the wave crest (particularly drastic in the case of boat B) is due to rather poor stability reserve, even in calm weather. *

* Note that changes in stability in waves are expressed in terms of righting lever variation. It is tacitly assumed that the effect of virtual weight variation in waves can be expressed conveniently in terms of righting lever GZ according to the formula:

$$GZ = \frac{\text{Righting moment}}{\text{Virtual weight}}$$

stability variation of the vessel operating in a following sea. As we already know from Fig. 92, stability in waves varies with time as the boat encounters succeeding crests and troughs, increasing in the troughs and decreasing on the crests.

A number of people have observed that a boat sailing fast finds herself in greatest danger of capsizing with the crest of a wave amidships, when running before a high following sea at a speed nearly equal to the wave speed. In such a condition, the boat may lose much of her transverse stability so that she capsizes or broaches-to if the position on the wave crest is maintained for a long enough time. One should realise that in this critical situation, when the boat becomes particularly vulnerable, a large and violent heeling moment may be applied to the boat through the action of wind and/or breaking seas. In an attempt to minimise this danger, experienced skippers usually reduce speed whenever this becomes approximately equal to that of the wave-train; the boat is then overtaken by the waves. Consequently, the time during which she is exposed to knockdown while on the wave-crest is reduced, and so is the probability of capsize.

The results given in Fig. 97 were obtained for a wave length (L_w) equal to the model length, and the wave steepness was in the order of $1/20\ L_w$ – rather gentle as compared with wave steepness that may be encountered during a storm.[80] Nevertheless, even in this relatively mild condition, the maximum righting lever in the wave crest (Fig. 97A) is reduced to about two-thirds of its magnitude in calm water, and only about one-half the value computed by the traditional method.

Looking at the stability curves of another vessel (Fig. 97B) – with lower GM and different shape from that shown in Fig. 96 – it is seen that, with the crest amidships, the righting levers reduce gradually or even become negative, over the entire range of heeling angles. As a matter of fact, this fishing boat, having insufficient stability to start with, capsized and sank on her maiden voyage. Let this example stand for many. Does Fig. 97B contain a clue?

Before you attempt to answer this question, first think attentively about a general observation made some 2400 years ago by the Greek philosopher Leucippus (the founder of atomic theory). He propounded a sort of law binding man to nature: 'nothing happens at random, but everything for a reason and by necessity'.

It might be added in this context that most yacht designers are not aware that the trim and wave-induced changes in actual, seagoing stability can be so large. One of the reasons is that stability curves are not normally used by them as one of the means of evaluating the seaworthiness or probability of capsize of a boat before she is built. Why is that? Perhaps the answer has already been given in a book entitled *What Should my Boy Study?* – it reads: 'it appears that the emoluments of the profession (yacht designer) do not warrant the study it entails'. What bothers yacht designers most is the driving power which is potentially in the sailplan combined with the stability of the hull which will keep that sailplan in an operating position, not lying flat on her side.

E. Influence of hull shape

Yacht designers seldom deliberately sacrifice speed for seaworthiness, especially when IOR boats are concerned. Since in most seas or oceans where races are sailed, storms occur much less frequently than fair or moderate weather, this approach seems to be justified. However, in the case of a blue water cruising yacht, the design requirements which contribute to seaworthiness may become of overriding importance. The question of immediate interest arises: does the hull shape (or more precisely its cross-sections) which as we know largely determine stability, also affect seaworthiness?

Let us consider first the related problem of how much seagoing stability depends on wave steepness. The wave-induced stability changes presented in Fig. 97 are relevant to the wave steepness in the order of $1/20$ L_w only. Of course, we may expect that these changes will be more conspicuous in steeper and bigger waves where the vertical accelerations, which are the function of the wave height and period (see Eq. 34), are greater. The effect of waves of varying height (steepness) on the righting lever is shown in Fig. 98.[82] It will be seen that, while in calm water the angle of vanishing stability is about 50 degrees of heel, in sufficiently steep waves the stability threshold may be reduced to a dangerously low level at 10 – 15 degrees of heel. Such a severe stability deterioration can well be regarded as a built-in timebomb, just waiting for the appropriate sea conditions to capsize the vessel.

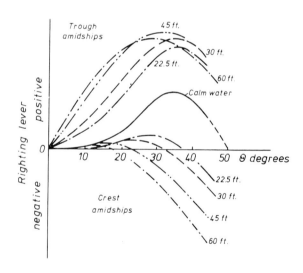

Fig. 98. Variation of the righting lever (stability) in waves of different size (steepness). As seen with the crest amidships, the vessel may lose much of its positive stability and capsize. By contrast, with the trough amidships, stability is greatly increased as compared with that in calm water. In general, for any given wave length and boat speed, the amplitude of up-and-down motion (and thus the wave-induced stability changes) is proportional to wave height. It will be shown that the changing roll-stability of the vessel as it travels through successive crests and troughs, can result in a peculiar coupling resonance (rolling + heaving motion), in which the boat may eventually capsize. Although the stability characteristics shown in this graph are exhibited by some fishing vessels, they are also of relevance to all sailing yachts.

Theoretical investigations and tests conducted on models in waves of various lengths and steepness, reported by a number of authors[82,83,84,85], have indicated that hull geometry, in particular the shape of its cross-sections, influence the vertical accelerations; and stability variations are, in turn, related

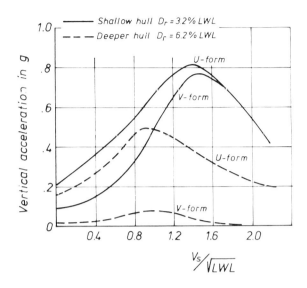

Fig. 99. *Effect of hull cross-section and depth (D$_r$) on vertical accelerations in the fore part of a vessel running in stern seas at different speed/length ratios (V$_s$/√LWL). It is assumed that the wave length is equal to or greater than the hull length. For wave lengths appreciably less than hull length, vertical accelerations (and, related to them, wave-induced stability changes) become less pronounced and therefore less important. Vertical acceleration is given in terms of acceleration due to gravity 'g'.*

to these vertical accelerations (Eq. 34 and Fig. 91). Thus, a boat running in the worst situation (i.e. in following seas with the wave crest amidships) will be more seaworthy with V-shaped deeply immersed sections than will that with a U-shaped or flat-bottom hull.

Figure 99 illustrates, although not directly, this effect in quantitative terms. Four curves give vertical accelerations for two hulls with different sections (V-shaped and U-shaped) and with different draft/length ratios. Resulting accelerations, given in terms of g, are plotted against speed/length ratio. Within a speed range up to about V$_s$/√LWL = 1.4, a hull with V-shaped sections will produce much lower vertical accelerations, and certainly give less trouble from slamming. As shown by broken line curves, the differences in accelerations become greater and more favourable for a V-shaped hull when the draft increases. Of course, apart from the shape of hull sections, a smaller boat will always be worse off in acceleration than a larger craft.

At higher speeds beyond V$_s$/√LWL = 1.6, U-shaped sections for a shallow hull may sometimes be advantageous; such a speed range is, however, well above the capability of a normal cruising boat driven by sails in average weather conditions.

The acceleration data relevant to the deeper hull with V sections (Fig. 99) may be regarded as roughly applicable to classic yachts such as those shown in Fig. 78A; while the data relevant to shallow hulls with U sections are applicable to contemporary IOR round-bottom yachts with large beam/draft ratio (Fig. 78B).

Referring to modern trends in yacht design, H. Barkla[85] remarked: 'Mathematics of a simpler variety show unequivocally that the sea is rougher for boats with the fashionable high beam/depth ratios'. Figure 100, based on Barkla's sketch kindly sent to the author, illustrates the point. In a similar

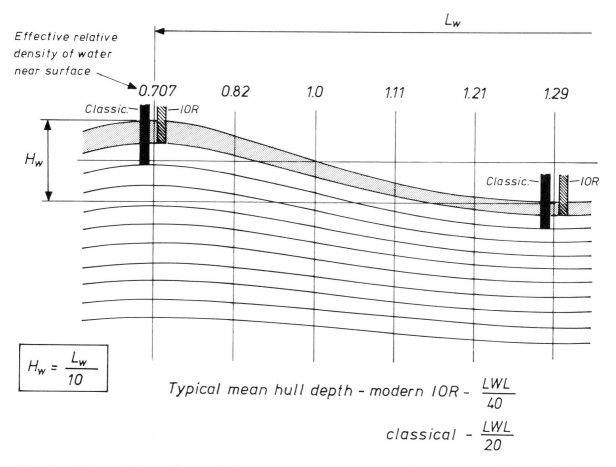

Fig. 100. *With a shallow hull, the effective wave is roughly that which is experienced at the surface. Assuming that the displacement of the hull is concentrated near the centre of buoyancy, the effective wave has a height less than that of the free surface by an* amount depending on the ratio of the mean depth of the hull to the wave length (L_w). The shorter the wave, the more important the hull depth as a factor for reducing vertical hull movement.

manner to that shown in Fig. 79, a wave may be considered to be formed by a series of imaginary layers which, initially horizontal (parallel) whilst the water is at rest, are distorted in such a way that their thickness is increased under the wave crest and correspondingly decreased under the wave trough. Spacing within these layers gives an idea of the variations in the effective weight density along the wave profile. Closer spacing indicates that the effective weight density is greater and numbers written above the wave profile give the numerical values of the effective weight densities within the water surface layers. The calculations are based on the assumption that the wave height (H_w) is 1/10 of the wave length (L_w). Since the imaginary layers below the surface rise and fall with diminishing vertical amplitude (due to successively smaller circular orbits) the differences in effective water density become gradually smaller. At a depth (h) equal to half the wave length, the orbital motion is negligible and so are the differences in effective density.

Following Froude, who first called attention to this consequence of orbital motion, we have already considered the significance of the effective wave slope on rolling, namely: a wide shallow hull in a beam sea follows a steep wave slope near the surface, while a narrow deep hull seeks its equilibrium position about a lesser slope at a greater depth. On this basis alone the latter hull form should be expected to have smaller angles of roll.

But there is also another aspect of the effect of diminishing wave motion with depth on the boat response. Referring to Fig. 100, Barkla[85] has demonstrated that, because the *effective wave height* falls off the deeper the mean depth of the hull, an IOR type of boat will have to go up and down farther than a classic type of boat which gets her hydrostatic lift from double the depth.

Small, vertical columns in Fig. 100 show schematically a marked reduction in hull depth, and also in displacement, for a sample of boats of classic proportions together with contemporary IOR type yachts. Barkla's argument goes like this: 'When beating into waves of the right length to excite resonant pitching and heaving, the effective wave height may be as much as 20 per cent greater for a dinghy-shaped hull than for a yacht of more traditional form. Other things being equal, which they are probably not, this would imply over 40 per cent more energy being dissipated in pitch and heave, and hence over 40 per cent more added resistance. For the builders of cruising yachts to ape the IOR trends towards flat bottoms and rhomboidal waterplanes is indefensible.'

'The real constitution of things generally hides itself'

Heraclitus
(Greek philosopher circa 540 BC)

11 Effect of Heaving Motion on Capsize Probability

Conspicuous rolling, caused by the synchronous wave action described in Chapter 8 is so evident to those who have experienced or studied it that, in almost all investigations which have been published on the subject of safety at sea, the simultaneous occurrence of another important cause contributing to capsize (also due to wave action) has been somewhat overlooked.

Every time a boat rolls in waves she usually heaves up and down. Let us now see what effect heaving coupled with rolling may have on her chances of survival in heavy seas. As shown in Fig. 101, a following or quartering sea overtakes the boat. She is rolling to port and at the same time heaving down from the wave crest marked 0 in sketch A. Her stability increases sharply because the instantaneous effective weight and buoyancy forces, being greatest in the wave trough, produce a large righting moment, which 'snaps' the boat rapidly to an even keel. In so doing she acquires considerable rolling momentum. A quarter of the encounter period later, the boat is timed to meet the next wave crest amidships (sketches B and C). In the meantime a portion of her rolling energy will be drained away by the work done against the water resistance (damping). However, at the starboard-up attitude, when the boat rises to the crest (sketch C) her roll-resisting moment and the angle of vanishing stability rapidly diminish, and are at their lowest when the wave crest is amidships (Fig. 98). This is a situation which is exactly opposite to that desired. Consequently, the angle of roll (Θ_2), reached when the crest is amidships, may become greater than Θ_1, reached when the boat begins to rise from the wave trough amidships position (sketch A).

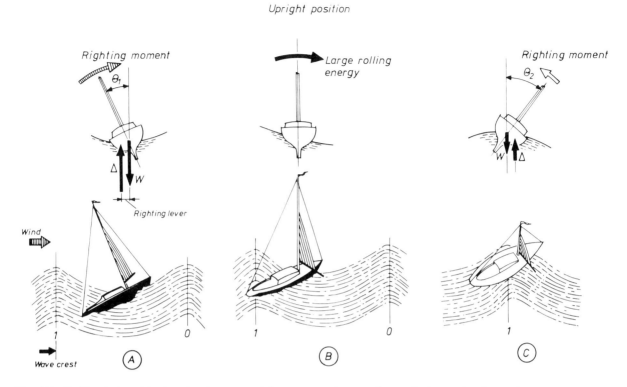

Fig. 101. *Rolling induced by heaving in waves. A large roll momentum imparted to the hull, due to increased stability in the trough, may cause capsize when the boat is lifted to the next crest, where her stability is drastically reduced again. It has therefore been argued that anything which can be done, through design, to minimise changes in stability, is of value in terms of seaworthiness. A deeply immersed vessel, which undergoes relatively small variation of stability in waves, should be less likely to experience capsize.*

We have another kind of wave-induced heeling caused by heaving coupled with wave-induced rolling. In scientific parlance such a coupling is known as *parametric excitation*. It occurs when one of the parameters controlling the motion of a physical system changes periodically with time. In this particular case, vertical change of the centre of gravity (G) of the boat due to heave is the 'villain' parameter.*

A girl shown in Fig. 102 on a swing unconsciously applies parametric excitation of the same nature as that of the rolling boat which simultaneously heaves in waves.

What lesson can yachtsmen learn from the swing analogy? It can be proved that the rapidity with which parametric rolling develops depends greatly on the initial value of the heel angle (in the situation of Fig. 101A) and upon the amplitude of heave. If both the initial angle Θ_1 and the wave height are large, the following angle of roll Θ_2 (sketch C) will be magnified substantially and may easily exceed the angle of vanishing stability, which is at its lowest in this particular attitude of the boat. But if Θ_1 is very small at the start, parametric

* That is not the change of the centre of gravity G inside the boat but the G change in relation to the average water level.

Fig. 102. *This painting was commissioned from Fragonard by Baron de Saint-Julien in 1766, who asked for a picture representing his mistress on a swing, with a bishop standing by while the Baron admired from the grass. Fragonard carried out the picture according to Saint-Julien's wishes, except that in place of the bishop he put an acquiescent husband giving a helpful push to the swing – an action analogous to the rolling motion induced by waves. The girl, changing energetically her centre of gravity by bending her legs (see one of her shoes flying away to the left), helps to increase the angle of swing; her action is analogous to an additional heeling moment induced by the up-and-down motion in waves (heaving).*

rolling may not develop. The boat will simply heave up and down with negligible roll. So, if one could eliminate or reduce heel in the first place, parametric rolling due to simultaneous heave would be unlikely to lead to a knockdown.

There is a situation in which the boat may be knocked down in quartering or following seas, even though there is relatively little initial synchronous rolling. It can happen when the boat is overtaken by exceptionally steep waves spaced at such intervals that the parametric excitation rapidly amplifies the rolling. Finally, when the boat rises to the next wave crest, and her close-reefed sails are no longer sheltered by the upwind seas but are exposed to the full force of the wind, she happens to be rolling heavily to one side, just at the time when her stability is at its lowest.

Such an event, simulated in controlled test conditions, is presented in Fig. 103. Though the boat is knocked down on a wave crest, her rolling motion prior to that fatal roll had given no clear sign that such a thing was imminent. Up to that moment, her rolling had passed through cycles with maximum and minimum angles of roll which did not seem to reach a significant size, so that a catastrophic roll angle beyond the angle of vanishing stability can be reached quickly. Just one heave in a steep, big wave may be sufficient to knock down the boat if she were already rolling in response to a number of waves of even insignificant height.

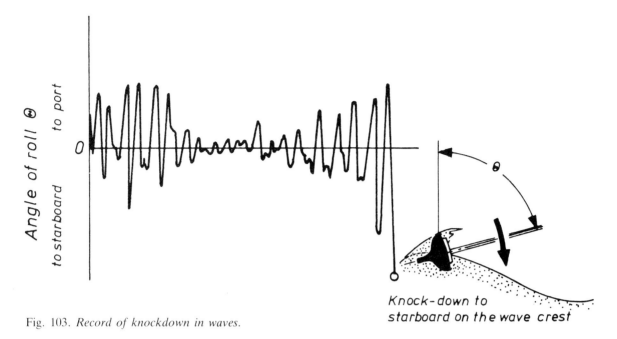

Fig. 103. *Record of knockdown in waves.*

Knock-down to
starboard on the wave crest

Such behaviour, not infrequently experienced in real conditions, is treacherous and misleading, since in one or two swings the rolling motion may become overwhelming. The rate of roll may increase so swiftly that the crew cannot possibly respond adequately (particularly when the rudder comes out of the water), and control over further events is lost.

As a matter of interest, a notable paper *The Ultimate Half Roll*[86] highlights the case in point where recently a coastal tanker, which complied with the IMO criteria for transverse stability, capsized suddenly on a wave crest in relatively light wind (Force 6–7) near the Swedish island of Gottland. The waves were about 5 m (16½ ft) high. Only two seamen survived.

A. Experimental confirmation of the heaving effect

The mechanism of parametric excitation (rolling due to heave) may be demonstrated by making a simple experiment. Attach a piece of string half a metre long to a bob, to produce a simple pendulum. Hold the upper end of the string between the fingers at the edge of a table in such a way that sideways movement of the pendulum support is eliminated (Fig. 104A). If some initial swinging motion is given to the pendulum then, by moving the string up and down at properly timed regular intervals, in the manner indicated in Fig. 104B, the swinging motion of the pendulum will be magnified more or less rapidly, depending on the magnitude of the vertical impulse (see Appendix 5).

Another analogy of rolling due to heaving, a child's swing, demonstrates the mechanism of energy transfer necessary to build up the motion. Each time the

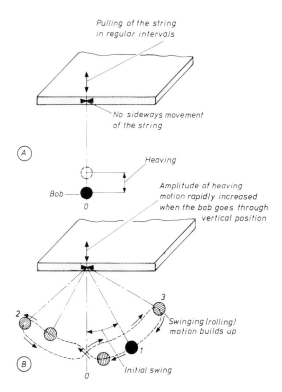

Pulling of the string in regular intervals

No sideways movement of the string

Ⓐ

Heaving

Bob

0

Amplitude of heaving motion rapidly increased when the bob goes through vertical position

Swinging (rolling) motion builds up

2

3

1

Ⓑ

Initial swing

0

Fig. 104. *Pendulum (swing) analogy of parametric rolling. In principle, the mechanism of parametric rolling (due to heave) in waves (not easy to grasp intuitively) is similar to that of a swing in which a child learns that by squatting (changing the centre of gravity of his body) at proper intervals, large angles of swing can be attained at the cost of a certain amount of energy. If performed by the reader, this pendulum experiment may be helpful in clarifying the mechanism of capsize when the boat rolls and heaves simultaneously. Large angles of swing can be reached in two different ways. First, by a person on the ground pushing the swing, while the child is* passive. *This is equivalent to a boat forced to roll due to the action of the wave slope alone. Secondly, by simultaneous and synchronised pushing, together with the* active *squatting action of the child on the swing. This is equivalent to simultaneous rolling and heaving of the boat in waves under synchronised conditions. Of course, the angles of swing (or roll) in the second case may build up rapidly; and catastrophic roll angles can be reached quickly if waves are large and steep. Just one big wave may be sufficient to knock down the boat, if she is already rolling in response to a number of waves of lesser height.*

swing is going towards the vertical position, a person on the ground supplies an impulse in the direction of the motion. If the swing is excited in this fashion, the amplitude may grow progressively. This is analogous to the wave action on a boat in resonant conditions.

The same effect is achieved, without any external help, by changing the position of the centre of gravity of the swing. To amplify a swing's motion, the child squats (pumps) when the swing is in its extreme position (1 or 2 in Fig. 104B), thus lowering the centre of gravity. It is not difficult for the incautious to cause the angle of swing to reach a frightening (if not a dangerous) magnitude and the swing may even be forced to approach the inverted position; and the greater the initial angle of swing and the greater the amplitude of the up-and-down movement of the CG, the more rapidly will the angle of swing increase. Of course the child could not possibly put the swing into motion, even by performing the most energic squatting and standing-up, if there were no initial swinging, no matter how small; and on this and this condition only, parametric excitation may occur and the amplitude of swing will grow.

The centre of gravity of the swing moves up and down in a similar manner to that of the pendulum bob of variable length, periodically describing an elongated figure of eight as indicated in the graph. The area within this trajectory represents the work done, i.e. the energy expended in order to increase the amplitude of oscillation, and this work is proportional to the vertical variation of the centre of gravity. In the case of a heaving boat this energy comes from the waves.

*'. . . those will survive whose functions happen
to be most nearly in equilibrium with the
modified aggregate of external forces'*
Herbert Spencer (1820–1903)
'Principles of Biology'

12 Rolling Inflicted by Rudder Action

One more component of rolling must be taken into account before we can
bring some order to the rather confused picture of causes and effects
responsible for sudden disaster at sea. Figure 105A depicts an equilibrium of
yawing moments when a yacht sails down-wind in an upright condition. The
yawing moment due to the action of the aerodynamic force (F_T), shifted by
distance (a), relative to the Centre of Lateral Resistance (CLR) is balanced by
the rudder action. The boat will maintain her straight course as long as there is
an equilibrium of moments, so that:

$$F_T \times a = F_{rud} \times b$$

When the boat begins to roll heavily, no matter for what reason, large
variations in yawing moment will also occur. Measurements taken by the
author in the wind tunnel during tests on a rolling rig indicate that – depending
on the distribution of the total sail area between the mainsail, headsail and at
times the spinnaker – an increase in yawing moment due to rolling can be
several times greater than that when there is no rolling. Yawing is usually at its
maximum when the yacht is heeling towards the side on which the boom is
rigged, as shown in Fig. 105B. The reasons for this are twofold. First, the
yawing moment lever (a) increases when the angle of heel increases. Secondly,
when the sail rolls, the resulting wind speed on which sail forces depend
increases too. Thus, wind pressure on the sail is greater and proportionally
greatest on the upper part of the sail, where the resulting wind speed is highest.
Consequently, the Centre of Effort (CE) of the sail forces developed in the
rolling condition is raised above the CE relevant to the static condition. As a
result, the yawing moment is greatly increased while rolling. Incidently, wind

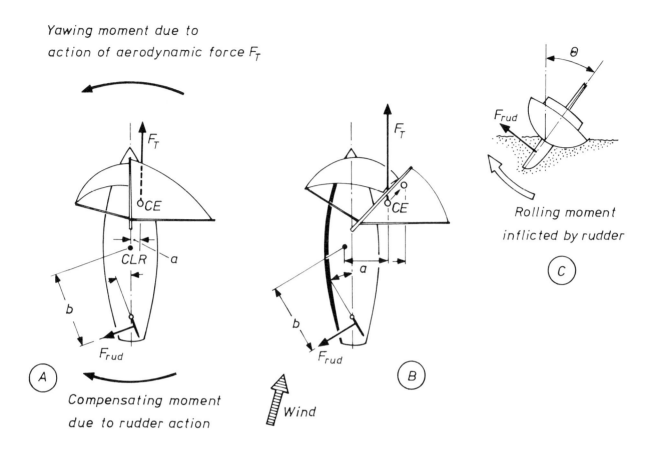

Fig. 105. *Rolling induced by rudder applied in order to control yawing. For the boat to maintain a straight course, the yawing moment caused by aerodynamic forces must be balanced by a compensating moment due to rudder action. When the boat heels, the resultant* aerodynamic force is shifted in such a way that the yawing moment increases; compare the magnitude of the yawing lever (a) in sketches A and B. If the boat rolls heavily, the aerodynamic moment becomes the dominating factor which controls yawing.

tunnel tests indicate that up to 60% more driving force may be produced when the rig is rolling – with roll angles approaching ± 30 degrees – than when the rig is steady. Thus, provided the maximum angle of roll can be kept under control (which in fact it can, by gradually increasing mainsail twist to reduce the maximum roll input from the rig), rolling can be advantageous; it increases the driving force from the sails and thus the speed.*

To correct unwanted deviation from the course sailed, caused by the aerodynamic yawing moment, the helmsman must increase the rudder force (F_{rud}), as shown in Fig. 105B and C by pulling the tiller to port. However, an application of helm to correct yaw inevitably exaggerates roll, so that the motion builds up. This coupled yawing motion caused by rolling can also be amplified by the orbital flow affecting the boat if she travels obliquely through the waves (Fig. 90). In such an unsteady flow condition, originated by rolling

---

* An increase in hull resistance due to rolling is small or, as the towing tank tests on a 5.5 metre model indicated, the hull resistance may even be reduced if the rolling angles are not excessive i.e. below ± 20–25 degrees.

and yawing motions, delayed effects on the sail as well as on the hull forces are to be expected. Thus the resulting motion of the boat, having certain inertia, will be unpredictable, in a sense that there will be a time delay between the rudder action and the boat response.

To maintain the desired heading in following or quartering seas, rudder control is indispensible to prevent excessive yaw. However, the helmsman may neither be capable of immediately anticipating yaw nor of applying the corrective moment at the same time as destabilising yawing occurs; a lag in boat response implies also a lag in the helmsman sensing future motion – a particularly relevant aspect of incalculable consequence if there is backlash in the steering system and the helmsman is losing control over the rudder blade movement, and consequently the rudder action through its centre-line position. This time-lag relationship between yawing and rudder, and their effects on the boat's motion is a complicated game. Admittedly, most sailors would probably agree that correct steering in these circumstances is something of a compromise between doing nothing at all and trying to maintain a straight course.

Observations made by practical sailors give some indication that timing of the helm action is as important as the amount of rudder applied. By improper timing one may amplify rolling in a vicious circle. Anticipation can also do the trick sometimes – pick a flat patch of water to avoid the roll which might otherwise be caused by waves. Skilled helmsman, by deliberately delaying the application of rudder, in an attempt to fight the rolling instead of the yawing motion, may achieve some degree of success at stabilising the boat without using much helm. Of course, the optimum timing of the corrective rudder action, to cope successfully with effects of rolling and yawing, will be different for different types of boats depending on their inertia, the actual sail area and configuration used in any given condition, and on the shape of the underwater part of the hull including keel and rudder. For instance, if the hull is of separate fin – keel/rudder type and the spade rudder is a deep one, a lot of rudder to control yaw is likely to be used, and that may roll the boat violently.

'This new ship here is fitted according to the reported increase of knowledge among mankind. Namely, she is cumbered end to end, with bells and trumpets and clock and wires, it has been told to me, can call voices out of the air or the waters to con the ship while her crew sleep. But sleep Thou lightly. It has not yet been told to me that the Sea has ceased to be the Sea.'

R. Kipling

13 Dynamic Metacentric Stability

What has been discussed so far in Chapters 7, 8, 10, 11 and 12 is a digest of the essential information on the nature of the most important and mutually interrelated causes, of both aerodynamic and hydrodynamic origins, which may lead to violent rolling and ultimately to capsize. These are:

(1) rolling excited aerodynamically (Chapter 7)
(2) rolling induced by waves (Chapter 8)
(3) rolling due to combined effects of heaving and stability variation (Chapter 11)
(4) rolling inflicted by rudder action (helmsman response) (Chapter 12)

The likelihood of the simultaneous occurrence of all these causes in unison, subsequently leading to ultimate knockdown, is somewhat remote; that is to say, it is as remote as the likelihood of meeting severe weather conditions during the whole sailing season. However, bearing in mind the so-called Murphy's inevitability law ('If anything can go wrong, it will, and at the worst possible moment'), it is not unreasonable to suppose that sooner or later the crew will face the danger of being knocked down. It seems justifiable therefore to identify a certain combination of the rolling motion components listed above in the context of dynamic metacentric stability in contradistinction to the static, and to define what the new term *dynamic metacentric stability* means.

It should not be confused with the term *dynamic stability* (without the adjective metacentric used in Chapter 7). This was defined as that property of a boat which causes her to maintain her steadiness or stability only by reason of her motion. Dynamic metacentric stability is narrower in its meaning, and can be defined as the energy available by virtue of the boat's righting moment to resist heeling energy coming as an input of hydrodynamic and aerodynamic origins (enumerated 1–4 above). In *Principles of Naval Architecture*, Vol. 1, p135, there is the following definition of this term 'The dynamic (metacentric) stability of a ship at given inclination is defined as the work done in heeling the vessel to that inclination.

To avoid knockdown, there must be some margin of righting energy left, after the heeling energy from the wind and sea has all been expended through damping, or absorbed (stored in the heeled attitude of the hull). But what does this mean in practical terms? How can one present and measure dynamic stability? To answer these questions we must briefly define the notions of energy and work.

For our purpose it is sufficient to say that energy is the capacity for doing work, and that energy can be stored in different forms or else dissipated ultimately in the form of heat. Wind has energy; it can do some work by driving sailing boats. Wind energy can also be stored in the form of wave energy, which can also do work on boats by pushing them around or causing violent motion. Thus energy and work are somewhat interchangeable. The product of force (F) times the distance (d) moved in the direction of the force is the physicist's definition of work; Work Done = Force × Distance (F × d).

A useful technique for presenting and calculating work done, or energy transfer to or from any physical system such as boat, can be used by plotting a graph of the force involved against the distance moved. This concept is illustrated in the force/distance diagram of Fig. 106.

If the force (F) is constant (sketch A) the graph is a line parallel to the distance axis (d). The work done or energy transferred can be established simply by finding the area under the line of the force/distance graph. In this simple case the area representing work done is given by the rectangle F × d. If the force (F) is variable, as shown by the curve in sketch B, the amount of work done can, with a little more difficulty, be found in exactly the same manner as before, by finding the area under the curve. In other words, the work done can be measured and its amount presented, for convenience, as an area.

A similar expression to one stating that 'work done is given by the product of force times linear distance' can be used for studying the rolling motion of a boat and her dynamic metacentric stability in rolling. In this case, the moment is equivalent to force, and the heeling angle Θ (angular displacement) to distance, d, so that we have:

Work done = Righting (or heeling) moment × heeling angle Θ (35)

To estimate the work which must be done by the elements or other disturbing heeling moments, to bring a boat to the point of no return, i.e. beyond the angle of vanishing stability, the stability curve can be used. However, consideration of the static stability curves for that purpose raises an important point of principle. It is customary in naval architecture to present hydrostatic stability calculations in terms of the righting lever (GZ) variation with angle of heel – as shown for example in Fig. 107A taken from the Fastnet

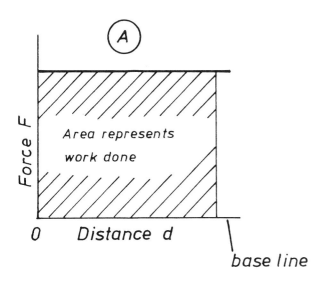

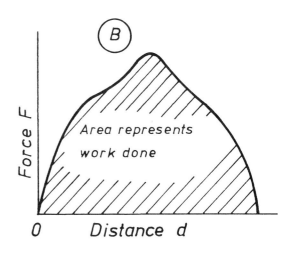

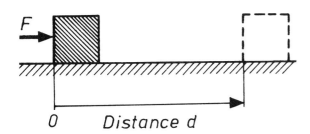

Fig. 106. *Force-displacement diagram.*
(A) Work done by a force (F) pushing a block against friction, is defined in physics as the product of the force (F) acting along the line of motion, times the distance (d) which the block moves along that line.
(B) Work done by a variable force (F) can conveniently be expressed as an area.

Inquiry Report. Such a presentation is, however, of no use for our purpose – quite apart from the fact that the curves shown can be misleading when comparing the stability of boats of different displacement. In other words, the righting lever could be used as a stability yardstick (when comparing stability of different types of boat) but only on condition that the boats in question, although different in hull geometry, have the same displacement; otherwise not.

According to formula 35, stability characteristics must be expressed in terms of the righting moment against heel angle, remembering that the *righting moment* (GZ × displacement) curve, and *not the righting lever* (GZ) curve, should be used to estimate the maximum rolling energy that can be absorbed before the boat will capsize. The two curves in Fig. 107B show hydrostatic stability of the same boats as in Fig. 107A, but now the curves are presented in proper coordinates, i.e. righting moment against the heel angle (Θ). It can be seen that the dynamic stability reserve, indicated by the crossed area under *Grimalkin's* curve, is distinctly smaller than otherwise might be suggested by the original curve of GZ shown in Fig. 107A; and this is entirely due to the

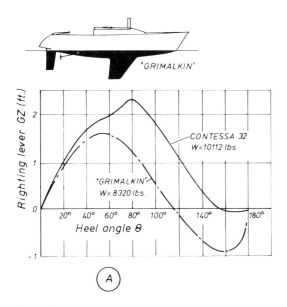

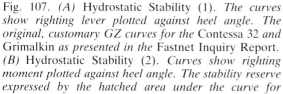

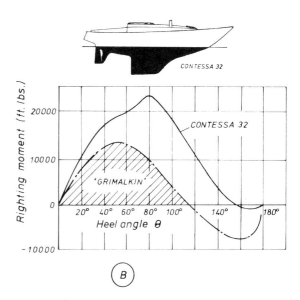

Fig. 107. *(A)* Hydrostatic Stability (1). *The curves show righting lever plotted against heel angle. The original, customary GZ curves for the* Contessa 32 *and* Grimalkin *as presented in the* Fastnet Inquiry Report. *(B)* Hydrostatic Stability (2). *Curves show righting moment plotted against heel angle. The stability reserve expressed by the hatched area under the curve for* Grimalkin *is smaller than that suggested by the original static stability curve shown in (A). In measurements of areas under the curve of righting moment, it is necessary to express the heeling angles in radians not degrees. Since there are 2π radians in a circle = 360°, therefore one radian = 57.3°, or 1° = 0.0175 radians.*

difference in displacements of the two boats in question. A corollary of this is that the heavier the boat, other things being similar, the safer she is in rough seas. Evidently, the work required of the elements to bring a heavier boat to an angle of no-return, reflected by the area under the stability curve, is greater.* This point needs some further clarification.

Displacement/length ratio $\Delta/(0.01\ LWL)^3$ which can be defined as a measure of load (Δ) put on a given length (with LWL assumed to be a representative index of the size of a boat) gives some idea of how heavy is heavy. Table 6 shows displacement/length ratios for a variety of existing boats, some of which are likely to be familiar to the reader.[87]

---

* Obviously, seaworthy boats should have a good reserve of righting energy, as measured by the area within the stability curve above the base line (Fig. 107B). The greater this area the greater the energy which the boat can absorb before the dangerous angle of vanishing stability is reached. It is seen in Fig. 107B that in this sense the hydrostatic stability reserve of *Grimalkin*, a rather modest representative of the 'modern' design trend, is less than half of that of the heavier *Contessa 32*. Thus, for this reason alone, *Contessa 32* could withstand a blow twice as hard as that which would knock down *Grimalkin*.

Table 6

$\dfrac{\Delta}{(.01\ LWL)^3}$	Boat	Δ (tons)	LWL (feet)	$\dfrac{\Delta}{(.01\ LWL)^3}$	Boat	Δ (tons)	LWL (feet)
500	Tradewind 33	8.68	25.8	285	Contessa 28	3.04	22.0
500	Endurance 37	9.3	26.5	285	Viking 8.5	3.75	2.36
470	Endurance 35	9.0	26.7	280	Jaguar 30	4.0	25.0
460	Tahitiana	9.0	27.0	275	Southerly 28	3.8	24.0
450	Barbary	7.0	25.0	270	Southerly 33	5.58	27.5
440	Bowman 36	8.3	26.7	270	Longbow	4.2	25.0
440	Nicholson 32 Mk XI	6.1	24.0	260	Viking 800	2.790	22.0
435	Tufglas 28 (Twister)	4.3	21.5		(Macwester 27)		
430	Pintail	5.18	23.0	260	Contessa 26	2.4	21.0
425	Vertue	4.2	21.5	255	Sunbird 32	4.5	26.1
415	Halberdier	9.1	28.0	255	Sadler 32	3.57	24.0
410	Fisher 34	11.0	29.9	250	Carter 30	3.04	23.0
400	Table Bay	12.0	31.0	250	Sea King 28	4.5	26.5
400	Sovereign 35	7.0	26.0	245	Contessa 35	6.25	29.5
400	Rustler	5.5	24.0	240	GK24	1.2	20.0
400	Nantucket Clipper	3.7	21.0	240	Viking 25	1.88	19.9
380	Samphire 26	3.4	20.8	240	Jaguar 27	2.5	21.75
365	Nicholson 35	7.0	26.75	235	Moody 39	8.1	32.5
360	Finisterre (Nic 38)	7.1	27.0	225	Starlight	3.12	24.0
350	Coaster	8.0	28.4	225	Nicholson ½ Tonner	3.35	24.7
350	Cornish Trader	6.0	25.7	220	Trapper 500	2.32	28.0
350	Seamaster 815	3.17	20.9	210	Corribee	0.89	16.2
350	Seamaster 915	4.0	22.5	205	Moody 30	3.6	26.0
340	Barbican 33	5.5	25.3	205	Moody 36	4.7	28.4
340	Atlantic	9.6	30.5	200	Salty Dog	2.5	23.3
335	Norske 35	10.0	31.0	195	Seagull	1.0	17.25
330	Vancouver 27	4.0	22.9	195	Nicholson 33	4.1	27.6
325	Voyager 30	4.3	23.7	180	Shaft 30	2.68	24.5
325	Cobra 850	3.46	22.0	180	North Star 26	2.25	23.25
325	Viking 30	4.46	24.0		(Offshore 8 metre)		
320	Hustler 35	5.41	25.75	175	Hustler 32	2.73	25.0
320	Mirage 37	6.7	27.5	165	Sonata 7	1.1	18.4
310	Centaur	3.0	21.3	165	Impala	2.05	23.2
310	Contessa 32	4.24	24.0	150	OOD 34	3.35	28.0
300	Warrior	5.5	26.4	115	Contention 30	2.68	28.7
300	Rival 38	7.68	29.5	110	Starflash	0.89	20.0
290	Mirage 28	3.1	22.0	110	Contention 33	2.4	28.4

This boat displacement spectrum can be subdivided into a number of categories in the following way:

Table 7

Displacement/length ratio	Category
450 and above	Very heavy
400	Heavy
350	Medium heavy
300	Medium
250	Medium light
200	Light
150 and below	Very light

It is noteworthy that some more recently built Ultra Light Displacement Boats (ULDB) have the displacement/length ratio reduced to 80 or even less!*

A. Displacement effect

Table 7 should give a sort of feel for what is heavy and what is light; although it leaves unanswered the whole matter of the relative merits of heaviness or lightness. D. Desoutter commenting on this point wrote: 'a lighter boat will need less sail area to make her go, and that may be valuable in racing. She may also be cheaper, both because her construction uses less material and because she requires a smaller rig with lighter spars and staying. In passing, though, it should be remembered that if you want ultra light weight the structure will have to be more sophisticated, and the standards of inspection and control much higher. It will be more like aeronautical engineering, and not cheap.'[87]

From the viewpoint of seaworthiness, however, strong argument can be given in favour of a heavy displacement hull. This primarily concerns the stability reserve indicated by the area under the positive stability curve (Fig. 107) which, in general, will be larger for boats with greater displacement/length ratio. Thus, for example, considering the data in Table 6, one might expect that the heavier *Contessa 32*, with her displacement/length ratio of about 310, should have a larger area under the stability curve than *Grimalkin* (her entry in Table 6 is shown by 'Nicholson 1/2 Tonner') with relevant ratio about 225. And indeed, Fig. 107B confirms such an expectation (see also the Table in Fig. 49, based on the Fastnet Race Inquiry Report, which gives slightly different values for $\Delta/(0.01 \text{ LWL})^3$ but is consistent in relative difference).

The fact that heavier boats will be less vulnerable to high accelerations, and hence have a much less tiring and sick-making motion at sea, is another advantage. But let us concentrate on the significance of the area under the stability curve in dynamic sea conditions when capsize threatens. The concept is presented in Fig. 108.

---

* One may expect that the ability of a ULDB to resist and absorb overturning moments before the angle of no-return is reached (Fig. 55) could well be five to six times smaller than that of a *Contessa 32* – the size of boats being equal.

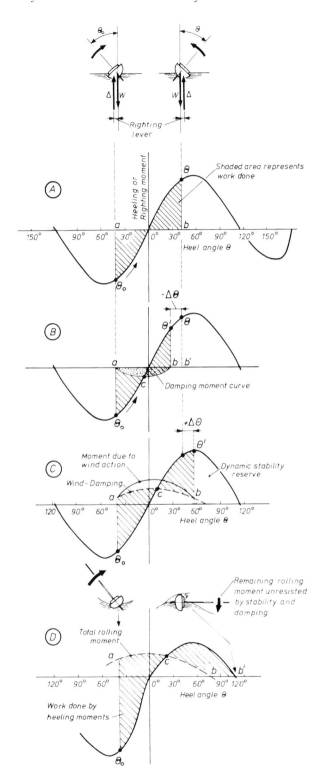

Fig. 108. Static and Dynamic Stability. *Note that in diagram C, the blank area to the right labelled 'Dynamic Stability Reserve' represents residual righting energy left after the first roll. Stability variation in waves, shown above in simplified manner, is rather underestimated by yacht designers, or even not taken into account at all. The stability in dynamic conditions is time variant, dependent on a changing centre of buoyancy and waterplane shape. Thus, the ultimate stability, as well as damping, are functions of the entire hull shape; particularly evident when, say, a wave crest is amidships and the waterplane shape changes drastically. In order to calculate the energy dissipated during the full cycle according to Eq. 28 (page 161) and Fig. 82B (page 152) one must take into account energy dissipated during the swing from port to starboard (as given by the area b, Θ^1, Θ, and b^1 in Fig. 108B) as well as that energy which will be dissipated in the return swing from starboard to port again. This second half of the full cycle is not illustrated in Fig. 108B because the drawing would look too complicated to grasp the basic principle.*

B.   Righting energy (*See Fig. 108*)

Graph A. This plots the static stability curve (righting moment against angle of heel or roll) for *Grimalkin* in the manner already shown in Fig. 92. The boat is temporarily heeled to port to an angle Θ_0, about 40 degrees in calm water. The work done by the disturbing heeling moment against the righting moment to bring the boat to that angle is given by the crossed area within Θ_0, a, $0°$. If the disturbing moment is suddenly removed and there is no damping due to water resistance (an idealistic assumption introduced for the sake of easier, step-by-step presentation) the boat will roll through the upright position and will be brought to rest momentarily at an angle of roll Θ, which is exactly the same as Θ_0 from which the rolling motion has started. Since no rolling energy has been dissipated into the water during the swing from port to starboard, the work done initially by the heeling moment operating when the boat was heeled from $0°$ to Θ_0 will be recovered in the subsequent swing from $0°$ to Θ and stored in the form of potential energy.[88] Thus, the respective areas representing work or energy transferred are exactly the same on the starboard as on the port side of graph A, i.e. areas Θ_0, a, $0°$ and $0°$, b, Θ are equal. In frictionless, flat-calm seas the rolling motion once initiated would last for ever.

   Graph B. This also refers to flat sea conditions, but damping due to water resistance is now present, and is indicated by the damping moment curve plotted below the horizontal axis. The dotted area represents the rolling energy which will be drained away through the work done by the hull and its appendages against water resistance during the roll from port to starboard. Since, under real conditions a portion of the energy, initially stored in the heeled position, will inevitably be dissipated, the boat will be brought to rest momentarily at the angle of heel Θ^1, which is smaller by $\Delta\Theta$ than Θ_0 (from which the rolling was started). The cycle of rolling motion will begin again, and the boat will perform a series of successive rolls to port and back to starboard, each being less than the previous one. The reduction in the roll angle $\Delta\Theta$ per swing can be found by adjusting the vertical line Θ^1, b in graph B by shifting it to the right or left in such a way that the relevant areas representing the energy stored in extreme roll positions to port and starboard (taking into account the energy lost given by the area a, c, b,) are the same, i.e.:

$$\text{area } \Theta_0, \text{ a, c, } = \text{area } \Theta^1, \text{ b, c}$$

This desirable reduction in the angle of roll by the amount $-\Delta\Theta$, entirely due to the loss of rolling energy through damping action, is shown in graph B. It will be seen that the dotted area representing damping a, c, b is equal to the area b, Θ^1, Θ, b^1, and indicates energy lost but which might otherwise be stored in the heeled position.

   Referring to Eq. 28, which reads $\dfrac{\Delta E}{E_{tot}} = 2\delta$, and its relation to the graphical presentation in Fig. 108A and B, it should be noticed that the total energy stored in the heeled position E_{tot} = area a, Θ_0, 0°. The fraction of energy lost due to damping per swing ΔE = area b, Θ^1, Θ, b^1. The larger the $\dfrac{\Delta E}{E_{tot}}$ ratio, the higher the decrement coefficient (δ), i.e. the faster the rate at which rolling extinguishes with time (Figs 82 and 86).

Graph C. Here again, this refers to flat sea conditions but, apart from the damping action, there is also operating the aerodynamically induced rolling moment shown by continuous line curve labelled *Moment Due to Wind Action.* * The area under this curve represents the work done by the wind to heel the boat. The broken line curve (Wind − Damping) below the former represents the resulting moment operating on the boat when the damping moment is subtracted from the aerodynamic moment. The crossed area Θ_0, a, c represents the total work (rolling energy) which must be absorbed during the roll from port to starboard. When studying this case of aerodynamically-excited rolling we should focus our attention on the two opposing components contributing to the resulting rolling motion, namely: the excitation component and the damping component. Their respective magnitudes will determine whether or not, and to what extent, rolling will grow with time. Magnification of rolling angles will continue until the rate of wind energy input due to sail action is matched by the rate of dissipation of wind energy in damping. In the case depicted in graph C, the aerodynamic moment is greater than that due to damping, thus the rolling angle (Θ^1), reached after a complete roll from port to starboard, is greater than Θ_0 by the amount + $\Delta\Theta$.

To the right of the demarcation line b, Θ^1 there is a blank area, below the stability curve, which represents the dynamic stability reserve. This reserve can, of course, be exhausted in a couple of rolling cycles, and the boat will subsequently be knocked down if nothing is done to reduce the magnitude of the aerodynamically induced rolling moment. This demonstrates explicitly that a high degree of damping, if achieved through the efficient action of a properly designed hull and its appendages, will effectively reduce roll amplitudes and also the boat's liability to knock down.

Graph D. Here we see a situation different from the flat sea. Now the sea is rough, and thus the static stability curve used before is no longer applicable. According to our findings discussed earlier, a boat's stability will be reduced on the wave crest and increased in the trough. As compared with the area under the stability curve in graph C (right side) the relevant area in graph D is much reduced, and so is the available righting energy of the boat to resist the heeling energy. This change is accounted for in graph D, and the small sketches above the stability curves illustrate the respective position of the boat in the trough and on the crest of the wave.

Additionally the total rolling moment, given by the broken line curve a, c, b, is greater than that in graph C, because new components of rolling motion

---

* The moment due to wind action may be periodic as discussed in Appendix 2. Thus the rolling moment produced by sails operating as a 'rolling engine' may be sufficiently strong to capsize the boat even in calm water.

operating in a rough sea have been added, namely: those due to wave action, coupling effects in heave, together with any component inflicted by the helmsman's attempt to reduce yawing. It will be seen that the energy stored in the port side attitude (in the wave trough), and given by the area Θ_0, a, c, cannot be absorbed during the roll to starboard and safely stored in the starboard attitude (on the wave crest). Clearly, the available energy-storing capacity of the boat in the starboard side attitude, i.e. her residual dynamic metacentric stability represented by the area c, b^1, b, is not large enough; evidently the area Θ_0, a, c is greater than the residual area c, b, b^1. And once the reserve of righting energy has been depleted, the consequence is inevitable. The mast will hit the water, whereby the remaining rolling energy may or may not be absorbed at the cost of structural damage to the rig.

Many of the IOR type of boats which have a low angle of vanishing stability will run out of righting energy when the mast nears the water. In such a rather topsy-turvy situation (Fig. 57) crew weight no longer augments the restoring moment but, on the contrary, contributes to capsize.

'Sir, I have found you an argument, I am not obliged to find you understanding.'

Samuel Johnson (1704–84)

14 Effects of the Design Features on Seaworthiness

By way of preview, it has been mentioned earlier that to proceed in an orderly and logical fashion, open to rational criticism, we must look at boat behaviour in rough seas as the response of a physical system to wind and wave forces. An awareness of the system concept as applied to boats is of unquestionable value to anyone seriously concerned with real situations in rough weather.

A. System approach to boat dynamics

In a similar manner to any other physical system subject to dynamic forces, a boat should be regarded as incorporating three basic component qualities:

(1) Moment of inertia (displacement of the boat and distribution of mass relative to the axis of rotation).
(2) Stability of the hull in terms of righting moment (taking into account the fact that the magnitude of the righting moment will depend on a number of factors, discussed earlier), which, as a rule, will largely vary in waves.
(3) Damping as a means of dissipating energy back into water and air.

Taken together, these components (1–3) and the way they are blended into an unified whole, determine the dynamic personality of the boat. And the implication is that, depending on their dynamic personalities, boats will respond differently to the same storm condition. In addition, there must also be taken into account the forces or moments which cause the motion of the boat,

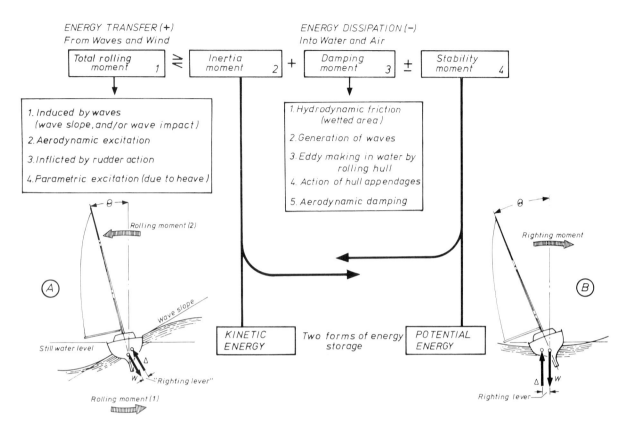

Fig. 109. *A boat in waves considered as a dynamic system. Basic components are: inertia (mass or weight of the boat, and its distribution relative to the axis of rotation), damping, and stability. This block diagram should assist in exposing the fallacy of seaworthiness criteria based on hydrostatic characteristics of the boat alone. Taken together, the basic components determine the dynamic personality of the boat; depending on their personalities, some boats are safer than others.*

i.e. an input or energy inflow from wind blowing on a rig and wave force.

These integral components of the boat in waves, considered as a system, are shown in the form of a block diagram in Fig. 109. They interact with each other in such a way that the whole becomes more than just a simple collection of the parts. Thus, when talking realistically about dynamic stability in a seaway and seaworthiness, we must consider the effect of all components operating and interacting simultaneously. The performance of a sailing vessel, be it a yacht or fishing vessel – as well as any other dynamic system – depends upon that of all its components, but transcends that of any one component. Referring specifically to seaworthiness it cannot, by implication of the system definition, be determined from the performance of any individual component (part) alone.

Although by its very nature a system cannot be described by the sum of single properties of its parts, it is possible to make significant distinctions by considering certain aspects of the action of its parts in the context of their design features. The system approach is finding out how these components interact with each other, to enable the whole to function safely or to achieve given goals. If any component cannot fulfil its particular function, the whole system is affected and may fail. Every part has a role to play. As we shall see, altering just one component can lead to quite unexpected consequences.

Virtually all systems we have to deal with in the real world – including ourselves – are open systems, in a sense that they depend for input (exchange of energy) on other systems, for instance the weather system. To quote an expert's opinion – only a cask full of wine with a good bung, gradually maturing inside the unchanging microclimate of a deep cellar, might be regarded as a small closed system; whatever happens inside the cask is a far cry from the dynamic event.

A sailing craft can be described as an open system which may be driven into non-equilibrium and disaster by increased energy inflow from wind and waves. A threshold of safety is reached when the energy input exceeds a critical amount that cannot be absorbed and/or dissipated through the dynamic interaction of the hull and sails with surrounding water and air.

The most common mode of capsize is the dynamic roll-over of the boat as a consequence of her response to rolling moments, exerted either by one catastrophic rogue wave or else due to action of a successive group of large waves. These may act (and usually do) in a cumulative manner, with other rolling moments of different origin. The block-diagram of Fig. 109, in which the boat is presented as a dynamic system, illustrates the point. To the left (below box 1) there are written four rolling moments which may knock down the boat. These are the essential, but by no means all, possible moments which may contribute to capsize. Another way of looking at the action of these constituents is to consider them as agents through which the energy of waves and wind is transferred and converted into the rolling motion of the hull. This is the reason why these rolling moments are listed under the common heading ENERGY TRANSFER (+).

The magnitude of the resulting (total) rolling moment will depend on whether or not the constituent moments operate in unison and, of course, on the severity of wind and sea. In sketch A of Fig. 109 there are shown for example, two rolling moments 1 and 2 operating in unison at the particular instant when the hull is on the rising slope of the wave. One of them is of hydrodynamic origin (1) and due to wave slope action, and the other (2) is due to aerodynamic excitation. When the boat rolls under the action of these moments, her motion is resisted and boxes 2, 3 and 4 indicate possible roll resisting moments. The meaning of the two small arrows ⇌ of opposite direction, drawn between box 1 and boxes 2, 3 and 4, is that the effect of the total rolling moment may either be greater or smaller than the combined effects of the roll resisting moments.

The word *possible* used when referring to the roll-resisting moments (boxes 2, 3 and 4) calls for some explanation. The reader may recollect that stability can either contribute to the rolling motion, and ultimately to the capsize (sketch A in Fig. 109), or resist the rolling motion (sketch B). This is the essence of Froude's metaphor 'The effect of stability is the lever by which the wave forces a ship into motion – if a ship were destitute of this stability, no wave that the ocean produces would serve to put her in motion.'

As illustrated in sketch B of Fig. 109, the stability moment resists the rolling moment at first. However, at the end of each swing the rolling energy stored in the heeled position of the hull will be returned as a fresh input to initiate rolling motion in the opposite direction. In other words, the wind and wave energy stored in the form of potential energy in the heeled position of the hull is periodically converted into kinetic energy of rolling motion and back again into potential energy.

Potential energy storage depends on a change in system configuration (heeled attitude of boat); and the amount of energy stored (ΔE_p) equals the work required to change the configuration (see Note 88). For a heeled boat, this change in potential energy equals the weight of the boat (W) times the change in centre of gravity position (Δh) relative to the upright position:

$$\Delta E_p = W \times \Delta h \tag{36}$$

Kinetic energy storage of a rolling boat depends on her mass moment of inertia (I_r) about the axis of rotation and the square of angular velocity ω (see Note 89), and can be estimated according to the formula:

$$E_k = \tfrac{1}{2} I_r \omega^2 \tag{37}$$

Thus, the rolling boat can be looked upon as a dynamic system which has two different forms of energy storage – kinetic energy (box 2 in Fig. 109) and potential energy (box 4). These are mutually interchangeable like a pendulum. Signs ± drawn between boxes 3 and 4 reflect this dual action of the stability moment operating interchangeably with the inertia moment. If there were no means whereby the energy inflow could be dissipated back to the environment through damping (box 3), the rolling boat would store more and more energy at ever increasing angles to and fro, until her dynamic metacentric stability was exhausted, the point of no return reached and the boat capsized.

It must be stressed here that the heading ENERGY DISSIPATION ($-$) written above box 3 with negative sign (Fig. 109), indicates that dissipation is associated with damping and not with either inertia or stability actions. These can only temporarily absorb and store the wave and wind energy in the cyclic manner decribed above. There is a distinct difference between the meaning of the words *absorb* (store) and *dissipate*.* As we have already pointed out in Chapter 13 when discussing this distinction, it is not just a matter of pure semantics, and cannot be overemphasized. To avoid knockdown, there must be some margin of righting energy left (Fig. 108D), after the heeling energy from wind and sea has all been dissipated through damping and safely stored through the action of stability, before the angle of vanishing stability is reached. For improved seaworthiness, it is highly desirable to get rid of energy inflow through damping (dissipation) rather than storing it.

Wasa's disaster (she sank on her maiden voyage in 1628) to which a short

---

* The following examples illustrate this difference. The energy you put into one of those spring-mounted punch balls is *stored* and will quickly be returned, perhaps to your discomfort. But the energy you put into stirring the Christmas pudding mixture is *dissipated*, and will not spring back. When a boat is rolled some of the energy input is used to stir up the water around her keel, and that is lost. But some of the energy is stored up and will reveal itself by returning the boat towards upright attitude and beyond.

reference was made in Chapter 8, may illustrate the point. According to available evidence 'four of her sails were set: foresail, foretop, maintop and mizzen, while she was in the shelter of the tall cliffs. Then, out of the shelter, the breeze caught the canvas. A powerful gust and she heels, rights herself and then heels again hard over to port. The water gushes into the open ports and she sinks swiftly in 110 feet of water under sail, pennants and all.'

Here we have an example of a vessel capsizing just after two rolls only. Apparently, the cumulative wind energy inflow during the first and second roll was greater than the righting energy available to restore the ship to the upright condition. In other words, the residual storing energy, i.e. residual dynamic metacentric stability left after the first roll, was not large enough safely to accommodate the rolling energy delivered during the second roll. If *Wasa* had possessed more efficient damping to quickly dissipate the wind energy input back into the water during the initial roll, she might not have gone to the bottom in her own harbour under peaceful conditions. Quite apart from insufficient damping contribution, the vessel evidently had little reserve of positive stability (as measured under the righting moment curve) and also a low angle of vanishing stability. But who was to blame? In subsequent legal proceedings the case was, in the end, dismissed without anyone being held responsible. Probably rightly so, since knowledge of the dynamics of capsize did not exist at that time. One may wonder: is this knowledge sufficiently comprehended today?*

A fundamental requirement of any reasonable theory is that the *predicted consequences* of certain design features incorporated in a boat considered as a system (Fig. 109) should agree with the empirical evidence both observational and/or experimental. Tests on models capsizing in breaking waves done recently in the USA, Japan and England, are of crucial importance in this context. In following chapters we will refer to these tests considering first the inertial effect (box 2 in Fig. 109) on seaworthiness.

B. Inertia effect – overview

*'It is by reason of dynamical rather than of statical relations
that an elephant is of graver deportment than a mouse.'*
                                        D'Arcy W. Thompson
                                        Growth and Form

Sailing boats in rough seas are subject to large and abrupt forces (loadings) of aerodynamic and hydrodynamic origins. The problem of predicting the hull response to these occasionally violent loadings is a rather complicated one. However, some generalisation is possible on the basis of boat inertia, namely: rapidly varying forces are transmitted to the hull, which responds in the same

---

* This is in spite of the fact that the basic factors playing significant roles in the dynamics of capsize have been known since W. Froude's time.

sort of way as a flywheel responds to arbitrarily applied torque variation. Depending on its mass moment of inertia, a heavy flywheel responds only slowly to changes in the torque magnitude, and so does the heavy displacement yacht to changes in the rolling moment due to singular or combined action of waves and wind.

The term transverse or *roll moment of inertia* (I_r) may be expressed as that property of the boat which manifests itself as a resistance to being accelerated and set into rotary motion by the action of rapidly applied rolling moments (box 1 in Fig. 109).

The mass moment of inertia:

$$I_r = m\ k^2 \tag{38A}$$

which can alternatively be rewritten as:

$$I_r = \frac{\Delta}{g}\ k^2 \tag{38B}$$

where k is the radius of gyration (gyradius).

It is to be noticed (Eq. 38B) that it is not just displacement which determines the roll moment of inertia; the gyradius is even more important, since I_r depends on the square of k. The contribution of rig to the moment of inertia illustrates the significance of the gyradius. As shown in Fig. 110A, the rig is a relatively small weight item in comparison with other contributions to the displacement of a typical modern yacht; it amounts to about 5% only. But, as shown in Fig. 110B, it dominates the roll moment of inertia, making up some 60% to 70% of the total moment of inertia.[91] This finding, although perhaps surprising to some readers, should not be unexpected bearing in mind that the centre of gravity of the rig (mast, rigging, wires, etc.) is a long way up from the axis of roll, and this distance – the gyradius (k) – is squared in Eq. 38B.

According to survey data (Fig. 110C) the weight of a typical rig has decreased by nearly 30% since the robust rigs of the 1960s; and this 'translates to about a 25% decrease in roll moment of inertia'![91] The ballast effect is also significant; its weight contribution (Fig. 110A) is in the order of 50% of the displacement. However, because its gyradius is relatively small, the ballast contribution to the total roll moment of inertia is about the same as that of the hull itself (Fig. 110B) – in the order of 15%.

Ballast location has become a controversial issue. On the one hand, bearing in mind stability and seaworthiness requirements, it should be located as low as possible; on the other hand, as a result of rating rule implications (tenderness ratio penalty) the ballast is sometimes deliberately located higher in the keel or even within the hull itself in order to maximise the handicap allowance.

The influence of the mast, and its concomitant effect on the roll moment of inertia relative to the probability of capsize in breaking waves, was clearly demonstrated in the American investigations.[92–95] Figure 111A is a graphical presentation of the tests on models termed 'two-dimensional'.[93]

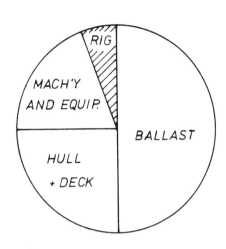

A.Distribution of weight

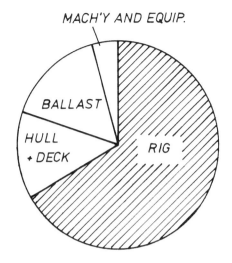

B.Distribution of roll
moment of inertia

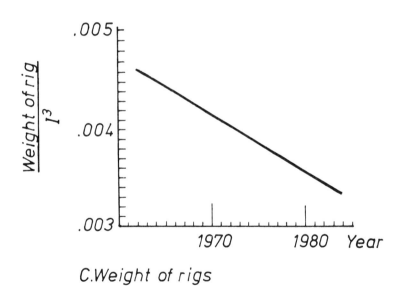

C.Weight of rigs
for typical sailing yacht

Fig. 110. *(A) and (B) Distribution of weight and roll moment of inertia for a typical contemporary sailing yacht.*
(C) Reduction in weight of rig over the last 20 years. Weight of rig is expressed as a ratio of weight (W) to cube of the 'I' measurement in the IOR handicap formula, which is defined in the rule as being the height of foretriangle *(and may be taken as roughly the mast height above deck).*

An analysis of the reasons for retirement in the 1977 and 1984 Sydney–Hobart race indicates that rig failure contributed to about 25 per cent of total retirements. Rig failure is by far the prime reason for boats' inability to reach destination. Designers as well as skippers must therefore assume that the boat may be subjected to rough sailing weather for days and that fatigue or weakness of the rig will be likely to show up as a failure.

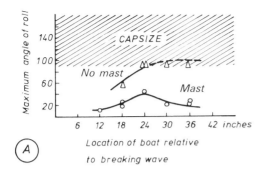

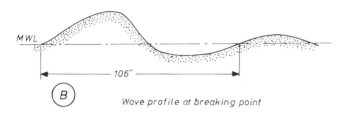

Fig. 111. *(A) The effect of the mast on capsize probabilities. It is seldom realised how much the total moment of inertia of a boat in rolling and pitching is due to the mast, sails and rigging.*

(B) The computer controlled wavemaker produced repeatable breaking waves at a given point downstream. Two consecutive pictures taken by the author illustrate the capsize of an IOR type of boat without mast.

C. Capsizing impact of a single breaking wave

'We may find one or the other physical theory very attractive. But its sole purpose is to induce observations which might eventually disprove it'

Sir Herman Bondi
British astrophysicist

Before Fig. 111A is interpreted, and the significance of the roll, moment of inertia is discussed in some detail, we shall digress for a while to consider the mechanics of breaking waves relevant to the capsize process. Experiments were carried out in a 120 ft long towing tank, where the computer-driven wavemaker was programmed to generate a wave train that would produce repeatable, deep-water breaking waves at a given point downstream of the wavemaker. A profile of the wave used for the tests is shown at breaking point in Fig. 111B. Figure 112 depicts the development of a breaking wave recorded in laboratory conditions at discrete time intervals, similar to the wave produced in the

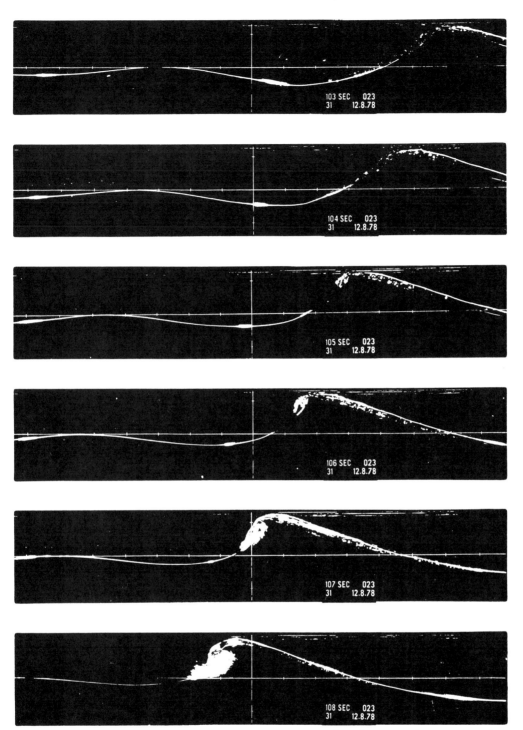

Fig. 112. *Breaking wave development recorded in a water tank at Edinburgh University. The high energy content in breaking waves is due to their large acceleration and velocity of water particles, as well as to steepness. A nearly vertical wall of water on the wave face becomes almost inevitable, particularly in conditions where a number of wave crests coincide and interfere with each other, thus adding their heights to produce a freak wave.* (Picture reproduced by courtesy of S. Salter and J. Taylor.)

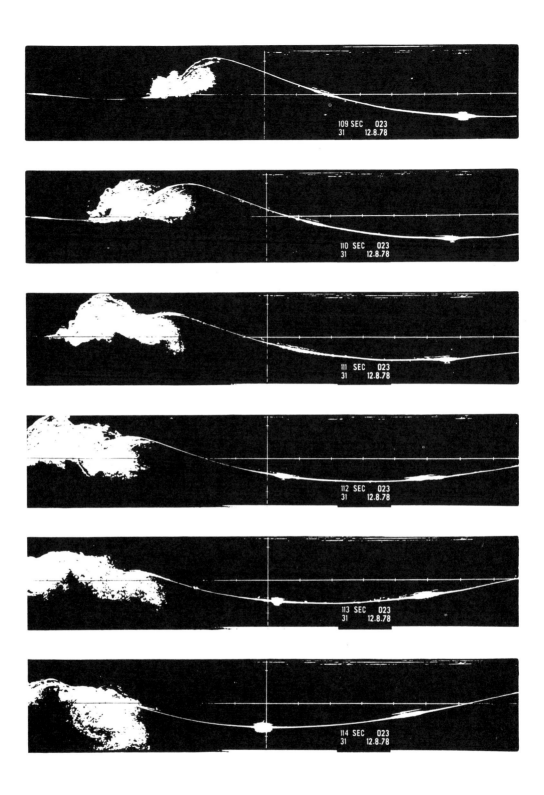

capsizing tests made in the USA to which Fig. 111 refers. Figure 113 presents the formation of a shallow water plunging breaker which corresponds to visual observation. As the wave progresses, it becomes asymmetric and its front steepens. At a later stage (sketches 3 and 4) a jet of water is ejected from the wave crest, with local velocity v_1 which is about 1.5 times the velocity of wave propagation (c for celerity):

$$c = \sqrt{g\,L_w/2\pi} \tag{39}$$

$$c = 1.34\,\sqrt{L_w} \text{ in knots (when } L_w \text{ is in ft)}$$

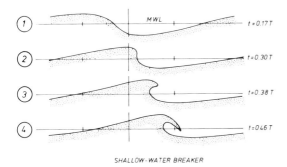

SHALLOW-WATER BREAKER

Fig. 113. *Close-up of a plunging breaker at successive time intervals (t), expressed in terms of the wave period (T), developing from an initial sinusoidal wave. This drawing is complementary to Fig. 93.*

Figures 114 and 94 show these local velocities and also local accelerations of water particles at the crest before and after the wave breaks. The maximum acceleration in this particular wave as shown is about three times the gravity acceleration (g). Small arrows marked c and g, drawn in each upper right corner of sketches A, B and C in Figs 114 and 94, indicate the magnitude of the velocity of wave propagation (c) and the magnitude of the acceleration due to gravity (g) respectively. These may serve as a reference. Notice, for example, that the forward part of the water jet in sketch C of Fig. 94 has an acceleration of about 1 g, directed vertically; the jet is falling freely under the influence of gravity, as experienced by a free jet from a hose. However, in some cases the emerging jet can have quite large velocities relative to the rest of the wave, sufficient to plunge far ahead of the crest. Subsequent evolution of the breaking wave depends on the place and instant of time where the falling jet touches the water surface. If it is near the crest, as might be expected from Fig. 115, the resulting splash may be directed down the wave, which then becomes a *spilling breaker*. As seen in Fig. 115, the plunging jet closes over the air beneath it to form a transient tube of a relatively short life span, before the wave breaks into a turbulent cascade of water.*

Experimental measurements made so far have revealed that transient local velocities (v_1) at the crest of a near-breaking or breaking wave may reach up to 2.8 times the velocity of wave propagation (c); and it seems likely that accelerations greater than 5 g may occur in natural waves.[96,97] These observations and measurements provide some rational basis for a more realistic

---

* The difference between *plunging* and *spilling* breakers is that the latter occur as the wave crest increases in height (the peak containing an angle less than 120 degrees). It then becomes unstable and finally slides down the forward slope of the wave in a torrent of foam.

Fig. 114. *Velocity field (distribution) within a plunging breaker in deep water. (A) is when the wave face becomes vertical, and (B) and (C) are some time after (A), when the crest is overhanging. The arrow marked c (top right) gives the magnitude of the velocity of wave propagation (celerity). (see also Fig. 94).*

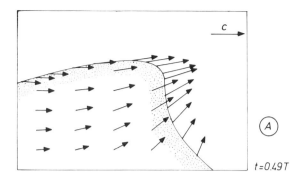

A

$t = 0.49T$

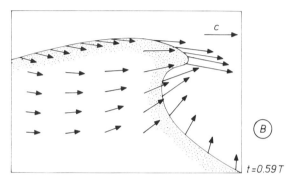

B

$t = 0.59T$

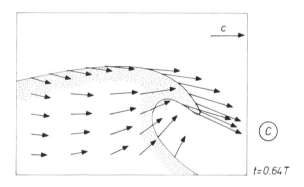

C

$t = 0.64T$

Fig. 115. *Plunging jet closing over the surf rider just before it descends towards the wave face with resulting turbulent splash-up. It is unlikely that the surfer will emerge in full control of his board after tumbling down the front of such a tumultuous breaking wave, characterised by intense vorticity.*

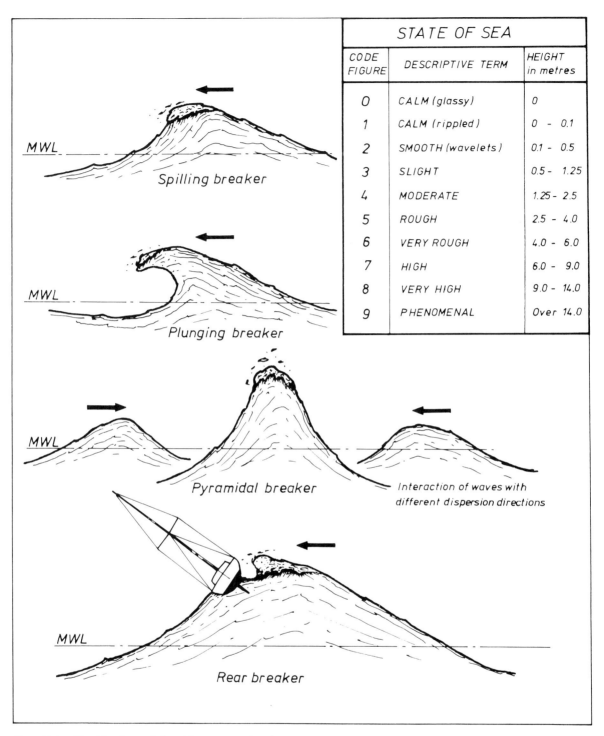

STATE OF SEA		
CODE FIGURE	DESCRIPTIVE TERM	HEIGHT in metres
0	CALM (glassy)	0
1	CALM (rippled)	0 - 0.1
2	SMOOTH (wavelets)	0.1 - 0.5
3	SLIGHT	0.5 - 1.25
4	MODERATE	1.25 - 2.5
5	ROUGH	2.5 - 4.0
6	VERY ROUGH	4.0 - 6.0
7	HIGH	6.0 - 9.0
8	VERY HIGH	9.0 - 14.0
9	PHENOMENAL	Over 14.0

Spilling breaker

Plunging breaker

Pyramidal breaker

Interaction of waves with different dispersion directions

Rear breaker

Fig. 116. *Classification of breaking waves in deep water. MWL stands for Mean Water Level. The table next to it gives dimension of waves generated by winds ranging from 1 to 70 knots.*

Wave and sea scale for fully arisen sea

SEA STATE	SEA-GENERAL DESCRIPTION	(BEAUFORT) WIND FORCE	WIND DESCRIPTION	RANGE (KNOTS)	WIND VELOCITY (KNOTS)	WAVE HEIGHT FEET AVERAGE	WAVE HEIGHT FEET SIGNIFICANT	T (AVERAGE PERIOD)	L_w (AVERAGE WAVE LENGTH)	MINIMUM FETCH (NAUTICAL MILES)	MINIMUM DURATION (HOURS)
0	Sea like a mirror.	U	Calm	< 1	0	0	0	–	–	–	–
	Ripples with the appearance of scales are formed, but without foam crests.	1	Light Airs	1-3	2	0.05	0.08	0.5	10 in.	5	18 min.
1	Small wavelets, short but pronounced; crests have a glassy appearance, but do not break.	2	Light Breeze	4-6	5	0.18	0.29	1.4	6.7 ft.	8	39 min.
	Large wavelets, crests begins to break. Foam of glassy appearance. Perhaps scattered white horses.	3	Gentle Breeze	7-10	8.5	0.6	1.0	2.4	20	9.8	1.7 hrs.
2					10	0.88	1.4	2.9	27	10	2.4
	Small waves, becoming larger; fairly frequent white horses.	4	Moderate Breeze	11-16	12	1.4	2.2	3.4	40	18	3.8
					13.5	1.8	2.9	3.9	52	24	4.8
3					14	2.0	3.3	4.0	59	28	5.2
					16	2.9	4.6	4.6	71	40	6.6
4	Moderate waves, taking a more pronounced long form; many white horses are formed. (Chance of some spray).	5	Fresh Breeze	17-21	18	3.8	6.1	5.1	90	55	8.3
					19	4.3	6.9	5.4	99	65	9.2
					20	5.0	8.0	5.7	111	75	10
5	Large waves begin to form; the white foam crests are more extensive everywhere. (Probably some spray).	6	Strong Breeze	22-27	22	6.4	10	6.3	134	100	12
					24	7.9	12	6.8	160	130	14
					24.5	8.2	13	7.0	164	140	15
6					26	9.6	15	7.4	188	180	17
	Sea heaps up and white foam from breaking waves begins to be blown in streaks along the direction of the wind. (Spindrift begins to be seen).	7	Moderate Gale	28-33	28	11	18	7.9	212	230	20
					30	14	22	8.6	250	280	23
					30.5	14	23	8.7	258	290	24
7					32	16	26	9.1	285	340	27
	Moderately high waves of greater length; edges of crests break into spindrift. The foam is blown in well marked streaks along the direction of the wind. Spray affects visibility.	8	Fresh Gale	34-40	34	19	30	9.7	322	420	30
					36	21	35	10.3	363	500	34
					37	23	37	10.5	376	530	37
					38	25	40	10.7	392	600	38
					40	28	45	11.4	444	710	42
8	High waves. Dense streaks of foam along the direction of the wind. Sea begins to roll. Visibility affected.	9	Strong Gale	41-47	42	31	50	12.0	492	830	47
					44	36	58	12.5	534	960	52
					46	40	64	13.1	590	1110	57
	Very high waves with long overhanging crests. The resulting foam is in great patches and is blown in dense white streaks along the direction of the wind. On the whole the surface of the sea takes a white appearance. The rolling of the sea becomes heavy and shock-like. Visibility is affected.	10	Whole Gale	48-55	48	44	71	13.8	650	1250	63
					50	49	78	14.3	700	1420	69
					51.5	52	83	14.7	736	1560	73
9					52	54	87	14.8	750	1610	75
					54	59	95	15.4	810	1800	81
	Exceptionally high waves. Sea completely covered with long white patches of foam lying in direction of wind. Everywhere edges of wave crests are blown into froth. Visibility affected.	11	Storm	56-63	56	64	103	16.3	910	2100	88
					59.5	73	116	17.0	985	2500	101
	Air filled with foam and spray. Sea white with driving spray; visibility very seriously affected.	12	Hurricane	64-71	> 64	> 80	> 128	(18)			

estimation of impact forces from extreme waves, with many applications for the design and safety of any waterborne craft.

Figure 116 illustrates four basic types of breaking waves and the table next to it gives dimensions of waves generated by winds ranging from 1 to about 70 knots.

Since large local velocities (v_1) within the crest (Fig. 114C) are inseparably associated with the breaking process and emerging high velocity jet, one may expect that the impact severity of a breaking wave should be greater than one which is non-breaking. And indeed, tests carried out in the towing tank by means of a dynamometer confirm that expectation.[98] Figure 117 represents this point. The lower line in plot A gives the variation of the force impulse against the wave height (H_w) for regular waves with no breaking crest. The upper hatched band indicates a much higher force impulse than would be expected for a given wave height; this is exhibited whenever breaking occurs. It is seen, for example, that the strength of force impulses in breaking waves is 4–5 times larger than that recorded in regular waves of the same height (H_w). A similar graph (Fig. 117B) gives the force impulse plotted against the crest front steepness as defined in sketch C of Fig. 117. Here again the bulk of the measurement points relevant to regular waves lies close to a straight line, but the measurements for breaking waves exhibit some scatter within the hatched band. Thus, one wave can deliver a greater capsizing impact than the other, even though height and steepness are similar. This demonstrates the difficulty in estimating accurately the severity of force impulses based on temporal records of the wave height or steepness alone.

The capsizing moment would appear largely to depend on local velocities within the jet (Fig. 114C). It is unlikely that these velocities can ever be precisely identical – particularly in natural waves which, as a rule, are the product of interference effects of a number of wave trains coming from different directions, and non-deterministic in nature. One thing is certain however, the capsizing power of a single episodic, breaking or erupting wave may be much greater than that due to the action of a train of regular, *non-breaking waves operating in resonant conditions*, whereby the roll angle may grow in a cumulative manner.

Figure 118, together with what follows, is intended to elucidate the issue in a qualitative if not strictly quantitative sense. The capsize of a boat lying broadside to an incoming breaker can be considered in two stages: *the first* is that of forced rolling inflicted by the wave steepness, and occurring simultaneously with lifting-up (heaving) of the boat towards the crest; *the second* is a rapid heeling, followed by sudden sideways drift (away) due to the impact of a high velocity jet discharged from the crest. Frames marked 1, 2 and 3 (Fig. 118B), based on a sequence of photographs taken in the towing tank, illustrate the first stage; the remaining frames illustrate a part of the second stage of the capsizing process, and a series of photographs in Fig. 119 complement visual observation of the event.

As might be expected, the capsizing energy transferred from the breaking wave to the boat during the first stage largely depends on:

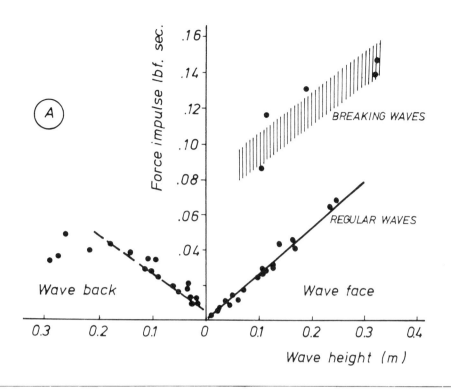

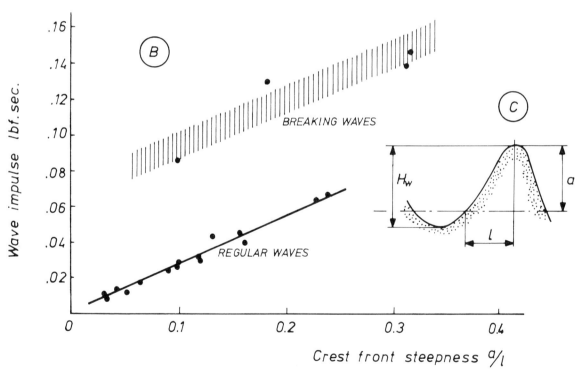

Fig. 117. *Plots A and B show the force impulse exerted in regular, non-breaking and breaking waves at different wave heights (H_w) and at different wave crest steepness, defined in sketch C. Measured force impulses plotted to the right of the vertical axis are relevant to the wave face, whereas those to the left are relevant to the wave back.*

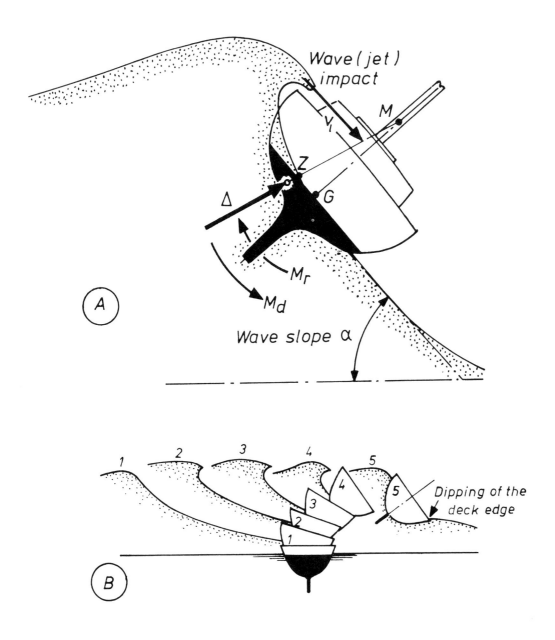

Fig. 118. *Basic capsizing forces and moments, and their effect on boat behaviour in breaking waves. Note that in situation A, the righting lever GZ becomes the rolling lever, where $M_r = GZ \times \Delta$ = rolling moment, and M_d = damping moment. The capsize trajectory recorded in sketch B is based on photographs taken in a towing tank (Ref. 92). The situation depicted in sketch A is an intermediate one between positions marked 4 and 5 in sketch B. With the hull now inclined at a large angle to the horizontal, the jet ejected from the wave slams against the topsides, imparting a strong overturning moment to the hull. With virtually no restoring stability moment, the jet impact moment may be considerably augmented by the tripping effect produced by immersion of the covering board (deck edge).*

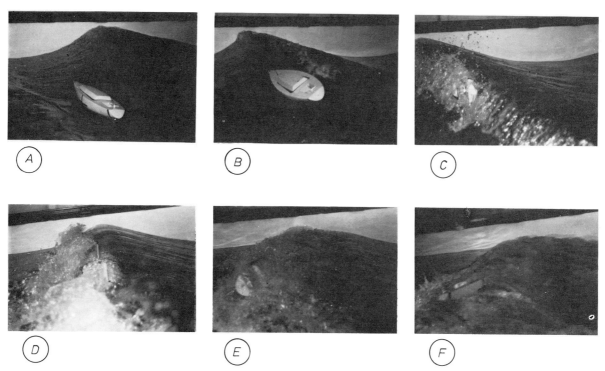

Fig. 119. *Photographs of capsizing sequence of an IOR type of boat (without mast) in breaking waves (Ref. 98). In picture C, the hull is engulfed in the spilling crest and thrown sideways with high acceleration. In picture D the keel rolls up out of the water, and the boat rights herself while drifting with the spilling breaker. If there were a mast attached to the hull, recovery from the inverted position might not take place, due to the large damping moment produced by the rigging.*

α_{max} – the wave slope (see Eq. 25)
GZ – righting lever (see sketch A Fig. 109)
Δt – time interval during which the boat is exposed to the wave slope action
I_{tot} – total inertia of the boat, including added mass (I_a), i.e. $I_{tot} = I_r + I_a$

The term *added mass* (I_a) requires some explanation. The total moment of inertia (I_{tot}) of a boat in motion depends not only on the mass of the boat herself and the distribution of her mass relative to the axis of rotation, i.e. her own roll inertia (I_r) as defined by Eq. 38B, but also on the inertia of water entrained by the hull underbody and forced to roll together with the hull, i.e. the added inertia (I_a); Figs 7, 10 and 16 may serve to illustrate the point.

The Colin Archer type of boat, or old pilot and fishing-boats, have large mass moment inertia for two reasons. First, they are of a heavy displacement type; secondly, the large lateral area of their hull underbody *entrains large amounts of water*. As a result, their added moment of inertia (I_a) is much higher than that of the modern, light displacement type of boat (B in Fig. 7).

In Chapter 8, a brief reference was made to the effect of the centreboard (CB) position on the rolling period of a Finn class boat. With CB down the rolling period T_n increased from 2.1 to 2.4 sec, i.e. by about 15%. Bearing in mind Eq. 20A, in which the roll moment of inertia is in the numerator, this increase is entirely due to the effect of added mass component. Were the lateral area of CB larger the effect of added mass would be more pronounced. One might therefore infer that contemporary types of boat built to the current International Offshore Rule should, for this reason alone, roll more heavily and be more susceptible of capsize than the older type of boat such as A, B, C, D, and E in Fig. 16.

Can this plausible inference be substantiated more rigorously?

Theory of capsize

Rolling energy (E_r) transferred to a boat and due to the action of wave slope can be mathematically expressed as follows[99]:

$$E_r = \frac{(\int_0^{\Delta t} M_r \, dt)^2}{2 \, (I_r + I_a)} \tag{40}$$

where M_r is the rolling moment induced by the wave slope. Many readers familiar with O level mathematics will remember the elongated S symbol as the more or less dreaded *integral sign*. It is not the author's intention to bring back those haunting memories. The reason for presenting Eq. 40 is to hint that even with the help of integral calculus (which is a major instrument for the natural scientist and engineer) it is extremely difficult to estimate accurately the energy inflow from the wave to the boat in dynamic conditions, i.e. when everything changes in time rapidly: wave slope, boat attitude, velocities and accelerations within the wave, etc, etc.

It would be rather misleading to give the impression that the solution to Eq. 40 is straightforward. In his book *How to Solve It* Polya emphasises the importance of understanding the problem, believing that the purpose of computing *is insight not numbers*. An adopted model for computation and/or experiments, intended to *prove or disprove* the underlying theory, may be crucial and it should be realised that, explicitly or implicitly, theory is always a starting point. It is most likely that the model used, be it mathematical or physical, will determine the answer to the problem we are seeking for. Much confusion may arise if the model does not fit reality, and we shall see soon that, indeed, this is frequently the case we must be aware of. Although computing and experiments are supposed to be the tools that supply the *correct* answer, we shall concentrate first on the physical insight and thereafter we shall critically interpret the available experimental results.

Bearing in mind Eq. 40 and the implications of Figs 109, 114 and 118, some difficulties must arise if one attempts accurately to estimate the inertial, damping and stability effect in waves. This is because the water flowing past the boat, considered as a dynamic system, can greatly diminish or augment her total inertia, her damping and her stability.

It looks as if Mother Nature was quite determined that we shall never be able to predict boat response and thus safety in rough seas with desired accuracy – leaving enough room for heroes and people of the Man of La Mancha stature who are somewhat conditioned –

> 'To dream the impossible dream,
> To fight the unbeatable foe,
> To bear with unbearable sorrow,
> To run where the brave dare not go . . .'[100]

Dreamers apart and referring to Eq. 40 again, some important generalisations, well supported by experimental evidence, are possible. For our immediate purpose, suffice it to realise what factors are in the numerator and what are in the denominator of Eq. 40. In other words, what factors (design factors amongst them) primarily determine the amount of capsizing energy received from a steep wave. And that is what really matters from the viewpoint of yacht designer, practical sailor and rule maker alike.

The magnitude of rolling moment (M_r) in the numerator of Eq. 40 depends, for a given displacement, on the wave slope (α), the righting lever (GZ) from Figs 118A and 120A, and the time interval (Δt) during which the boat is exposed to the wave slope action. That is:

$$M_r \propto (\alpha \; GZ \; \Delta t) \tag{41}$$
where $\propto$ designates 'is proportional to'

The form of the sea surface, defined mathematically as a 'random moving surface', is unpredictable in the sense that both the slope (α) and the time interval (Δt) are *independent* variables, not amenable of human intervention. Thus, one of the ways a hazardous wave/boat encounter, and the capsizing energy inflow to the boat, can be mitigated is to change GZ, a *dependent* variable which the designer and rule-maker may control. The smaller the GZ, the less energy will be transferred from the wave slope. This is what theory (as incorporated into Eq. 40) implies, and it is evident from Fig. 120A that, other things being equal, the beam of the hull determines GZ. Wider boats with larger GZ should be more susceptible of capsize and therefore less seaworthy than narrower ones. Is this theory consistent with experiments?

Three models were chosen for investigation of the beam effect on capsize probability. The body plan and static stability curves of three beam-variants of the fin-keel parent model 1 are presented in Fig. 120B. The parent model is based on a 1/13 scale version of a modern yacht of about 33' (9.75 m) LOA and 4.5 tons displacement. Righting moment curves, calculated on the assumption that the centre of gravity (G) lies at the flotation line, show significant variation in hydrostatic characteristics. Thus, comparison of the two curves for extreme models 2 and 3 reveals that the wider beam raises the maximum righting moment at the expense of an increased area of inverted (negative) stability.[98]

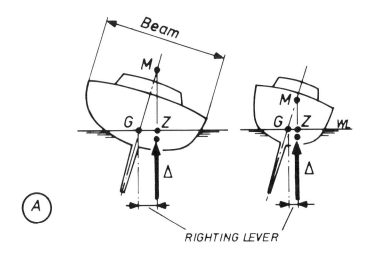

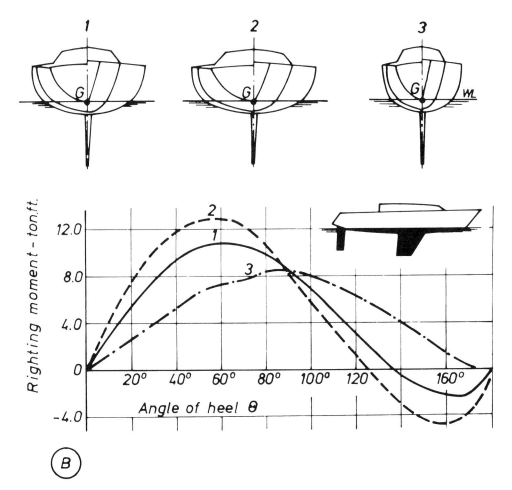

Fig. 120. *(A) The effect of beam on the righting moment. Position of the centre of gravity (G) relative to the waterline remains constant.*
(B) Body plans of three beam variants*
(1) Parent form.

(2) Wide hull.
(3) Narrow hull.
Together with relevant static stability curves of a fin-keel IOR type yacht LOA 33 ft (10 m), beam 10.8 ft (3.3 m) and displacement 4.5 tons.

* See also Addendum on page 275.

234

Three scaled-down breaking waves of heights approximately 5.5 m, 4.5 m and 4.0 m (full size) were used, and the behaviour of each model was investigated at three attitudes to the waves: beam on, 20 degrees off the stern (quartering seas) and stern square on.

According to the English test results, beam was found to be 'the most significant parameter in its effect on capsize'.[98,101] It has a greater influence on capsize behaviour than any other design parameter such as, for example, displacement, inertia, freeboard or area and shape of hull appendages. This is summarised in Table 8.

Table 8
Capsize related characteristics*

Design parameters	*Maximum knockdown angle*	*Range of inverted stability*	*Downwave control*
Wider Beam	✛	✛	▬
Lighter Displacement	+	+	–
Higher Centre of Gravity	●	✛	–
Higher Freeboard	●	+	●
Larger Lateral Keel Area	●	●	✛
Higher Roll Inertia	●	●	●
More 'Traditional' Hull Shape	●	–	✛

In the 4.0 m and 4.5 m waves, the narrow model (3) was only knocked down to 120 degrees whereas the parent and the wide model (1 and 2 in Fig. 120B) were rolled over completely. The wide model (2) rolled to a higher heel angle as it rose up the wave face prior to being struck by the breaking crest, and on the impact the *leeward deck was seen to dip into the unbroken wave face.* By contrast, the narrow model (3) appeared to absorb the breaking crest impact by *slipping sideways* (ahead of the wave) rather than by rolling. In the 5.5 m wave all the three beam-variants were fully inverted, but the narrow model was the only one to right itself. The wide model therefore was not only more susceptible of capsize but also less likely to recover from an inverted attitude. And, indeed, it required another breaking wave impact to bring the model upright. It should be stressed in this context that all models tested were without masts. Had the wide model 2 possessed a mast and rigging, and had they been left intact after capsize, the hull might have remained floating upside down for a rather long time – dangerously long for the crew to survive. Another episodic breaking wave, similar to that which capsized the boat, is unlikely to come quickly. Besides, the damping generated by the mast and rigging, deeply immersed in relatively quiet water as compared with the breaking waves on the surface, may be sufficiently large even to prevent re-righting.

As many dinghy sailors have learned, once a boat has turned turtle with

---

* A thick ✛ means a stronger effect than a thin +, thus 'wider beam' in the first column is more prone to being knocked down. A thick ▬ indicates a strong negative effect, and a thin – indicates less negative effect; ● means no noticeable effect.

Fig. 121. *Once a boat with large negative stability is stuck in the mast down position, it is extremely difficult, if not impossible, to bring her upright again. Quite apart from a quantity of trapped water which may be of* considerable weight (and must be raised in the righting process), the drag resistance of the mast and rigging can be beyond the righting power of wave action alone.*

rigging vertically down (Fig. 121), it is sometimes extremely difficult if not impossible to right her without outside assistance.

So far we have considered the energy input from a wave during the *first stage* of the capsizing process (Fig. 118A), i.e. that due to wave slope action. The second and eventually final stage begins when the boat is struck by the breaking crest, or by the jet of water emerging from the crest. The energy transferred during the impact (E_i) of duration Δt, can be expressed in a similar manner to Eq. 40 as:

$$E_i = \frac{(\int_0^{\Delta t} M_i \, dt)^2}{2 \, (I_r + I_a)} \tag{42}$$

where M_i is the impact moment which in turn can be expressed as:

$$M_i \simeq 1/2 \, \varrho \, A \, C_D \, v_1^2 \, r \tag{43}$$

where ϱ – density of sea water (1.99 lb sec^2/ft^4)
A – area of the hull superstructure subjected to wave impact
C_D – drag coefficient of superstructure exposed to wave impact
r – impact moment lever

Again, as in the case of Eq. 41, it is difficult to evaluate the integral of Eq. 42, i.e. the magnitude of the impact moment (M_i) because A, C_D, v_1 and r all vary with time. Furthermore, the time interval (Δt) during which the boat is exposed to the impact cannot be established.

Thus, the capsize event may broadly be categorised as non-deterministic in nature. A deterministic event would be that which can be predicted accurately on the basis of some explicit mathematical relationship. Unfortunately, all data which go into Eq. 42 are random or probabilistic in nature and therefore non-deterministic. And this implies that sheer luck or the 'wheel of fortune' should somehow be accommodated into the mathematics of capsize.

It is, however, certain that, for a given boat, the impact energy (E_i) is much higher than the rolling energy (E_r) transferred from the wave slope. To quote, the major feature of model behaviour during an encounter with a wave is: 'If the wave is not breaking, then regardless of steepness there is no danger of capsize'.[98] This observation is in agreement both with the theory (exposed in Eqs 40 and 42) and with measurements presented earlier in Fig. 117, provided that no other forces, such as wind forces on rig, are acting. An inspection of Eqs 42 and 43 will reveal that the water jet emerging at the crest is a principal carrier of wave energy. The exponent of power relevant to local velocities (v_1^4) explicit in these Equations, i.e. the fact that the impact energy received (E_i) depends on the fourth power of v_1, explains the devastating effect of the jet. In other words it is not the height of the wave that causes the capsize, but the high velocity of the mass of water (kinetic energy) which strikes the hull.

It should be added that, at the end of the first stage of capsize event (Fig. 118A), the boat is ill-prepared to resist the final blow from the breaking crest. The wider the boat (higher GM), the greater the angle of heel reached at the moment of impact. It follows that the area of the hull exposed to the jet is also larger (Fig. 122). Hence, impact energy is directly linked to hull geometry.

Fig. 122. *A beamy boat which behaves like a raft (i.e. heels away from the nearest crest) is vulnerable to the coup de grâce (see also Fig. 119). As a result of action of the water jet (with its high energy content) on the exposed area of the hull, the boat is usually catapulted into a more or less violent capsize.*

Since the area (A) of the hull superstructure subjected to wave impact goes into Eq. 43, the question arises: What is the effect of freeboard variation on capsize probability? Observation of the behaviour of a modern boat 1 (Fig. 120B) with a typical coachroof, and an identical model but with higher freeboard and a flush deck (Fig. 123), revealed no difference in their propensity to capsize.[98,101] But, once capsized, the model with the lower freeboard had a greater tendency to self-right. The fact that the model with higher freeboard remained inverted on more occasions was attributed to its slightly greater range of negative stability (compare the static stability curve in Fig. 123 with that relevant to model 1 in Fig. 120). This observation is recorded in Table 8 under the heading Higher Freeboard.

American tests[93,95] have also hinted that, other things being equal, variation in freeboard alone has little or no effect on capsize probability. A plausible explanation is that when large beam is associated with low freeboard, such a combination will cause the lee rail to submerge earlier, at a smaller angle of heel. Once the deck edge is under water (Fig. 57), stability rapidly diminishes because a tripping effect accelerates the capsize. Generous freeboard may offset the tripping effect, thus causing the hull to slide along the wave face

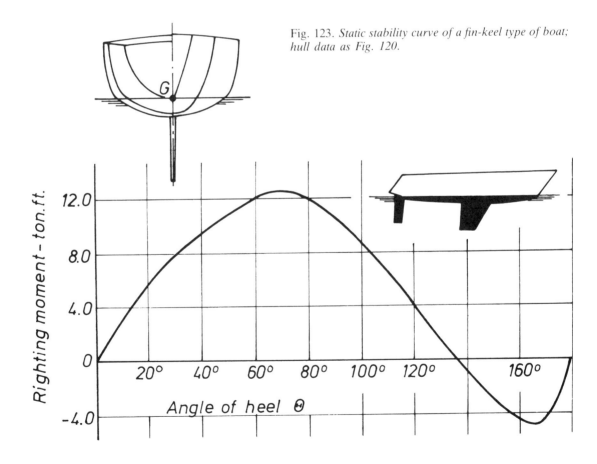

Fig. 123. *Static stability curve of a fin-keel type of boat; hull data as Fig. 120.*

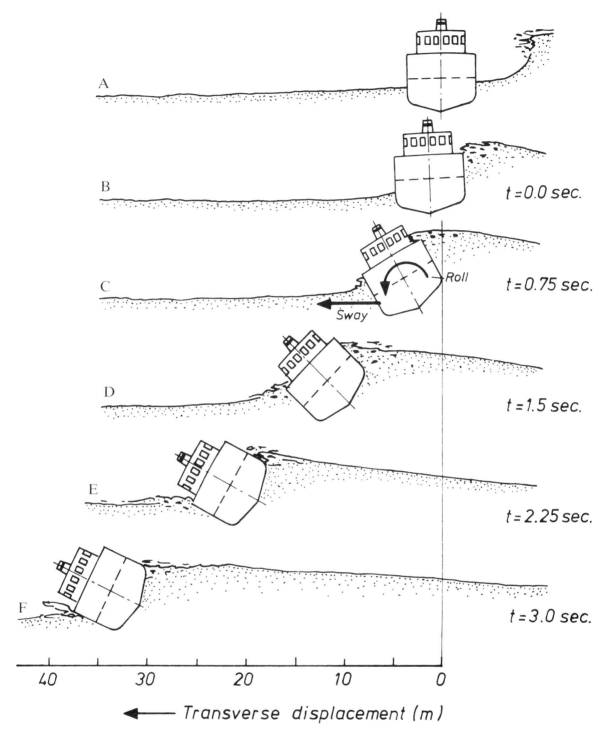

A

B   *t = 0.0 sec.*

C   Roll   *t = 0.75 sec.*
                                      Sway

D   *t = 1.5 sec.*

E   *t = 2.25 sec.*

F   *t = 3.0 sec.*

40   30   20   10   0

⟵ Transverse displacement (m)

Fig. 124. *Capsize sequence of fishing vessel Helland-Hansen. This was caused by a breaking wave which hit the vessel broadside while under way at 6 knots. The skipper observed the wave with a height of about 16 ft (5 m) approaching from the port side; he reduced speed and held his course. The vessel was hit by the wave and the slam was felt but not heard by the survivors. During a period of 5–6 seconds the ship listed about 60° and, being hit by subsequent waves, reached her angle of no-return at about 80° and sank sideways after about 20 minutes. (RINA paper 'The capsizing of M/S Helland-Hansen' edited by E.D. Dahle and O. Kjaerland, 1977.)*

rather than to dip into the water. However, because a larger area of the hull is initially exposed to breaking waves, the advantage of having higher freeboard for one reason is somewhat cancelled for another.

Conclusions relevant to freeboard effect[93,95,98,101] reached by researchers in England and the USA are at variance with tests made on fishing vessels in Norway. To improve seaworthiness of the Norwegian fleet the following recommendation has been made: 'Bulwarks (equivalent in principle to higher freeboard), although providing protection in moderate weather, are dangerous in breaking waves. They increase the wave moment . . . Rails, combined with low bulwarks if necessary, should therefore replace high bulwarks on small vessels'.[99] Capsizing tests conducted in a large towing tank with the model positioned broadside to the waves revealed that: 'The only effective measure was to remove the bulwark, which gave a substantial decrease in heeling angle' The effect of bulwarks (and thus the hull area A) on the impact energy transferred to the boat when she is struck by a breaking wave is indirectly shown in Fig. 124.

Yet another capsizing test on a 1/13 scale model of a 66 ft offshore supply vessel conducted in the USA (and reported in Ref. 108) also indicated that: 'The effect of bulwarks was detrimental in high waves, capsizing occurred with a lower wave height with the bulwarks in place (freeing ports open) than with bulwarks removed'. The same argument applies to the deckhouse effect. On the one hand, it has been argued in Ref. 99 that a weathertight deckhouse extending from side to side substantially improves a boat's propensity to right herself; on the other hand, it also increases the area exposed to waves from the side. Consequently 'the recommendation is presently valid only for the conversion of existing deckhouses to superstructures', which implies that doors, hatches, and windows should be of stronger construction.

D. Significance of inertia and displacement

'To the question, What shall we do to be saved in this World? there is no other answer but this, Look to your Moat.'

George Savile, Marquis of Halifax (1633–1695)
A rough draft of a 'New Model at Sea'

The inertia effect has been briefly discussed in Chapter 14B where the boat inertia was considered to be analogous to that of a flywheel. Thus, a heavy flywheel is expected to respond only slowly to changes in torque magnitude; so does a heavy displacement yacht to changes in rolling moment due to the combined action of wind and waves. In other words, the larger the inertia (that is, the larger the displacement and/or the gyradius (k) (see Eq. 38B), the smaller should be the change in heeling motion (heeling acceleration and heel angle) for a given heeling moment imposed by the action of breaking waves. On inspection of Eqs 40 and 42, it is seen that, indeed, our expectation must be correct, because the roll moment of inertia (I_{tot}) multiplied by 2, is in the denominator of these equations. Hence, the rolling or impact energy to be transferred from the breaking wave to the boat is *inversely proportional* to her inertia.

In the light of what has been discussed in the previous chapter, we may interpret the test results presented in Fig. 111A. For each individual test the model lay still in the water, beam-on to the oncoming wave and in various locations with respect to the breaking point of the wave (Fig. 111B). The benefit of the higher roll moment of inertia due to the presence of a mast is evident.[92] Although the impact forces and accelerations were severe enough to capsize the model without the mast, with the mast in place the model became immune against this particular wave of specific height.

The location of the model relative to the breaking point appears also to be crucial, and there is a critical region (critical location) within which the model without a mast would always capsize. Upstream of this region the model would ride over the waves.

Let us translate this finding into real life. The boat in position marked a along the wave profile 1 in Fig. 125 might, just might, safely ride over the incoming wave face. Considering further stages of the plunging breaker

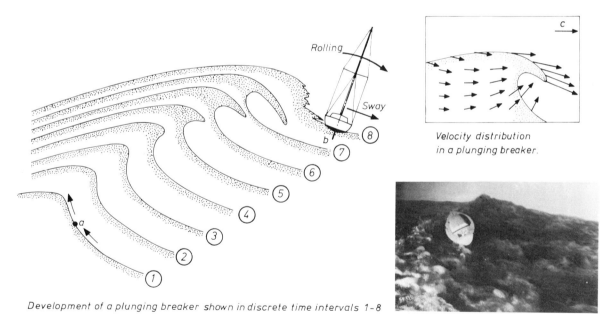

Velocity distribution in a plunging breaker.

Development of a plunging breaker shown in discrete time intervals 1-8

Fig. 125. *Probability of capsize depending on the position of the boat in relation to the breaking crest. When the boat is positioned well down stream from the breaking point, she may drift without capsize. Such a situation is shown in the photograph, which illustrates a model of an IOR type of boat. When the kinetic energy of the wave jet is diffused into the breaking process, the boat is less susceptible to capsize.*

development (wave profiles 2–8), it is seen that the wave gradually steepens and a mass of water builds up, overhanging the wave face. If trapped within this critical region of breaking wave growth a small boat has very little or no chance at all of avoiding capsize. In this case, a significant portion of the wave energy is being converted from the potential energy of an elevated crest into the kinetic energy of a mass of water rapidly accelerating in a roughly horizontal direction (in the form of a jet discharged from the crest – a powerful water hammer (Fig. 114)). This constitutes the major threat to any boat which has not enough roll moment inertia to withstand the blow. Downstream from this critical region, i.e. from position b along the wave profile 8 in Fig. 125, the probability of capsize gradually decreases because a large portion of the kinetic energy of the water hammer has already been diffused into a less dangerous turbulent mass of water. (Photograph in Fig. 125.)

These experiments (Figs 111 and 125) seem to indicate that the Wheel of Fortune plays an important part in a survival situation, namely: a boat in a gale is likely to encounter a number of waves having enough energy to capsize her. Capsize may not occur, however, if the boat is not actually trapped within the critical region, i.e. the boat is well upstream or downstream from the spot where plunging breakers develop their dangerous power to capsize.* It should also be noted (Fig. 111A) that the boat which has lost her mast and rigging becomes more vulnerable to a second capsize, i.e. smaller waves than those which caused her initial capsize and dismasting become potentially dangerous. According to Fig. 110, dismasting can reduce a boat's moment of inertia by a factor in the order of 250–350%. Thus, in terms of the roll moment of inertia – 'a dismasted 40 foot boat suddenly becomes a 30 footer. She then becomes a candidate for repeated rolling in waves much smaller than those she might otherwise survive'.[94]

To investigate further the influence of mass moment of inertia on the capsize probability, more variations of the inertial characteristics were allowed to the model.[92,93] The models were constructed in such a way that, by means of adjustable weights, both the total mass (displacement) and the distribution of mass (gyradius k) could vary about the rolling axis. This allowed the models'

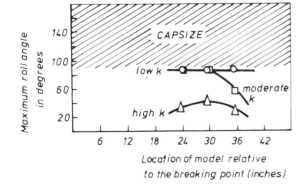

Fig. 126. *Effect of inertia (radius of gyration, k) on capsize probability. In considering the significance of roll moment of inertia, one should keep in mind that the capsize process is essentially a contest between wave impact, which tends to roll the boat, and inertia, which tends to resist the roll-over.*

* Let us remind ourselves of Bill King's experience of being rolled in *Galway Blazer II*, 1000 miles WSW of Cape Town in 1968. To quote from his book *Capsize*: 'The wind started to die down. At about Force 9 I decided to go out on deck. I took the hurricane hatches off and went aft to

resistance to roll and capsize to be varied according to implication of Eqs 40 and 42 discussed earlier.

It will be seen from Fig. 126 that the influence of the roll moment of inertia is quite significant. Under the same breaking wave characteristics, for a high gyradius the maximum roll angle was 45 degrees, while for a low gyradius there was 100% capsizing. In this particular experiment the magnitude of gyradius named *High k* was less than twice that named *Low k*. As in the previous test (Fig. 111), the location of the model in relation to the breaking point appeared to be another strong factor influencing capsize.

Figure 127A illustrates the combined effect of beam and gyradius on the capsize probability.[93] It has been found that the roll gyradius of modern ocean racers varies between 0.62B and 0.78B, where B is the maximum beam of the yacht; characteristics of sample ocean racers are given in Table 9.

Table 9

LOA ft	B_{max} ft	Displacement lb	GM ft	k ft	$\dfrac{k}{B}$
47.9	13.6	28,800	4.66	9.93	0.73
49.0	13.5	27,400	5.08	10.60	0.78
44.2	11.0	20,800	3.34	7.58	0.69
48.5	13.9	26,700	4.70	9.78	0.70
46.4	13.8	24,000	4.76	8.60	0.62
46.2	13.3	23,000	4.79	9.88	0.74
46.0	12.4	27,500	3.52	9.59	0.77

Beam was chosen as a design factor to non-dimensionalise the gyradius on the assumption that a hull with a larger beam would tend to have an increased weight distribution, and vice versa. The method of establishing the gyradii (k) of yachts listed in Table 9 was a relatively simple matter; the metacentric heights (GM) of these yachts were known and the roll period was measured. Since, according to Eq. 20C, the natural period of rolling is related to both k and GM, i.e.:

$$T_n = 1.108 \frac{k}{\sqrt{GM}} \tag{20C}$$

then

$$k = \frac{T_n \sqrt{GM}}{1.108} \tag{44}$$

look at the vane-steering ... Then, as if led by a guardian angel, I returned to the enclosed cockpit for a piece of rope to secure the foresail ... A few seconds later she was rolled through 360°, carrying away the top of her foremast and springing the mainmast. It seems that the first lull after a heavy blow may be the most dangerous time for freak waves.' This by no means unique accident illustrates that almost any offshore yacht can get caught at the wrong time in the wrong place and not be able to avoid rolling over or capsize.

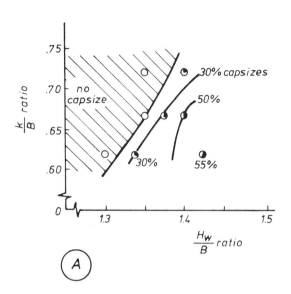

Fig. 127. (A) The effect of roll gyradius (k) and wave height variation on capsize resistance.
(B) The effect of displacement (Δ) and wave height variation on capsize resistance.
The darkened portion of each circle represents the percentage of capsize events recorded in ten different locations relative to breaking waves, and observed twice each; thus every circle represents twenty observations. Parameters held constant were gyradius, centre of gravity, beam, and keel area.

In Fig. 127A the variation of gyradius (k) in terms of k/B ratio relevant to yachts in Table 9, is marked on the vertical axis. Along the horizontal axis there are marked ratios of wave height (H_w) to the maximum beam (B) of the model tested. Three different wave heights were used, but the beam was held constant. Other parameters such as displacement, centre of gravity and keel area remained constant. It will be seen that by increasing the inertial component (gyradius k) the model can withstand higher waves with a considerably lower percentage of capsizes. This is consistent both with theory (Eqs 40 and 42) as well as with the results shown earlier in Fig. 120.

If one recalls Eq. 38B.

$$I_r = \frac{\Delta}{g} k^2$$

it becomes evident that the displacement (Δ) contributes to the roll moment of inertia (I_r) in direct proportion, while the gyradius (k) is a second power effect, i.e. when k is increased twofold the moment of inertia should increase fourfold. In other words, an increase in displacement, although beneficial, should not be expected to be as effective an anti-capsize dodge as a similar percentage increase in the roll gyradius; and Fig. 127B confirms this conclusion. As in graph A, the $\dfrac{H_w}{B}$ ratio is marked along the horizontal axis, while variation in displacement (Δ) is represented along the vertical axis. If, for example, the gyradius (k/B ratio) is increased by 25% (from 0.60 to 0.75, graph A), the non-capsizing wave ratio H_w/B is increased from 1.30 to 1.40. On the other hand, if displacement (Δ) is increased by the same 25% (from 5.00 to 6.25 lb, graph B) the non-capsizing wave ratio H_w/B is increased from about 1.31 to 1.34 only.

Results of experimental investigations conducted in America into the mechanics of capsizing in breaking waves (Figs 126 and 127) appear to suggest explicitly that – let us quote – 'The roll inertial characteristics of a vessel provide the single *most dominant contribution to capsize resistance*'. In other words, the moment of inertia seems to exert the largest influence on this critical event.[93] However, this conclusion is at variance with those derived from tests carried out elsewhere.

In Table 8, which summarises the effect of basic design parameters on capsize probability, higher inertia appears to be insignificant. In Ref. 101 we read: 'The roll inertia of the fin keel parent model (see Fig. 120A) was reduced by 40% to simulate the loss of mast and rigging. This alteration did not affect the yacht's propensity to capsize'.

Fig. 128. *Three models representing over 50 years of yacht design include, all scaled to the equivalent of 32 feet:*
Left. Tally-Ho, *the winner of the 1927 Fastnet. Due to severe weather, of the fifteen yachts which started the race, only two completed the course:* Tally-Ho *and the American* La Goleta.
Centre. New York 32, *a traditional hull design.*
Right. Standfast, *a modern fin-keel design.*

In widely publicised articles on capsize in breaking waves written by D. Jordan[103], a number of tests on small models – representing older designs (Fig. 128) as well as modern ones built to the IOR specifications – were described. Let us quote: 'I used a horizontal jet of water (not natural waves) to simulate the crest of a breaking wave. I then evaluated the dynamic behaviour of various hull designs and determined the effect certain design variables had on capsize vulnerability. This early work[103,1,2] led to two broad conclusions. *First*, it is unlikely that any changes in hull design that could reasonably be applied to modern sailing boats would have had a significant effect on the number of capsizes that occurred in the Fastnet storm. *Second*, a drogue of the proper size and strength deployed from the stern can pull a boat through a breaking wave crest and in many, if not all cases, can prevent capsize'.[103,3]

These conclusions are based on a chain of arguments and observations, to give a sample: 'The fact is that three designs (Fig. 128) had about the same capsize performance, even though each has certain undesirable design features;

Tally Ho has a full length keel, a large topside area and a short rig. The *New York 32* has a light displacement (relative to *Tally Ho*) and half-length keel. *Standfast* has light weight and more topside area than the *New York 32* . . . In any case, one thing seems clear. A modern design does not show markedly inferior performance to an older design when it is struck abeam by a breaking wave crest . . .'.[103]

The second of Jordan's conclusions stems directly from the first. Since all yachts, no matter how different they are in the design characteristics, have about the same propensity to capsize, therefore we should concentrate on the engineering design of the drogue as the capsize preventing device. Convincing as these 'findings' might be to some, a question remains: what lessons relevant to inertia and displacement effects can be learned by a diligent and critical reader from all those conflicting test results published so far in scientific reports and articles?[98–103] Probably he will be confused – whom to believe?

E. Conflicting conclusions – who is right?

'One of the first duties of man is not to be duped'
Carl Becker

One of the elementary laws of contradiction in logic postulates that a proposition and its negation cannot be simultaneously true. If we agree on that, then we must also agree that there must be a weak link (possibly concealing ignorance) in one of two chains of argument which led to almost diametrically opposed views on the influence of roll inertia on the capsize probability.

A few general remarks on experimenting with models, and the alleged scientific facts they reveal, appear to be appropriate here. The trouble with boat model testing is the one which always arises with any model testing in dynamic conditions, namely the notorious difficulty in maintaining dynamic similarity between a full scale specimen operating in real conditions and the model in laboratory conditions. Ideally, the laboratory model subjected, say, to wave action, should consist of a scaled down representation, possibly true in every respect, of the real situation experienced in full scale. If this requirement is to be satisfied, the wave input and model response investigated in the towing tank should, to a reasonable degree of accuracy, be comparable to full scale behaviour. And so reasonable predictions can be made. This implies that, before the tests are actually carried out, we should know fairly precisely *what we are going to investigate and why*. In other words, some sort of theory, even though tentative at first, should precede experiments. After all it is better to have a provisional theory, which can be criticised and eventually corrected through testing, than to have no theory at all.

A widely accepted view expressed by Sir Karl Popper[104] is that scientists should spare no pains to criticise and test the theory in question, in an attempt to expose those points which are vulnerable. If the outcome of a test shows that the theory (or conclusion) is erroneous, then the theory is eliminated. In

Peut-on prévoir
de telles catastrophes ?

Fig. 129. *An artist's impression of a gigantic wave, a few seconds before it hit Hawaii on 1st April 1946, destroying everything in its path.*

science there is no room for paradoxes or contradictory theories; trial and error is essentially a method of elimination. If we are lucky we may secure, by an intelligent experimentation, the survival of the fittest theory, by elimination of those which are less fit or even plainly wrong. Otherwise an investigation can quickly degenerate into meaningless testomania, which not infrequently produces only harmful disinformation. Modern testomania, somewhat encouraged by the existence of computers printing numbers at terrifying speed, becomes mainly a new form of old wives' tales.

Comparison of tests on different models, such as shown for instance in Fig. 128, could be most deceiving if the experiments were done in waves not compatible with the inertia properties, the effect of which was to be investigated. To be more precise, it is perfectly possible to apply such a breaking wave impact that anything on the water surface will eventually founder or will be smashed to pieces. Figure 129 presents an artist's impression of a gigantic wave which hit Hawaii on 1st April 1946. In the face of such a castrophic wave, the inertia of any boat shown in the picture, no matter how large it might be, becomes irrelevant as a survivalibility factor. Even the largest vessel could not immunise herself against the overwhelming power of such a wave.

Bearing this in mind, let us consider now what sort of conclusion would be derived from the test results, as presented in Fig. 127A, if the investigations were carried out in higher waves of, say, $\dfrac{H_w}{B}$ ratio larger than 1.5. In all probability the conclusion reached would be that the roll moment of inertia is not an important factor. Fortunately, the American experimenters were clever enough and designed the test in such a way that the waves produced in the tank were not too high to obscure the effect of relatively small variation of the inertia of the model tested. From a perusal of the reports[91,92], it becomes evident that they appreciated the guiding roll of the basic theory of dynamic system behaviour.

It will be recalled that Fig. 109 depicts in the form of a block diagram the basic components of a boat (considered as a dynamic system), together with their internal connections. Components of this diagram can alternatively be translated in the form of equations, such as for example Eqs 40, 42 or 43, in which a number of important variables determine the wave input and inertia effects. Once the equation is written down, the effect of selected variables on the system behaviour can be studied by varying the magnitudes of the variables (look again at which variables are in the numerator and denominator of Eq. 42), and by observing (through experiments) the changes in a boat's behaviour as a function of these variations. Remembering that the double value of the total roll moment of inertia of a boat is the denominator of Eq. 42, it should not be surprising to learn that this parameter *must* play a significant role in the capsizing process. And indeed, tank experiments (Fig. 127), the Fastnet statistics (Fig. 45) and theory, all agree that the probability of capsize increases with decrease in the roll moment of inertia, i.e. broadly speaking, with decrease in size of the boat. The higher vulnerability to capsize of small yachts of low inertia is a fact of life.

In interpreting the significance of Fig. 127, attention should be drawn to the fact that the capsizing process is largely, but not entirely, a contest between the wave impact moment (which tends to knock down the boat) and her inertia (which resists this action). Bigger boats with higher roll moment of inertia have therefore a better chance to win this contest. The 1979 Fastnet experience of 303 yachts ranging in length from about 28 to 80 feet LOA, exposed to virtually the same waves and wind, has provided evidence in favour of the bigger boats.

However, bigger from the viewpoint of capsize vulnerability does not necessarily mean longer. It will be seen from Table 6 that the displacement/ length ratio of boats of identical length (LWL) may vary by a factor of five or even more. As a result, a heavy displacement type of yacht may have as much as five times greater roll moment of inertia than that of an ultra-light displacement boat of the same length.

Figure 130A and B illustrates the effect of length and displacement on the roll moment of inertia.[94] Thus, two yachts of length about 45 feet (see two darkened circles in graph A) may vary by a factor of almost five (500%!) in their roll moments of inertia. This fact should be kept in mind, since size (usually length) of a boat determines the yacht's eligibility for offshore racing. For instance, the lower limit for the 1979 Fastnet was 21.0 IOR rating. If we compare the roll moment of inertia of the two boats of length about 28 ft in class III (crossed circles in graph A), we will find that they differ in the roll moment of inertia by a factor of 2.4; this factor will determine their

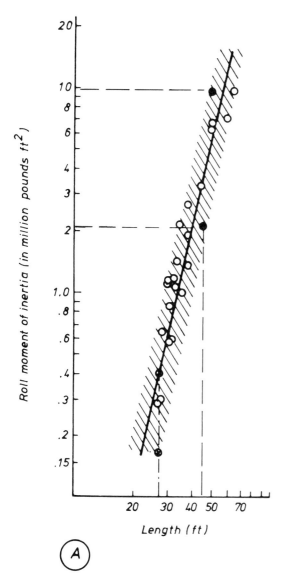

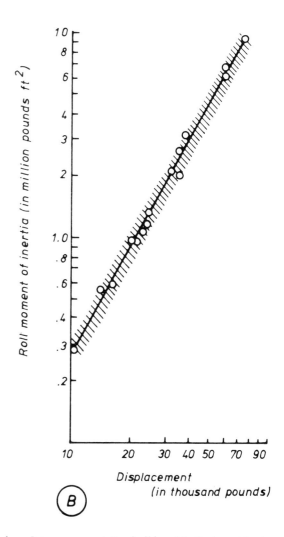

Fig. 130. *Effect of length of hull (A) and of displacement (B) on the roll moment of inertia. In order to accommodate large variations in magnitude of the roll moment of inertia, which vary roughly as L^5* (where L is a representative hull length), the logarithmic scale is used for the roll moment of inertia as well as for hull length and its displacement.*

vulnerability to capsize. Those two allegedly identically sized boats will differ markedly in their vulnerability to capsize, i.e. a capsizing wave for one is likely to be non-capsizing for the other. One may rightly argue that in the hopefully not too distant future, eligibility for offshore racing should be based on the inertia principle rather than on rated length alone.

F. Inertia – stability interrelation

*'There is another design that is far better. It is the design that
nature has provided. It is pointless to superimpose an
abstract, man-made design, on a region as though the canvas
were blank. It isn't. Somebody has been here already.
Thousands of years of rain and wind and tides have laid
down a design.'*

William H. Whyte *The Last
Landscape*

It is seen in Fig. 109 that inertia and stability are closely intertwined, in the
sense that a rolling boat has two forms of energy storage – kinetic energy (box
2) and potential energy (box 4); and these are mutually interchangeable as in
the case of a pendulum.

The question of how a boat acquires kinetic energy has partly been answered
in Chapter 14 (Figs 118 and 119). A large amount of rotational energy can be
transferred to the boat in a collision with breaking waves; this energy can be
quantified by evaluation of Eqs 40–43. In terms of rotational inertia, we can
express the kinetic energy of a rolling boat resulting from wave impact as:

$$E_k = 1/2 \ I_r \Omega^2 \tag{37}$$

This formula is analogous to the better-known expression for kinetic energy of
an object in linear (translational) motion, i.e.:

$$E_k = 1/2 \ m \ v^2$$

Thus, the moment of inertia (I_r) of a rolling boat plays the same role in
rotational motion as mass (m) plays in linear motion, and the angular velocity
(Ω) in rotation is analogous to the linear velocity (v) in rectilinear motion.
Deliberate attention is drawn to this fact, and the reason is this: when a boat is
struck abeam, as shown in Fig. 118, she does not only roll but she is also lifted
up, sometimes almost clear of the water, and thrown violently sideways drifting
with the breaker. Figures 124 and 131 illustrate respectively this sequence of
events leading to capsize of a fishing vessel, and a life-boat exposed to a
breaking wave.[105] The crew of a large 46 foot ketch *Inland Princess*, which
sank on 5th August, 1980 in a hurricane, described the breaking wave impact
as follows: 'The boat didn't feel stable anymore. In fact, all thirty tons of her
were literally being lifted off the crest and thrown sideways into the trough'.[106]
And, as experts assure us, steep waves are invariably preceded by a deep
trough.

At the instant when the wave strikes (Fig. 124) the boat receives two forms
of kinetic energy: one rotational and another translational (sketches B and C in
Fig. 131).

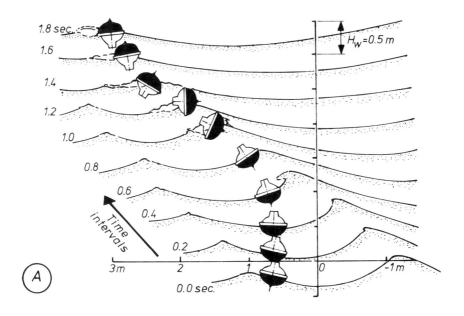

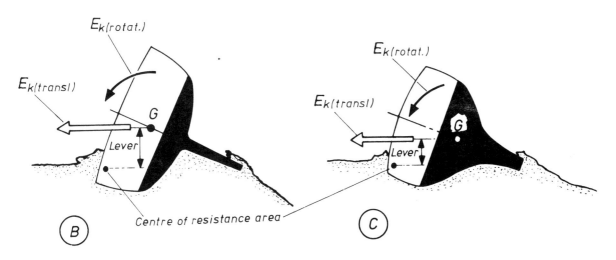

Fig. 131. *(A) Capsize sequence pattern for a lifeboat with an angle of vanishing stability (θ_0) = 120° in a breaking wave (see Fig. 132).*
(B) and (C) Due to wave impact, the energy transfer from the wave to the boat is of two kinds: rotational (rolling) energy $E_{k(rotat)}$ and translational energy $E_{k(translat)}$. If the lee rail of the descending hull is deeply submerged, as in the case of a beamy boat, the translational energy may be rapidly converted into additional rolling energy. In other words, an already rolling boat may experience an additional snap roll which will accelerate the capsize; the magnitude depending on the area of submerged hull and the lever between the CG of the hull and the centre of lateral resistance distinguished in sketches B and C. According to radio controlled model tests in transient breaking waves, to which reference is made in Fig. 165, a narrow hull is less susceptible to capsize when beam on to the seas.

As the boat begins to *roll she also sways*, being swept along with the wave for about 30 metres (100 ft) in full scale (between position B and F). In sufficiently high waves the rolling boat may even be completely wrapped into the turbulent crest as depicted in Fig. 119C–E.

The total energy (E_{tot}) transferred to the boat may be expressed as the sum of the two forms of kinetic energy:

$$E_{tot} = E_k \text{ (rotational)} + E_k \text{ (translational)} = \tfrac{1}{2} I_r \Omega^2 + \tfrac{1}{2} mv^2$$

where m   is the mass of the boat $= \dfrac{\Delta}{g}$

   v   sway velocity; (other notations have been explained earlier).

The division of total energy (E_{tot}) into these two components appears to be of some practical consequence. However, it is not an easy matter to estimate how the wave impact will be distributed between rotational and translational kinetic energy of the boat.

In principle, we are dealing with a shock-like loading on the hull, in which case the duration and strength of the jet discharged from the crest are not fully predictable, and neither is the boat's response. Another reason is that the momentum transferred from the wave to the boat, both rotational ($I_r \Omega$) and translational (m v), depends on hull attitude, i.e. course sailed relative to the breaking wave at the moment of impact. Three basic approaches to waves can be considered:

(1)   beam-on; either lying a-hull (stationary) or moving forward prior to the wave impact.
(2)   bow-on; either directly head-on or slightly oblique to the wave crest.
(3)   stern-on; running before the wave crests and attempting to control the ensuing surfing motion.

Of course the boat's roll inertia (I_r), her displacement (Δ) and her dynamic stability reserve (as given by the area under the positive stability curve together with the angle of vanishing stability, Figs 55, 56 and 58) will all play their parts in determining the boat's response to the three different situations.

For example, one can argue that the worst roll-inducing situation occurs when the boat is under wind pressure and already heeling away from the oncoming breakers. As discussed earlier (Figs 79, 80), a beamy, flat-bottom, raft-like boat will tend to roll away from the crests; this tendency can be seen in Fig. 131A if one compares the boat's attitude along the wave profile in the time intervals marked 0.4–0.8. At the moment of impact, the rotational energy of an already-rolling boat will be greatly augmented by the roll momentum transferred from the wave (Fig. 131A, time interval 1.0). Besides, the boat with her large hull area dangerously exposed to the breaker (Fig. 122), is prepared to receive a huge blow which will rapidly translate her down the wave. On her way, the lee rail will submerge and, once the deck is under water (Fig. 131B), it will tend to resist translatory motion (tripping effect). As a result, an additional, snap-rolling moment occurs which, when added to the existing rolling moment, can rapidly accelerate capsize. This sudden acceleration of rolling motion due to the tripping effect is evident in Fig. 131A, if one compares the heel angles of the boat recorded in time intervals marked 1.2–1.6. Thus, the tripping effect can be looked upon as a means of rapid energy conversion: from translational into the rotational energy.

An older boat of heavy displacement type (Fig. 131C) will behave differently in a similar situation. She will tend to roll towards the crest, therefore her less beamy hull will expose less area to the breaking wave. And, indeed, the capsizing tests in breaking waves have shown that the model with long keel, of three times the lateral area of the standard fin-keel, reached a far lower angle of heel at the moment before wave impact than the standard fin-keel model (Fig. 120B). Besides, according to Eqs 40–43, less energy will be transferred from the wave on account of her larger roll moment of inertia. Sketches B and C in Fig. 131 are self-explanatory, in the sense that the older type of boat (C) will be less susceptible to rapid conversion of her translational energy into rolling energy. Consequently, her rolling energy in position indicated will be lower than that of the IOR type of boat (B).*

As already mentioned elsewhere in this book, survival ultimately depends upon whether the energy transferred from wind and waves is greater or smaller than the energy which the boat can safely absorb and dissipate. If the energy input cannot be matched before the angle of vanishing stability (capsize threshold) is reached, the boat cannot successfully combat the perils of the sea. A large area under the righting moment curve (see 'safe zone' in Figs 55, 56 and 58), which is a measure of the maximum rolling energy required to capsize the boat in calm water, becomes the primary safety factor in survival situations.

Capsize experiments carried out in Japan[105] have confirmed the close link between the range of positive stability (area under the righting moment curve) and the height of breaking wave necessary to capsize a lifeboat. Figure 132 depicts the midship section of the hull, together with four different stability curves. The profile of a typical transient breaking wave in which the model was tested is shown in Fig. 131A. To produce models of the same shape but with different stability characteristics, the centre of gravity (CG) was adjusted vertically in such a way that the positive stability range was 60°, 90°, 120° (original) and 132°. Obviously the model with the lowest CG position has the largest range of stability. To examine the correlation between the capsizing probability and the stability range, the models were exposed to the action of breaking waves of increasing height. Subsequently, a critical wave height was established in which a model of given stability range marginally capsized; the results of the tests are shown in Fig. 133. Along the horizontal axis there is marked the stability range in terms of the angle of vanishing stability of four models tested relevant to Fig. 132C. Along the vertical axis there is indicated the wave height corresponding to full scale conditions. The broken line in graph A specifies the demarcation between the capsizing and non-capsizing waves.

The Japanese researchers concluded that 'it is ascertained that as the range of stability becomes wider, a boat tends to be more difficult to capsize, in other

---

* See supplementary remarks on page 275 in the Addendum to Figs 120B and 135A.

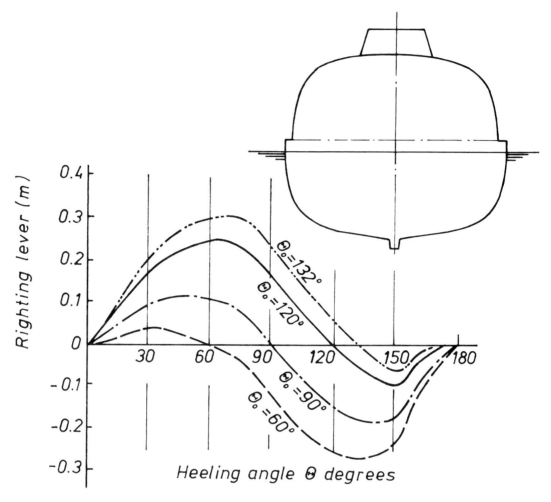

Fig. 132. *Four static stability characteristics of the same boat with different positions of centre of gravity. These can be distinguished by the angle of vanishing stability* θ_0, *and the relevant positive and negative areas within the stability curves and horizontal* θ *axis (see also Fig. 134(A)).*

words, the critical wave height in which the boat marginally capsizes increases as the range of stability increases.'

Although such a conclusion appears to be compelling in the light of experimental evidence, nevertheless the effect of a common factor linking susceptibility to capsize with both the stability and roll moment of inertia has tended to be overlooked. This factor is the distribution of mass within the hull. From research on capsizing (Figs 126 and 127) already discussed, we have learned that the gyradius is a dominant variable in capsize sensitivity. Referring to tests in Fig. 133, the change in position of CG might be, and most likely was, as important a variable in increasing the gyradius as it was in increasing the

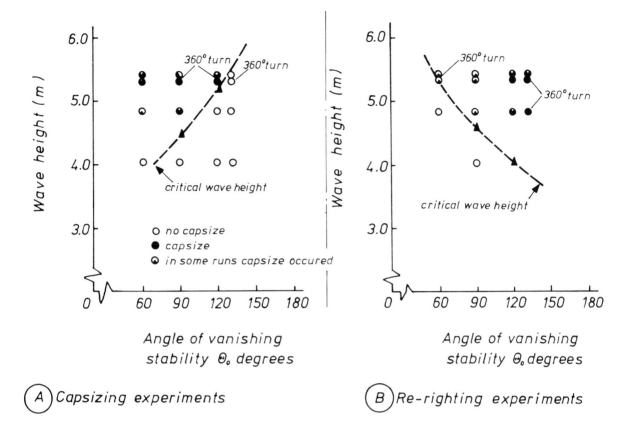

A Capsizing experiments

B Re-righting experiments

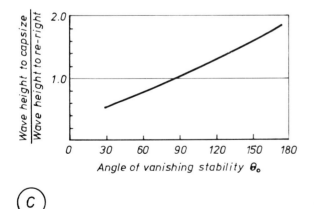

C

Fig. 133. *Capsizing and righting tests on a lifeboat (Ref. 105). In (A) and (B), the labels '360° turn' show when the model turned 360 degrees and then righted. (C) gives the ratio of capsizing wave to the righting wave, which depends on the range of positive stability, i.e. the angle of vanishing stability (θ_0). Although these tests were devised so that just the effect of stability range on capsize was to be investigated, there was also the hidden effect of variation of gyradius which was neither distinguished nor separated; the two effects are therefore lumped together.*

range of positive stability. By changing the vertical position of CG, the other factors remaining the same, the Japanese scientists changed two variables at the same time. However, the advantageous effect on capsize resistance was attributed to one variable only – stability. Of course they cannot be accused of prejudiced collation of the evidence. A definite lesson can be learned from this and other research such as, for instance, that relevant to Fig. 128; one cannot expect to find fully warranted uncontradicted information on the subject of seaworthiness, if one ignores the fact that all parts of a boat (Fig. 109) interact or are mutually interrelated.

It has been observed that science may be anarchical in method, unpredictable in content, and subversive in effect; so, be receptive to the implications of Fig. 109 – Newton's laws cannot be defied without incurring setbacks. The subject of dynamics grew up with Newton's laws of motion.

Graph B in Fig. 133 shows the result of righting experiments. Tests were done in a similar manner to the capsizing tests, i.e. the same models were exposed to transient breakers but in an upside-down attitude. The broken line specifies the boundary between the righting and non-righting waves. It will be noticed that, as the range of stability becomes wider, the critical height of wave necessary to right the boat becomes smaller. From the data presented in graphs A and B, an important ratio of the capsizing wave to righting wave height can be established. The result shown in graph C indicates that not only is the boat with a large stability range the less likely to capsize, but she is much more likely to be righted by successive waves much lower than the ones which capsized her.

Japanese test results[105] are in agreement with the American tests (described earlier) as to the effect of the model position prior to the breaking point of the wave. Three different basic situations have been distinguished:

(1) if the position of the model is upstream of the breaking point, i.e. the wave breaks after passing the model, capsize does not occur.
(2) if the model is in close vicinity to the breaking point, capsizing is likely to occur and its probability depends on both wave height and stability range (graph A in Fig. 133).
(3) if the model is situated downstream of the breaking point, i.e. the wave breaks before the crest reaches the model, capsize does not follow and the model merely drifts with the breaker.

These and other capsizing experiments in a transient breaking wave seem to indicate that, when the range of stability exceeds 150 degrees the boat becomes almost immune against capsize. If capsized, she will right soon, rotating 360 degrees in most cases due to residual turning momentum imparted in the course of the capsize event.

When translating these findings into the sailing boat situation, one should keep in mind that the experiments were conducted on lifeboat models, i.e. boats without high mast, sails or rigging. For that reason, the test results may be applicable without great error to dismasted boats; and masts are frequently carried away at some point of the capsize event. As already mentioned, in the case when mast, rigging and possibly sails have been left intact after capsize the

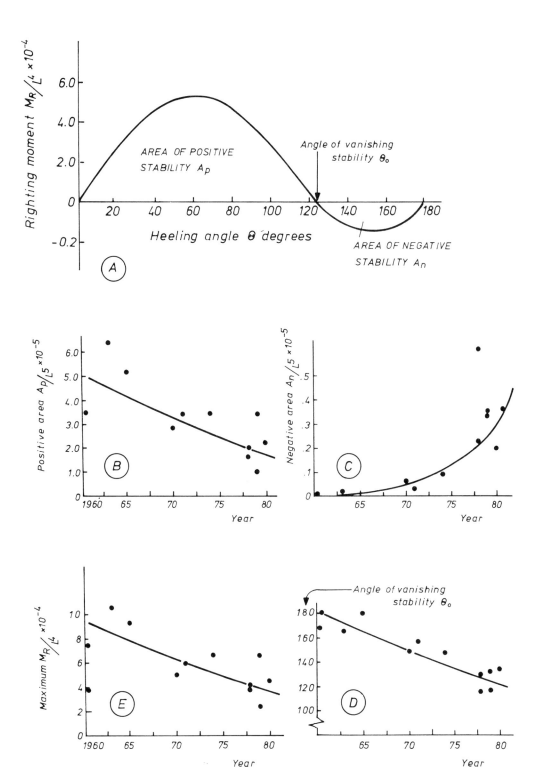

Fig. 134. *Trends in hydrostatic stability characteristics of yachts designed since 1960, as epitomised in Fig. 135. It should perhaps be borne in mind that the positive area (A_p) under the righting moment curve, is a measure of the energy required to capsize the boat in calm water; this area can be much reduced in waves.*

The negative area (A_n) is a measure of energy required to right the boat from an inverted attitude. A glance at graphs (B), (C), (D) and (E) will suffice to show that the evolution of yachts since the early 1960s has been orientated towards less and less seaworthy craft, with lower stability and smaller angles of vanishing stability.

situation is far more complex. The damping generated by rigging in the inverted attitude, may be sufficiently large even to prevent re-righting, unless another episodic breaker is met. But this is unlikely to happen quickly.

Since the stability range together with other characteristics of the righting moment curve (plotted as a reminder in Fig. 134A) play an important part in the capsizing process, the question may arise: how do contemporary yachts fare in this respect as compared with older types of boat? Graphs B–E give the answer. They are based on analysis of a number of data and drawings provided

Fig. 135. *Development in hull design (since about 1960). Noticeable changes in the displacement/length ratio $(\Delta/(.01\,L)^3)$, and shape of hull cross-sections, are largely* responsible for reduction in stability and seakindliness (as shown in Fig. 134).

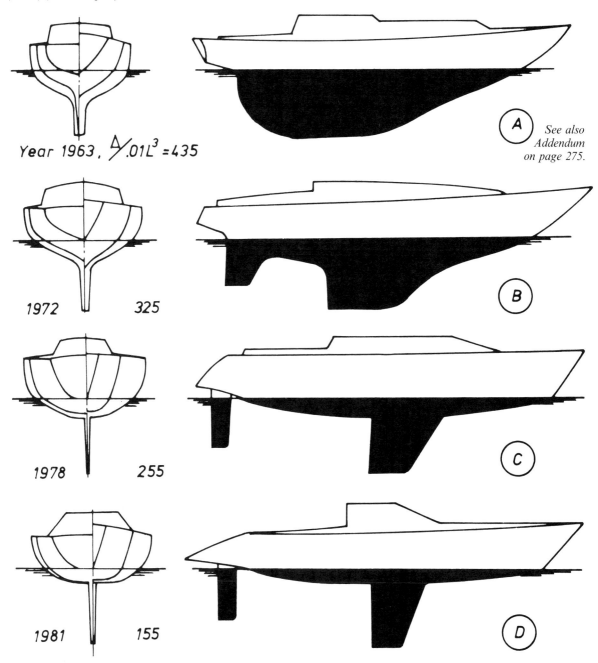

Year 1963, $\Delta/.01L^3 = 435$

A — *See also Addendum on page 275.*

1972   325   B

1978   255   C

1981   155   D

by yacht designers[98] relevant to yachts built over the period 1960–1980; some of them are shown in Fig. 135. These were considered to be the most significant in terms of design changes likely to influence the capsizing probability.

Graphs B and C in Fig. 134 clearly demonstrate a general tendency towards less safe boats. The positive area under the righting moment curve has been reduced to less than half, and at the same time the negative area has increased dramatically. The data presented are expressed in non-dimensionalised terms, in such a way that proper allowance was made for the variation in size of the boat (the waterline length).

Graph D shows the variation of the angle of vanishing stability. This reflects, in a different way, the variation in the range of positive stability (graphs A–C). Thus, this range has been reduced from about 180 degrees (common in the 1960s) to about 120 degrees for the more contemporary sample yachts. For the sake of completeness, there is also demonstrated in graph E the trend towards much lower value of the righting moment maximum; about half of that characteristic of the traditional yacht form.

Needless to say, according to strict definition of self-righting property, a boat should have a stability range of 180 degrees. This is the typical characteristic of the weight-conditioned stability of yachts of type A in Fig. 135. At no angle of heel does this heavily ballasted hull lose its positive righting moment unless, of course, it has been damaged during capsizing and flooded. Figures 134 and 135 illustrate convincingly how much offshore racing and cruising yachts owe their pedigree to the formative power of the rating rule.

The IOR does not deal explicitly with range of stability, nor does the IOR measurement include sufficient data to establish the righting moment variation with angle of heel. However, the hull line data of the Measurement Handicap System (MHS) as presently taken, allow stability to be calculated even though the effects of deckhouse, cockpit, etc. on the stability range are neglected. And the stability range of the MHS fleet reflects accurately enough the stability limits of yachts built to the IOR.[94]

As seen in Fig. 136A, the stability range, i.e. angle of vanishing stability, of the bulk of the USYRU offshore fleet holding current MHS certificate, lies between 110–130 degrees, and the European IOR fleet does not differ in this respect. If the deckhouse is taken into account, it can extend the stability range by 10–20 degrees depending on the ratio of the deckhouse volume to the hull volume.

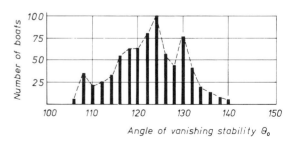

Fig. 136. *Angles of vanishing stability of the Measurement Handicap System fleet. Deckhouse and cockpit volumes were not considered when establishing these static stability curves.*

The probability of becoming trapped stable in an inverted attitude – an extremely dangerous situation for the occupants inside the hull and the crew hooked-on on deck – is related to the range of positive stability. In an interesting paper, Kirkman[95] made an attempt to estimate the righting probability assuming a certain distribution of energy in breaking waves. Another, tacit assumption was that intact mast and rigging do not impare a boat's ability to recover from an up-side-down position. According to him 'the yacht with 120 degree range is almost three times less likely to be trapped than the 90 degree range yacht, and the 150 degree range yacht over ten times less likely; the 175 degree yacht one hundred times less likely.'

Interestingly, the older fleet of proven cruiser-racers, as typified by *Dorade* (Fig. 31 or type A in Fig. 135), had just such an advantage over the present IOR fleet of ocean racers. As more empirical data are brought into prominence, such as for instance the influence of intact rig on the righting process, this preliminary probability estimate of being caught in an upside down stable mode will certainly be corrected. Most likely boats with a narrow range of positive stability will fare even worse than predicted by Kirkman.[95]

It has been admitted that the process of selecting, or even designing, a boat is largely a self-deluding justification for an entirely emotional decision. Different people have different, not to say contradictory, ideas about the effects of certain design features on seaworthiness. One may wonder in this context how many owners of yachts built to the IOR are aware of the peculiar stability time-bomb carried by the IOR fleet? Will self-delusion lose its power in the light of experimental evidence and physics of the capsizing event discussed so far?

G. Action of keel

'Irrationally held truths may be more harmful than reasoned errors'

T.A. Huxley

In Chapter 9 attention was drawn to the effect of damping on rolling. According to the theory originally developed by Froude, the inherent damping which every boat possesses to varying degrees of efficiency, may become her only protection against the danger of capsize. Without damping – to use Froude's forceful language – 'she would always be, in the strictest sense, at the mercy of the waves, and with waves of even approximate co-periodicity the mercy would be inexorably destructive'.[73]

Yet, in a recent article written by the author of a report on capsizing tests, to which a reference has been made earlier[98] we read: 'The fin-keel parent model (Fig. 137) was fitted with a keel of three times the area of its design keel. This modification did not alter the capsize behaviour of the yacht in beam seas'.[101]

The above conclusion appears to contradict Froude's statement; and certainly will be very welcome to ardent defenders of the fin-keel concept, who

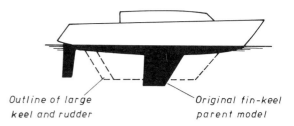

Fig. 137. *Model of a hull tested with two different keel and rudder configurations.*

Outline of large
keel and rudder

Original fin-keel
parent model

maintain that reduction of lateral area is not a culprit in the modern yacht's vulnerability to capsize. One contradictory fact is enough to dispose of any theory. Does this recent test conclusion invalidate Froude's finding and, incidently, the classic theory of dynamic system behaviour as diagrammatically presented by the pertinent components of the system in Fig. 109?

No, as we shall see, it does not. Capsize in a transient, *single* breaking wave in beam-on attitude is only one of the many situations in which the sailing boat may be knocked down. It is a rather rare event in the sense that, when the boat is struck abeam by an overwhelming breaker, the water jet usually has sufficient power to lift the hull almost clear of the water and throw it on its side. This mode of capsize may also be the final stage of the capsizing process initiated by other causes, which ultimately lead to a beam-on attitude to the breaker. In such a final stage, the keel and other hull appendages play a subordinate part, as the means whereby capsizing energy can effectively be dissipated. However, this does not imply that, in every other situation in which capsize may occur, the hull appendages play an equally insignificant part.

It is known that a common mode of capsize is dynamic roll-over, as a result of action of an external rolling moment exerted either by one catastrophic rogue wave or by the successive action of a train of breaking or non-breaking waves. These may act in a cumulative manner, with other rolling moments of different origins, as listed below box 1 in Fig. 109, in which the significance of damping due to effective keel action is shown to be of paramount importance.

Capsize may also be caused by a number of other different mechanisms which, individually or in combination, can lead to knockdown in waves of any relative heading to the boat. For instance, violent broaching due to loss of directional stability may easily end in capsize, caused by the combined action of the dynamic forces exerted by the waves, rolling induced by sail forces and centrifugal force generated by the turning motion. Again, in such a circumstance the keel and the rudder – their areas, aspect ratios and planforms – are primary factors which determine whether or not the boat can be kept under control.*

Damping

Turning attention to the damping moments listed under the heading ENERGY DISSIPATION (—) in Fig. 109 box 3, it must be said that the subject of damping is

---

* The observation just quoted from ref 101 and relevant to Fig. 137 should be interpreted in the light of test results described on page 253, that is the tests on the behaviour of a light displacement fin-keel model as compared with the heavy displacement type of yacht with a long keel. Little can be gained by increasing the lateral area of the keel if at the same time other factors which increase the boat's propensity to capsize in a breaking wave, such as low mass moment of inertia, low angle of vanishing stability and large beam remain unchanged. It should also be added that the tests on the model fitted with a keel of three times the area of its original fin-keel (Fig. 137) were performed in the largest breaking waves of height about 5.5 metres in full size (see page 235). Although there was little discernible difference in capsize behaviour, nevertheless the long

more significant than is widely believed, and is not quite so well understood as it deserves. So far in our discussion, we have mainly dealt with rolling motion involving no loss of energy originating from waves and wind. In practice, it is impossible to have motion without some dissipation of energy into the surroundings. Thus, every rolling hull disperses energy into the water. Certain hull forms, however, are more effective in this respect than others; and the role of the keel as a damping device for extinguishing rolling is far from immaterial.

Another way of looking at the action of damping is to regard it as a mechanism through which the energy storing capacity of the hull, i.e. the dynamic stability reserve available to absorb rolling energy (Fig. 108C), is retained or saved from too rapid exhaustion. Once this capacity had been exhausted, capsize is inevitable. In other words, if the hull does not have sufficient damping ability to keep pace with the input of energy, nothing can then prevent a roll over. This is the reason why a high degree of damping is so important a factor in seaworthiness.

To illustrate this point further, consider again the two extremes of hull: traditional type with long keel (Figs 10 and 83) and the contemporary IOR type with high aspect ratio fin-keel (Fig. 84). The question is whether the rolling motion of these two types of hull will be the same in similar rough sea conditions? One does not need to be a prominent yacht designer to guess, without much hesitation, that these boats will behave differently in waves. However, if we ask which of these two types will roll less and why, we may expect much confusion and argument. It is always harder to identify a person's premises than to identify his conclusions. This is inevitable whenever there is no reliable information which might eliminate ill-reasoned theories. As far as the hull damping action is concerned, there are surprisingly little data available, probably because the effects of damping have been somewhat underestimated or even ignored by present day yacht and fishing boat designers.

Let us try to perceive the purpose and physical meaning of some features incorporated in the hull shapes depicted in Figs 10 and 83. The profiles below the waterline of these exceptionally seaworthy boats reveals a deep hull with soft bilges and a long keel. Intuition tells us that such a shape must have large inherent roll-damping properties, and indeed the data presented in Fig. 138 corroborate our expectation. The graph indicates the *damping inefficiency* of various hull sections, by which it is meant that the section with the largest inefficiency factor requires the greatest assistance in roll damping from keel or bilge keels. It can be seen that the inefficiency factor reaches its maximum (least damping) at a section coefficient (C_x) of 0.78 corresponding roughly to a semicircular section. This is a typical section of modern racing boats, or indeed of a log. As the section coefficient diminishes (Fig. 138 left) and the underwater hull acquires a deep V-form or a modified Y-form along its whole length, as shown in Figs 10 and 82 roll-quenching is considerably improved. When the C_x value is close to 1.0 (Fig. 138 right), relevant to the box-like sections of merchant ships or sailing barges with sharp bilge corners, the hull itself becomes inherently effective in dissipating rolling energy.

On the basis of tests on bilge-keels, it can be concluded that the most

---

keel version did show slightly improved course keeping qualities.[98] Were the models tested in gradually smaller waves (4.5 and 4.0 metres) the conclusion about the effect of keel area and its configuration might be different – and certainly more favourable to the long keel. After all, as already mentioned earlier, the behaviour of any sailing craft must be analysed as a system by taking into account all its components as shown in Fig. 109.

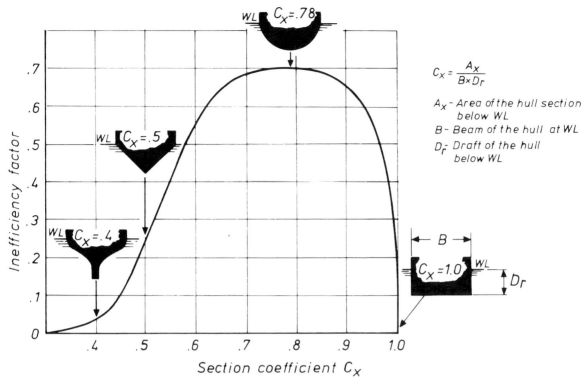

Fig. 138. The effect of hull cross-section on roll-damping.

efficient keel is the longest one which can be mounted along the hull centreline. This is because the damping force resisting the rolling motion, increases progressively as the keel increases. For reasons which will be discussed later, the long keel of low aspect ratio, shown in Figs 10 and 83 is more effective as a roll-damping device than that of high aspect ratio shown in Fig. 84.

Fin or long keel

How then can the current trend towards small lateral (wetted) area of a hull be justified? The answer is not hard to find – an uncritical application of science in an attempt to achieve a single objective regardless of the side effect consequences. Because the wetted surface area as a friction drag factor of some importance is not rated under the IOR rule, designers may gain an advantage in terms of speed by cutting it drastically. This inevitably leads to change in the keel aspect ratio from low to high, which appears to be desirable from purely speed performance.

Past experience has been repeated. As recorded in Fig. 28A, the type of hull built to the Seawanhaka Rule about 1882 is a good example of exactly the same attempt – reduction of hull friction by cutting its wetted surface; other examples are shown in Figs 28B and 29. Alas, by gradually reducing the wetted area of the keel, with the rudder still attached to it as in Fig. 28A and B, a point is reached where the boat becomes unmanageable – too small a leverage to steer and keep her firmly on course. This control problem came into sharper focus in the 1960s in the 5.5 Metre class (Fig. 146). The measurement rule has subsequently been changed to allow for fin-keel and separate rudder configuration – a common feature of hull shape by the end of the 19th century (Fig. 28C–E), which has survived in all sorts of dinghy hulls and small day-racers until now.

This concept was reintroduced in the 1930s by van de Stadt to offshore cruiser-racers and after some reluctance it was accepted by almost all yacht designers. As van de Stadt recalled: 'In the 1951 Fastnet race, *Zeevalk* (built in 1949, Fig. 139A) was second overall. In strong westerly winds, *Zeevalk* (35 ft in LWL) was able to go faster than the 57 foot *Circe* with Rod and Olin Stephens in her crew. At that time Olin was not aware of the possibility of the separate keel and rudder. Even in 1964 I could not convince him of the advantage over the long keel. Dick Carter changed his mind in 1965 after winning the Fastnet in *Rabbit*'.[107]

Winning boats influence designers for the succeeding years, and this explains why rivals ultimately look alike. Fig. 139A–D shows a number of planforms

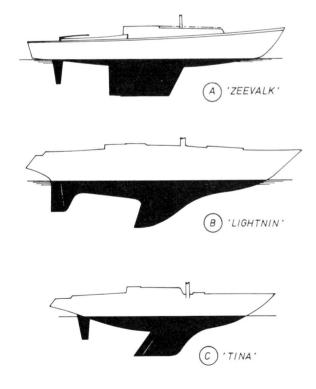

(A) 'ZEEVALK'

(B) 'LIGHTNIN'

(C) 'TINA'

(D) 'STORMVOGEL'

Fig. 139. *Some well-known yachts with separate keel/rudder configurations.*
(A) Zeevalk, designed by van de Stadt (built in 1949). LWL 35 ft (10.7 m).
(B) Lightnin, designed by Sparkman & Stephens. LWL 28.75 ft (8.75 m).
(C) Tina, designed by R.E. Carter. LWL 26.6 ft (8 m).
(D) Stormvogel, designed by van de Stadt. LWL 59.3 ft (18 m).
In low speed régime (speed/length ratio [$Vs/\sqrt{L}$] below 0.8), friction drag contributes about 70 per cent of the total resistance of the boat. One of the most notable features of these boats is the relatively small wetted area of their hull appendages; this is particularly noticeable in the case of Lightnin.

which incited wide international interest in a 'new' type of hull underbody. One can clearly see the tendency to cut down the amount of lateral area, which in the past seemed to be so important. In the case of *Lightnin'* (Fig. 139B) the lateral area of the fin-keel was reduced to the bare minimum, which was estimated by taking into account only the speed performance of the boat sailing under normal (not rough) weather conditions. Her noteworthy shark fin-keel in profile was inspired by an aerodynamic theory which suggests that little side force (lift) is developed by the area of fin behind the maximum draft, almost all of it being produced by the part of the keel immediately adjacent to the leading edge.[59] The complementary assumption was that the only function of the keel is to balance, in combination with the hull, the side force (heeling force) produced by the sails. The two other functions of the keel, namely its contribution to efficient damping (when needed), and to good directional stability and controllability downwind in rough weather seem to have been somewhat ignored or forgotten.

Consider first the aggregate effect of the hull and its appendages in roll damping. From Fig. 140 it will be seen that the sources of resistance to rolling may be divided into four parts:

(1) The frictional forces between the wetted surface of the hull and the surrounding water.
(2) Generation of water waves by the hull's roll to and fro.
(3) Resistance due to eddy making in water entrained by the rolling hull.
(4) Hydrodynamic lift (side force) generated by the keel whenever the resultant flow meets it at an angle.

These components of hydrodynamic damping are not equally significant. The frictional resistance offered by a bare hull of substantially circular section, as shown in Fig. 140A, is relatively small. The aggregate damping effect of the remaining sources of resistance to roll (Fig. 140B and C) – without taking into account possible damping action of sails – may be credited with contributing about 90% of the total rolling energy dissipated into the water.

Since rolling and the associated water flow are both unsteady and complex, the actual flow pattern developing round the hull cannot be depicted in any easy manner. For our purpose it will be sufficient to illustrate the water flow in a much simplified, schematic way as though it were momentarily steady and frozen. In sketch B it will be seen that, as the hull rolls anti-clockwise from its original position, there are surface disturbances generated along each side of the hull, with a bulge on its left and a hollow on its right. When the swing is reversed, as depicted in sketch C, the flow pattern of displaced water is also reversed. These periodically created disturbances on both sides of the hull manifest themselves as waves that move away from the rolling boat, and have continually to be replaced by fresh waves – each new creation involving a certain expenditure of energy.

Apart from the surface waves, each roll sets up a flow of water around the keel, dead-wood and other flat surfaces lying along the hull centerline. When the boat is underway and rolling begins (Fig. 141), the relative waterflow

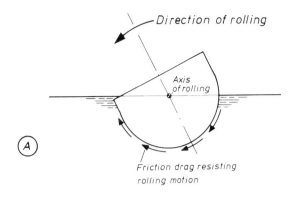

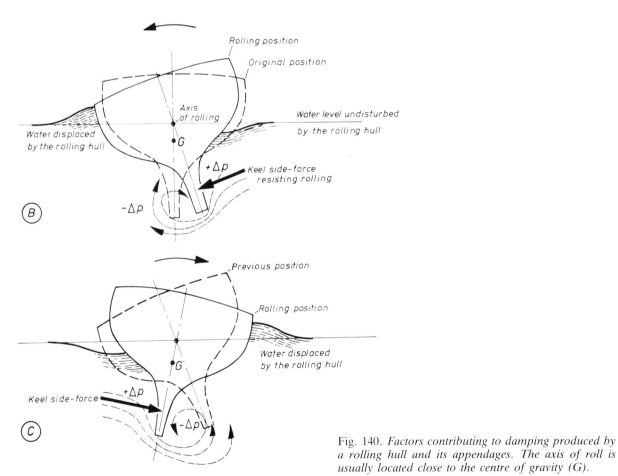

Fig. 140. *Factors contributing to damping produced by a rolling hull and its appendages. The axis of roll is usually located close to the centre of gravity (G).*

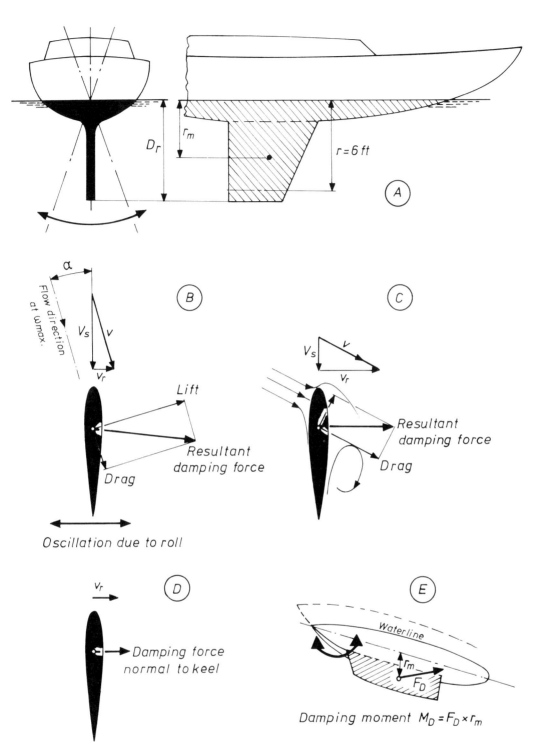

Fig. 141. *Simplified explanation of damping forces operating on a rolling fin keel at different boat speeds (V_s); (B) normal speed, (C) reduced speed, and (D) no forward speed, rolling only. The resultant damping force developed on the keel increases in proportion to the square of the resulting flow velocity (v), which is the* *sum of boat velocity (V_s) and velocity induced by rolling (v_r). Damping forces produced in unsteady flow conditions are much more complicated due to the so-called hysteresis, or memory, effect, which is discussed in the following chapter.*

around the keel is determined by the boat speed (V_s) and the sideways movement of the keel (and the separate rudder for that matter) at a certain angle of incidence, which can be small or large depending on boat speed and a number of other factors indicated in Fig. 141. The keel then acts as a cantilever hydrofoil. The dynamic positive pressure ($+ \Delta_p$) builds up on the advancing side, and the negative pressure ($- \Delta_p$) on the retreating side. Eventually the flow round the keel may separate (stall) if the boat speed ahead (V_s) is small or nil, and so the flow angle relative to the keel is dominated by the sideways motion of the keel alone. In such a case, the flow separation and resulting eddying developing behind the retreating side of the keel is undoubtedly of fairly large scale and does not decay quickly. Consequently, after a few rolls the whole surrounding water in which the keel swings back and forth is filled with eddies rotating at random. This confused mass of water offers much less resisting sideforce, indicated in Fig. 140B and C by thick arrows labelled keel side-force, than would undisturbed water flowing fast and without separation around the keel. Besides, a rather peculiar potentially dangerous and quite unsuspected effect may begin to operate. This will be explained comprehensively in the following chapter.

The advantageous effect of boat speed on damping is thus due to the keel constantly coming in contact with fresh portions of water that have not been set into turbulent motion by previous oscillation. The faster the boat moves ahead the greater the side force generated and the more effective the damping and the smaller the angle of roll.

Despite the fact that a great deal has been written about the roll damping effect of bilge keels (after W. Froude had recommended their use in 1865), the relevant test results and technical literature still furnish conflicting information about their effectiveness.[108] Why is that? Before a plausible answer can be given, it is important to distinguish between the two quite extreme situations in which bilge-keels and keels for that matter, are expected to be effective as roll extinguishers. One is when the boat is sailing at a steady speed in a seaway; the other is when the boat makes no headway, for instance, when heaving-to or lying a-hull, i.e. when the keel operates at zero or close to zero speed.

In the first case, when sailing with speed, the prevailing angle of incidence (α) of the keel relative to the resultant flow direction may be below that at which the stall occurs. As we shall see, such a no-stall flow is most likely to prevail when the aspect ratio (AR) of the keel is low. The keel then damps rolling mainly by virtue of its lift; this is shown in Fig. 141A and B. The boat sails with a speed V_s = 5 knots (8.4 ft/sec) and rolls rhythmically within heel angles of ± 20 degrees (to port and then to starboard and back again). Consider the flow around the keel when it reaches maximum angular velocity (ω_{max}) in the middle of the roll, from one side to the other. Sketch B refers to a narrow, horizontal strip of the keel area at a certain radius, r = 6 ft, from the axis of rolling. The flow direction is determined by the boat speed (V_s) and the velocity component (v_r) induced by a swing of the keel. It will be see that, when the keel swings to the left, the resultant flow velocity (v) is different from velocity (V_s) when there is no roll. The instantaneous incidence angle (α) at distance (r) depends on the variation in direction of the resultant flow (v) which, at the instant shown, is the sum of V_s and v_r. Assuming that the period of rolling $(T_n) = 4$ sec, we may calculate the instaneous incidence angle (α) as follows:

The angular roll velocity:

$$\omega = \frac{2\pi}{T_n} = \frac{6.28}{4} = 1.57 \text{ radians/sec} \tag{45}$$

Maximum angular velocity (ω_{max}) reached in the middle of swing from $\Theta = +20°$ to $\Theta = -20°$ (expressed in radians, $\Theta = 20°$ is $\frac{20}{57.3} = 0.35$):

$$\omega_{max} = \omega \times \Theta \tag{46}$$

$$= 1.57 \times 0.35 = 0.55 \text{ radians/sec}$$

Maximum translational velocity (v_r), due to roll at the radius (depth) $r = 6.0$ ft:

$$v_r = \omega_{max} \times r \tag{47}$$
$$= 0.55 \times 6.0 = 3.3 \text{ ft/sec}$$

Instantaneous angle of incidence (α) in this condition:

$$\alpha = tg^{-1} \frac{v_r}{V_s} \tag{48}$$

$$= tg^{-1} \frac{3.3}{8.45} = 21.3°$$

At smaller depth $r = 3$ ft, the instantaneous angle of incidence (α) relative to the keel would be less, i.e.:

$$\alpha = tg^{-1} \frac{1.65}{8.45} = 11.0°$$

When roll angle (Θ) approaches 30° the instantaneous incidence angle near the tip of keel would be about 30°; and will gradually increase when the rolling angle increases.

In the second case when the boat speed (V_s) is small or zero the instantaneous angle of incidence (α) of the keel relative to the flow velocity (v) will, as a rule, be well above the stall angle. In such a situation the keel damps almost solely by virtue of its drag as shown in Fig. 141C. Assume that the boat rolls within $\Theta = \pm 30°$ and her speed $V_s = 1.0$ knot (1.69 ft/sec). Following the calculation pattern as before, it can be shown that the instantaneous angle of incidence is likely to be about 71° near the tip of the keel (r = 6 ft), and about 56° at one-half of this depth (r = 3 ft).

When the speed is zero (Fig. 141D), the angle of incidence at which all sections of the keel operate, no matter what depth, becomes 90°. In such a situation, the damping force generated on the keel depends entirely on the velocity induced by rolling alone. This is directly proportional to the radius (r); that is, the sections farther down towards the tip of the keel will be subjected to progressively greater velocity. Thus, the roll damping moment becomes a function of r^3. The reason is as follows: let r_m be the mean distance from the axis of rolling to the centre of pressure of the keel; when the boat acquires the maximum angular velocity ω_{max}

$$v_r = \omega_{max}\ r_m \tag{47}$$

The damping force (F_D) normal to the keel and operating at distance (r_m) will be (Fig. 141E):

$$F_D = C_n \frac{\varrho\ v_r^2}{2}\ A \tag{49}$$

where C_n = the non dimensional coefficient given in Fig. 142
ϱ = the mass density of salt water (1.99 lb sec²/ft)
A = the area of the keel

Substituting formula 47 into 49, we have:

$$F_D = C_n\ \varrho/2\ A\ r_m^2\ \omega_{max}^2 \tag{49A}$$

Thus, the damping moment (M_d) resisting rolling will be:

$$\begin{aligned} M_D &= F_D \times r_m \\ &= C_n\ \varrho/2\ A\ r_m^3\ \omega_{max}^2 \end{aligned} \tag{50}$$

The whole subject of damping is one in which a high degree of precision is not to be expected. Thus, formula 50 can give only an approximate estimate of damping moment actually generated. Nevertheless, it clearly hints that keel effectiveness at zero speed depends primarily on the draft of the hull (D_r in Fig. 141A). The deeper the hull, the longer the mean radius (r_m); and therefore the larger the damping which increases in proportion to the cube of r_m.

Another important factor in this formula is the lateral area (A) of the hull underbody, to which the damping moment is directly proportional. The significance of these two factors becomes evident if we take into account the effect of resultant flow velocity (v) on the damping force shown in sketch B of Fig. 141 (when the boat moves with speed V_s) and compare it to the damping force produced in the zero speed condition when velocity due to roll (v_r) is much smaller than v (sketch D). Since damping varies as the square of the resultant flow velocity, one should expect that in the second case (sketch D) damping may only be a fraction of that which is produced by the keel of a boat sailing with forward motion. On the basis of the preceding reasoning, it therefore appears that the keel of a truly seaworthy boat should be designed primarily for the survival situation, i.e. zero speed, and this implies large lateral area and depth of the hull underbody.

This inference is rather self-evident because a situation may arise when the

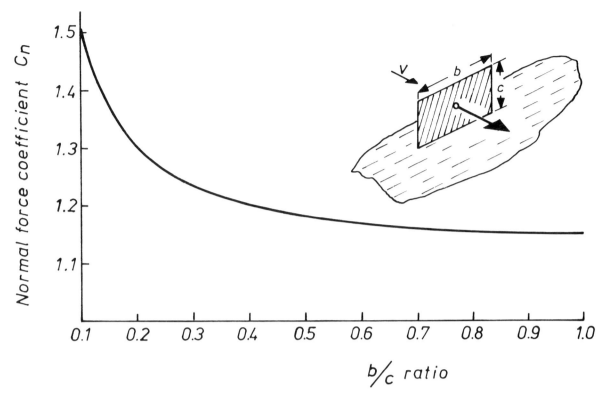

Fig. 142. *Normal force coefficients for plates attached to flat surfaces in uniform flow (C_n). In the case of a keel attached to a hull submerged in non-uniform flow, coefficient C_n as given above should be regarded as a rough approximation only.*

boat cannot be sailed with speed. It could be due to rudder failure, exhaustion of the crew, damage to the rig, extreme severity of the weather, etc. The seaworthy boat should then be able to defend herself (and the crew) against the perils of the sea; and the choice between the boat of type A or B in Fig. 7 may become a matter of life or death. This ties up with an observation made after his Atlantic crossing in the 25 foot yawl *Seabird* in 1911 by T.F. Day, then the editor of *Rudder* magazine: 'My long experience in small boats has taught me this: that if a boat is a good boat, when real trouble comes she is best left alone. She knows better what to do than you, and if you leave her alone, she will do the right things, whereas nine times out of ten you will do the wrong'.

Regrettably, there is practically no information on damping effectiveness of the keel forms usually applied to sailing yachts. However, tests on bilge-keels as they are normally applied to shipform hulls show that their share in the total damping of rolling may amount from 70% to 90%. Figure 10 illustrates one of the solutions to this problem, already found by men of the past for whom the only guide of trial and error (and memory too) was a stern teacher. The sea is exactly the same today as it was centuries ago, it has not changed to favour the survival of boats built to the man-made International Rule.

To avoid the accusation that the author is waging a personal crusade against the contemporary IOR type of boat, the following should be stressed. By drawing attention to Fig. 10, the author is not advocating a slavish return to the old forms of hull evolved in the past; neither does he believe implicitly that the hull shapes of those boats were designed on the basis of an immutable, final truth about seaworthiness requirements discovered once and for all by the early builders, and that for this reason there can be no improvements. Certainly one may argue that such a type of boat had a relatively mediocre speed performance especially in light winds, and was sluggish in stays and liable to get in irons when tacking, and so on. However, her seaworthiness qualities were regarded as outstanding; and it would be foolhardy to believe that there are means by which man can achieve some chosen ends without some side effects or penalties.

The conditions in which those boats had to operate *all year round* were described by E. March in his book *Inshore Craft Of Britain* as follows: 'The shores of the Bristol Channel run in eastward for about 100 miles, gradually

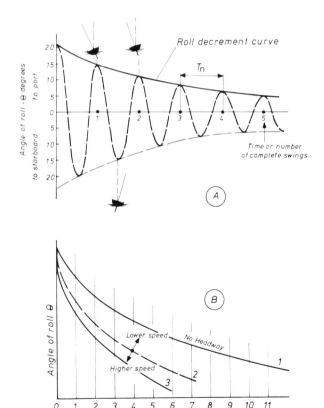

Fig. 143. *Roll decrement curves in a flat sea. In graph (B), curve 1 is with no headway, while 2 and 3 are taken with increasing speed. The higher the speed of the boat, the larger the roll-damping.*

converging until they meet the river Severn. This funnel shape and the swift tidal movements meeting the fierce current from inland, kick up vicious seas, and the channel is noted for its great tidal range, 48 ft in places at springs, the second highest in the world. These conditions demanded a very fine type of pilot boat, one easily handled in crowded waters yet able to face the full force of an Atlantic gale and above all having easy motion when lying-to on station'.

Speed effect on damping

Figure 143A demonstrates in some quantitative sense the critical dependence of damping on boat speed. There are plotted three roll decrement curves of the form presented earlier in Fig. 82 and relevant to calm sea conditions in which, nevertheless, heavy rolling may be incurred due to aerodynamic forces alone (Fig. 36). One curve applies to the situation when the boat makes no headway, and the two others when she is moving ahead. The advantageous effect of speed on damping efficiency of the hull underbody is dramatic. A hull itself, even without keel or bilge keels may have sufficient inherent damping when under way. For example, rolling tests on a shipform hull with rather slack midship sections, showed as much roll-damping for a bare hull at 15 knots, as at zero speed when fitted with bilge keels.

A further illustration of the influence of speed on rolling is given in Fig. 144. This time the model (with and without bilge-keels) was tested in small waves of steepness ratio (H_w/L_w = 1/43 and 1/86), and ultimate rolling angles were

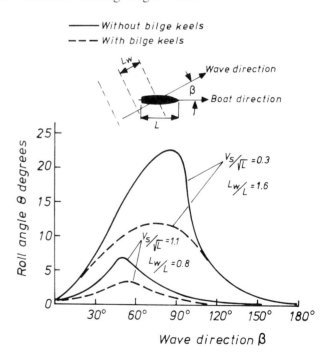

Fig. 144. *Model test on the influence of bilge keels on rolling angles. The lower set of curves is relevant to steepness ratio $H_w/L_w = \frac{1}{43}$, while the upper set applies to steepness ratio $H_w/L_w = \frac{1}{86}$.*

plotted against the wave direction (see sketch at the top of Fig. 144). Quite conspicuous peaks in the two sets of curves – one representing a high speed/length ratio $V_s/\sqrt{L} = 1.1$ and another a low ratio $V_s/\sqrt{L} = 0.3$ – are indicative of resonance conditions when the rolling period of the boat is about the same as the period of encountered waves. It will be seen that when resonance occurs, the influence of damping action is greatest; and at low speed the rolling angle $\Theta = 23.0$ degrees without bilge keels, is reduced to about one half if bilge keels are applied. At higher speed the rolling angle of $7°$ reached without bilge keels is reduced to about $3°$. These test results give some quantitative answer to the question of why, in a survival situation, active rather than passive tactics are usually successful and those who are able to maintain some speed and directional control fare better. Outside resonance the influence of damping gradually decreases, as should be expected according to Fig. 74.

One should bear in mind that the data in Fig. 144 are relevant to boat behaviour in relatively small waves of low steepness. Since according to Eq. 25 the maximum angle of roll depends on the wave slope, in stormy, steep waves an accumulation of rolling may be rapid indeed and extreme slopes may be lethal to small boats. Although it is unlikely that a boat with efficient damping can be capsized through synchronism alone, resonance may be a contributory factor; for instance, if a rolling boat already inclined far to leeward is struck by a breaker on her windward side. If, in this situation, the leeside rail dips under water, the danger of roll-over becomes imminent. The old rule still holds and always will, namely: in survival conditions when no sail can possibly be carried, it is the waves of a storm not its winds, that the mariner has to fear most. But it should not be forgotten that, after all, waves on the water surface are a form of stored energy which was transferred from the wind in the first place.

Addendum to Figs 120B and 135A

The behaviour of the light fin-keel form 2 shown in Fig. 120B was compared with that of a traditional yacht with long keel shown in Fig. 135A. The tests were made using free radio control models which were fitted with a motor driven propeller and rudder to allow them to be manoeuvered around the tank through the breaking waves.[98]
It was hoped that these tests would allow the development of a feel for the behaviour of the various models under conditions similar to those experienced full size. Marked differences in behaviour were observed. Thus, the light displacement fin-keel yacht appeared to be considerably more difficult to handle, particularly when running before the waves. The rudder seemed to have little influence on the ultimate directional control of the model. The boat nearly always broached broadside on to the breaking wave and, once in this position the model usually capsized, rolling quickly through 180 degrees (Fig. 122). More alarmingly, on many occasions the model remained float-ing upside-down (Fig. 121 right) and would not return to the upright position even when struck by further large waves.

On the few occasions that a reasonably straight course down the wave was held by the model, the bow buried into the trough or back of the receding wave and the stern rose up leading to a violent 'pitch pole' type of capsize that would clearly be catastrophic at full scale. This phenomenon was rarely observed with the traditional, long-keel yacht with a larger displacement/length ratio. The traditional hull form seemed to be more easily controlled running before the waves and held its course, surfing ahead of the wave with no tendency to broach.

When broadside to the breaking wave, the traditional yacht was usually knocked down to near horizontal but returned quickly to the upright position. Reducing the displacement of this form i.e. its mass moment of inertia, it could be induced to undergo a number of 360 degrees rolls but never remained in the inverted position.

'What is wrong with our ships will just make heroes of ordinary mortals, there is not any possibility of curative action'

Sir Rowland Baker

15 Directional Stability and Steering

In an article *Evolution of the Modern Cruising Boat* written by one of the most prominent American designers to whom we referred earlier[68], one can read: 'Good directional stability comes from separating the keel and rudder as much as possible. If the example of darts and arrows having feathers only at their aft end can't convince you of this logic, then perhaps the Lord's work in designing birds and fish might be of some help'.

Then, having concluded that 'there is no such thing as the ultimate, perfect cruising boat', the designer ends his article in this way: 'The ideal cruising boat, just as any other type of beauty, will always be in the eye of beholder'.

Those words reflect pretty accurately a common view, but it is one which does not get us very far. The beauty criterion, as applied to boats, is not merely mistaken but dangerously mistaken. It implies purely subjective judgements which in all probability will clash with the requirements of the relentless sea. A boat which appears beautiful in some eyes may not please the sea; and that can be fatal.

The *fin-versus-long-keel* controversy, still unresolved, is the central issue whenever desirable characteristics of cruising boats are discussed. It has become something of a sore subject and a very fascinating one to the point that, not infrequently, half of any particular club does not speak to the other half. For instance, racing people are inclined to believe that the cruising population 'have poor skills, slow boats and slower minds'[109]; and, as distinct from the cruiser, 'the modern racing boat is intended to be driven to the limit and to win races'. For that reason the argument goes on, 'one should put into some sort of perspective all photographs (such as that produced in Fig. 39) showing modern racing yachts in various states of disarray'.[110]

One may, of course, reply that by sailing boats to the limit of their capability, i.e. by carrying more sail area than is prudent in given weather conditions, broaching and capsize are more likely to occur. Any vehicle can be driven to the limit and eventually destroyed, i.e. any fool can drive a car fast enough to kill himself. In this respect there appears to be no basis, external to human agreement, by which we might distinguish between sense and nonsense. Not so many years ago such an extreme attitude towards racing as that which is acceptable today was commonly regarded as a *bad seamanship*. As to the pictures, the photographers are not by nature vicious people and cannot be blamed for taking shots of modern IOR type of boats 'in various states of disarray'. The fact is that those boats tend to behave in an unseaworthy manner in strong winds. And if the two types of boat, say D or E and G or H in Fig. 16 are sailed equally hard by equally determined crews, the contemporary IOR type H will certainly invite the attention of photographers because of its spectacular behaviour.

Does 'good directional stability' come from separating the keel and rudder as much as possible? How does that square with reports from experienced people that yachts with a short fin-keel and a separated rudder sometimes prove unmanageable even in not necessarily rough seas, as shown in Fig. 39?

The former opinion seems to be well supported by test results from one of the research establishments: 'a well-located high aspect spade rudder is far superior to a rudder behind a keel or long skeg. This finding may surprise those sailors who believe that long keel yachts have better fixed control stability'.[111] Thus science appears to be against many blue water skippers who are convinced that there is no place in long range cruising for anything but the traditional full-length keel configuration.

Let us inquire whether the assertion given by the researchers is credible. What test observations have led them to it? Having had time to digest the original report[112] one finds that the towing tank tests on the seakeeping and steering properties of sailing yachts were made on *non-rolling models in calm water conditions*. The tacit assumption was that the yacht which is superior in calm water will also be the best in a seaway. But that assumption sweeps aside the basic physics of a yacht's behaviour or response in heavy seas. Tests in calm water are quite unable to simulate the operation of the underwater part of the hull in large waves – the very conditions in which directional stability and steering efficiency are of paramount importance. They are the two qualities which determine whether the boat will be manageable, or the broaching tendency will become uncontrollable or dangerous.

A. Conflicting requirements

Before we attempt to see why boats are difficult to manage off the wind, and even occasionally to windward, we must be sure of the nature and meaning of the terms *directional stability* and *control*, or *steering*. Confusion about those concepts is largely responsible for the wide gap in the fin-versus-long-keel controversy.

Directional stability is the propensity of a boat, once disturbed by wind or wave forces, to return to her original straight, compass course. Allied properties are course-keeping ability or the ability to self-steer. No sailing boat can be designed in such a way as perfectly to fit this definition: a return to her precise original course. Although the directionally stable boat tends to return to a straight track after being disturbed, she generally will settle down on a new heading to a greater or lesser extent different from the original one. The use of rudder is then needed to bring her back to the desired course. How much rudder-power will be needed depends on the inherent directional stability of the hull and keel, and on the *nature* and *magnitude* of the disturbing forces.

One more element should be added – the helmsman's contribution. Because of the asymmetry of her sailplan a sailing boat is not directionally stable. Usually she tends to luff up when the helm is released (weather helm). Nevertheless, the combination of boat and helmsman can be stable even though the boat herself is not. But as yet we cannot predict for sure, at the design stage, how directionally stable the boat-helmsman system will be and in what conditions the boat will become unmanageable.

The basic function of the *rudder control* or *steering* is twofold. On the one hand it must restore and maintain the equilibrium between wind and water forces whenever the directional stability is disturbed. Additionally, the rudder must produce non-equilibrium of aero and hydrodynamic forces to provide manoeuvrability – a glimpse of the obvious, it steers the boat! But the real point is that these two rudder functions should be achieved in all weather conditions; both in calm and in stormy conditions.

In fact it is impossible to design one boat which will fully satisfy the two demands of, (a) utmost degree of directional stability and (b) a high degree of manoeuvrability. Directional stability conflicts with lively steering. The more directionally stable a boat, the less controllable she is, and vice-versa, the less stable the more manoeuvrable.

Steering

Good course-keeping in heavy weather, achieved with minimum helmsman fatigue, is favoured by cruising men as a feature of seaworthiness. A good cruising boat should bring her crew to their chosen destination as easily and comfortable as possible. Lack of this virtue can be extremely exhausting, and ultimately dangerous.

As described by Rod Stephens: 'with some boats he could rest on the helm and light a cigarette, with others one does not have time to before the yacht yaws and the spinnaker takes hold'.[113]

An evolution of the yacht *Bay Bea* shown in Fig. 145 may further illustrate the problem of handling. The yacht, as originally developed in the tank, was built with a traditional long keel. Subsequent testing, however, revealed that a shorter keel (less wetted area) would improve the windward performance. The hull was then altered as shown, with the rudder faired directly at the aft end of

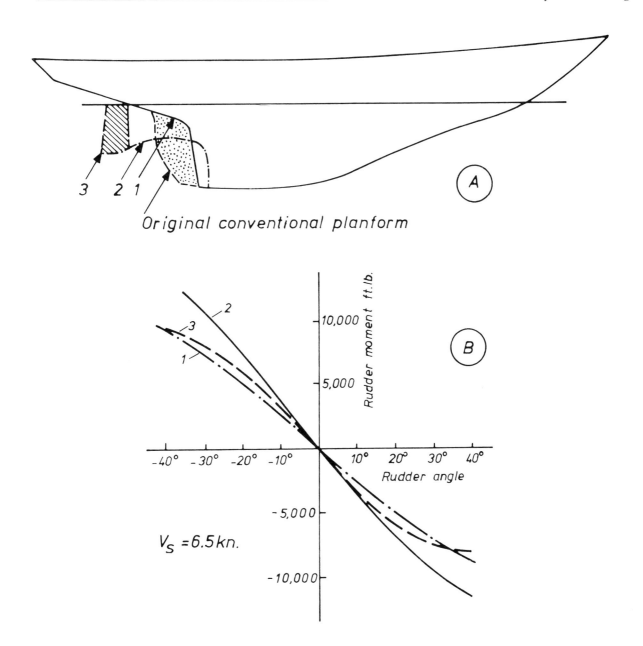

Fig. 145. *Rudder and keel profile variations for* Bay Bea, *tested around 1966 by Sparkman & Stephens; LWL = 43.75 ft (13.3 m), displacement = 21,000 lbs and SA = 740 sq ft (69 m²).*
(1) Shortened keel. Better performance but poor handling qualities.
(2) Final arrangement. Rudder with skeg moved aft gave good handling qualities.

(3) Similar to 2, but with separate spade rudder.
About the same time, S & S were also testing Intrepid, *which became the first 12-metre with a separate keel and rudder. Rudder moment (or turning moment) produced by three configurations at V_s = 6.5 kts, distinguished in sketch (A), and given in sketch (B), should be understood in the light of Fig. 105, i.e. the rudder moment = $F_{rud} \times b$.*

the keel. In this modified form performance to windward was better, but alas she exhibited a steering problem downwind – to put it mildly. As reported by Mr. Haggerty her owner, 'in one race on the leeward leg, the boat could not be kept on course and she broached-to, rolled-over, righted and resumed course 33 times in 3 hours'.[113] This can be a bit disconcerting and wearing on the crew, if not downright dangerous. Anyone who has broached-to in bad weather knows how unpleasant it might be. The interesting point is that such a relatively small reduction of the lateral area of the initial conventional planform (see dotted part of the hull underbody in Fig. 145A) resulted in such a drastic deterioration of steering efficiency as described above.

Subsequent development in the tank led to the measurement of rudder turning moments for a number of arrangements 1–3 indicated in Fig. 145A, and graph B shows the results of tests. It will be seen that at 30 degrees rudder angle (configuration 2, rudder moved aft with skeg), there is about 40 per cent more turning moment available than with the rudder forward as in configuration 1. For the separate spade rudder configuration 3, there is only 8 per cent more turning moment available at the same 30 degree rudder angle. One other interesting observation is that the spade rudder produces less turning moment than the same rudder with skeg.

Studies of the flow character in the rudder's vicinity suggest that, by properly fairing the after waterlines of the hull ahead of the rudder so as to form a sort of skeg, the wake can be cleared up, thereby permitting stronger flow to the rudder.[114] These test results demonstrate that there are also other aspects of hull design to examine when looking for reasons for poor steering (and even unmanageability) than just the profile or the position of the rudder alone.

Over the last thirty years the lateral area of the keel proper has been reduced to less than half that of the 1956 designs. As mentioned earlier, the primary motivation for this departure from traditional planform was the fact the model test on a 5.5 metre yacht (Fig. 146) in calm water showed that a certain reduction in resistance could be obtained by the use of small chord keels with less wetted area.[115] While this finding was borne out in windward sailing, it entailed a penalty in downwind controllability. An immediate solution was obtained by moving the rudder aft and adding skeg area. However, 'this solution is not without its dangers, for being further aft, the rudder at large heel angle is brought closer to the water surface and may ventilate'[114]; that is to cause leakage of air to the suction (low pressure) side of the rudder blade, which results in a partial breakdown of lift and thus rudder power. It will be seen in Fig. 147 that, at relatively small angles of heel, both the rudder and the keel are partly above the water and ventilate simultaneously. In rough seas off the wind, when the boat is rolling, large yawing moments may be induced by the combined effect of wave and sail forces. This may well call for a large – 300 per cent or even more – increase in steering power, which the rudder may not be capable of delivering, thus the broach cannot be avoided – ventilation is a mild word for what it entails!

Fig. 146. *Variation in lateral area of a 5.5-metre class boat. The original 5.5-metre rule stipulated that the rudder had to be fitted to the after edge of the keel in the conventional manner. In the course of keel evolution towards a higher aspect ratio of ever-decreasing width (chord), in an attempt to improve boat speed by even a fraction, a point was reached where the boats became uncontrollable in rough seas. The rule has been altered in such a way that the rudder may either be attached to the keel or separated, with or without a skeg. Since the turning axis of the hull is not far from the leading edge of the keel, a rudder hung on the trailing edge of a short-chord fin has a relatively small lever. Thus, in rough conditions, rudder power*

Rudder after modification

may be insufficient to maintain a straight course. An immediate solution was obtained by moving the rudder aft and adding a skeg. This remedy is not without danger for, being further aft, at large heel angles the rudder is brought closer to the free surface and may ventilate (see also Fig. 147).

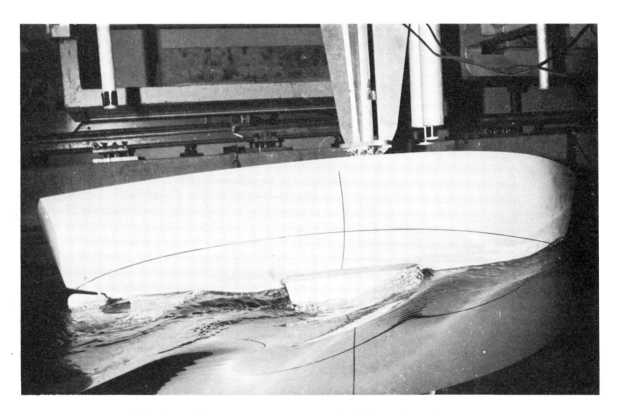

Fig. 147. *Excessive heel when rolling or turning may give rise to a number of hydrodynamic effects, which in turn may seriously impair directional stability or rudder power. One of these effects is ventilation of hull appendages when the root of the fin-keel or top of the rudder is brought near to the water surface. This may cause leakage of air to the suction (low pressure) side of the appendage, and result in a drastic breakdown of lift (side force). In such a case air communicates, through a sort of spiral vortex, with the flow of water near the leading edge of the keel or rudder. Normally at low angles of heel, the rudder blade is shielded from air leakage by the stern. A wide, shallow draft hull as shown above instigates this ventilation at smaller heel angles than a deep, narrow hull.*

Speed performance requirements

Aspect ratio (of both keel and rudder) becomes relevant at this point. If maximum speed is our over-riding objective, and we follow that idea through to its logical conclusion, the size and shape of the keel should primarily be determined by the amount of side force it must produce at minimum drag, which is not infrequently wrongly equated with minimum wetted area. The design problem then reduces itself to finding – by tank testing or by trial and error – this minimum size which is consistent with good close-hauled performance. Consequently, the hull of the speed-dominated racer with her small fin keel and separated rudder of high aspect ratios as depicted in Fig. 84 may seem to be a triumph of rational design. The justification is fairly straightforward, namely: the speed that a sailing yacht can make directly against the wind (V_{mg}) is usually taken as the criterion of sailing performance. The higher the V_{mg} at given true wind velocity (V_T), i.e. the higher the V_{mg}/V_T ratio, the better the chances of success in racing, particularly around a triangular course. It can be shown that V_{mg}/V_T is directly related to lift/drag (L/D) ratios of the rig and the hull, including its appendages,[59] in other words:

$$V_{mg}/V_T \simeq (\frac{L}{D})_{sail} + (\frac{L}{D})_{hull}$$

In general, the higher the aspect ratio of the rig and hull appendages the higher the L/D ratios.

However, the other function of the keel is to produce effective damping against rolling, and that of the rudder to maintain its steering power regardless of weather. The crucial question is: will these appendages perform their functions as satisfactorily in rough seas as they do in calm water conditions? Certainly until the answer has been found, the controversy of fin versus long keel will persist.

B. The effect of rough water

There are a number of important differences between boat motion in heavy seas and in calm water. These differences are related to the behaviour of the water itself, which (it hardly seems necessary to say) is very different in rough and calm.

The basic principles of wave motion in deep water have been earlier shown in Fig. 90. The wave profile is marked by a broken curve, while the points marked on the circular orbits give the positions of free surface water particles at specific times. If after a certain lapse of time the water particles moving in their orbits change their relative position – in this example by one twelfth of the circumference of the circle – then the crest of the wave will shift by the equivalent distance. This new position of the wave is marked by the continuous curve. It must be emphasised that a travelling wave is a passage of motion only, not of water. The actual movement of the water particles that compose the wave is relatively small, and contained within orbits.

While the water particles are executing one orbit about their position at rest, the crest of the wave will shift from position 1 to position 2, by a full wave length L_w. If the height of the wave H_w (which is twice the orbit radius 2R) and the wave length are known, the maximum velocity of orbital current at the surface, u_o, is found from:

$$u_o = \frac{7.1\ H_w}{\sqrt{L_w}} \qquad (32)$$

where u_o is in feet per second when H_w and L_w are in feet.

Hence, the higher the wave the faster the orbital current. The *importance of this relation cannot be overestimated*. It results in orbital flows of varying speed and direction, depending on which part of the wave surface is involved. The effect of water particles revolving in orbits is such that at the wave crests the water is moving in the direction of the wave advance, but in the troughs in the opposite direction. The intensity of the surface currents moving with the wave is represented in Fig. 90 by arrows of varying thickness, the thickest portion of

Fig. 148. *Relationship between maximum orbital velocity (surface current, see Fig. 90) and the size of waves. The steepness of wave is the prime factor which determines the magnitude of surface current, and hence directional stability and controllability. With increasing size of waves, particularly their steepness, yawing and* broaching *tendencies become more and more acute until directional stability is seriously impaired or even lost. Heavy displacement boats are subjected to relatively smaller deviations from course, on account of their greater mass and inertia.*

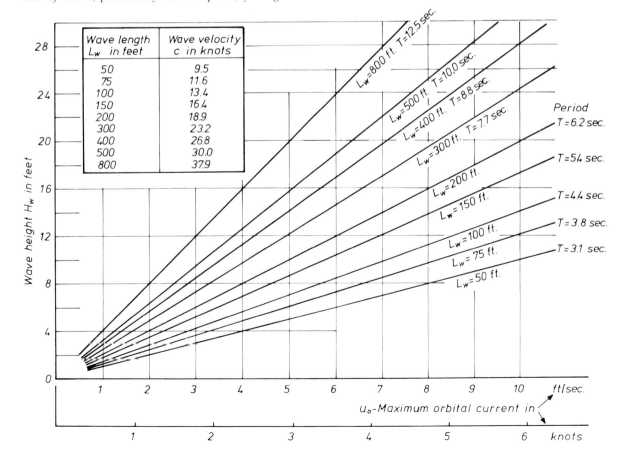

the arrow corresponding to the area where the current is strongest. Figure 148 gives plots of maximum surface current velocities for a range of wave lengths, periods and height likely to be encountered during deep sea heavy-weather conditions.

In passing it can be remarked that the radii of wave orbits decrease rapidly with depth (Fig. 149). For example, at a depth H_w equal to 1/10 L_w the ratio R/R_s is about 0.5, so the orbital current at that depth will be about half that at the surface. By the time a depth H_w equal to 1/2 L_w is reached the size of the orbit decreases to about only 4% of that at the surface. A submarine or a fish may thus easily escape the fury of the sea by submerging to a depth where the wave orbits are relatively small and the water is still. Now, having looked at the water itself, let us consider its flow relative to the boat.

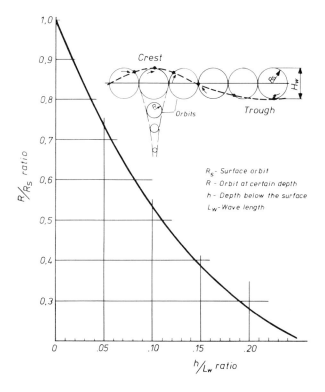

Fig. 149. *Relationship between the orbital radii (orbital velocities) at the surface, and at various depths of water. The size of the orbits decreases rapidly (exponentially) with depth. For example, at a depth equal to half the wave length, the size of orbit (and thus the orbital velocity) is only about 4 per cent of that at the surface.*

As shown in Fig. 90 in oblique seas the angle of incidence at which the water meets the hull, the keel and also a separated rudder, is subject to considerable variation due to the orbital current. Different parts of the hull find themselves in different positions along the wave profile. In contrast to the steady flow in calm water, local flows create yawing moments which will tend to divert the boat away from the prescribed compass course. For example, the boat in sketch 90B sailing downwind at an oblique angle will be affected at that instant by the orbital flow tending to initiate yawing to port. This is indicated by the thick black arrow. A couple of seconds later, after the wave crest has passed

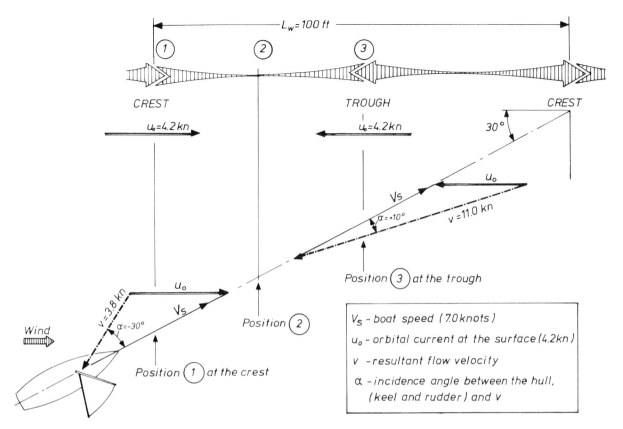

Fig. 150. *The effect of surface current (u_0) = 4.2 knots, expected in a wave of length (L_w) = 100 ft and height (H_w) = 10 ft, on the flow around the hull of a boat sailing down wind with V_s = 7.0 knots. The course sailed relative to the crests is 30°. Note the large variation in v from 3.8 knots at the crest to 11 knots in the trough. Associated variations in the incidence angle (α) from −30° at the crest to +10° in the trough, are large too. These imply that resulting variations in the hydrodynamic forces developed on the keel and separated rudder – tending to deviate the boat from the selected course – may be very large indeed. These work to the disadvantage of shallow, light displacement boats with separated keel and rudder of high aspect ratio.*

underneath the hull and the boat is facing the back of the wave ahead, the moment will be reverse and the boat will yaw to starboard. Evidently, the magnitude of the unsteady, oscillating yawing moment will largely depend upon the strength of orbital flow, and the resulting variation of the incidence angles of the hull and its appendages.

To give some feel for the magnitude of what we are talking about consider a boat sailing downwind in an oblique rough sea, at a direction 30 degrees to that of the wave motion, with speed V_s of 7.0 knots (Fig. 150). The wave length L_w is 100 feet and its height is 10 feet. From Fig. 149 we find that the wave velocity c is 13.4 knots and the maximum orbital current u_o is 7.1 ft/sec (4.2 knots). When the surface orbital current u_o is superimposed on the forward motion of the boat, the angle of incidence of the water on the hull and fin-keel is varying from −30 degrees at the crest (position 1) to + 10 degrees at the trough (position 3). The respective resultant flow velocities (v) are: 3.8 knots at the crest and 11 knots at the trough. At the intermediate position 2, where the effect of orbital flow is negligible, the keel temporarily operates at zero incidence, and the resultant flow around it is equal to the boat speed $V_s = 7.0$ knots.

These periodic changes in incidence angle and flow velocity are further modified by the flow variations imposed on the hull and its appendages when the boat is forced to roll due to aerodynamic excitation. Assuming, for example, that the depth of the keel is 6 ft, the period of rolling $T_n = 3.0$ sec, the boat speed = 7 knots (11.8 ft/sec) and the angle of roll $\Theta = 35°$, we find that the maximum angular velocity ω_{max} at the tip of the keel will be 1.28 rad/sec. The relevant maximum linear velocity due to roll will be $v_r = 1.28 \times 6.0 = 7.68$ ft/sec. Thus, the instantaneous maximum angle of incidence of a periodically rolling keel would be in the order of:

$$\alpha = \pm\, tg^{-1}\, \frac{v_r}{V_s} = \pm\, tg^{-1}\, \frac{7.68}{11.8} = \pm\, 33 \text{ degrees}$$

And this may greatly augment the variation in the incidence angle of hull appendages caused by the effect of orbital current (Fig. 150).

All these periodic rapid changes in the angle of incidence and relative flow velocity – on which, in turn, the magnitude of side forces developed on keel and rudder depend – will occur in 3 seconds, i.e. half of the wave encounter period, which is about 6 seconds. Self-evidently, this constitutes a fundamental modification to the calm water situation. As a result the boat will tend to yaw periodically to either side of the prescribed compass course. Experiments indicate (Fig. 151) that the oscillatory yaw moment reaches a maximum at a boat heading relative to direction of wave propagation of 120 to 150 degrees, or roughly the same heading for a spinnaker reach downwind.

The waves encountered in stormy weather are predominantly short crested, and irregular in length. Usually a variety of steep, short waves are superimposed on the longer ones. To maintain a straight course in such an

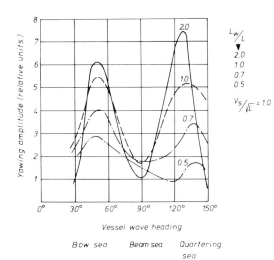

Fig. 151. *Oscillatory yaw moments versus angle of heading relative to waves. Apart from heading angle, the magnitude of yawing moment (and proportional to it, the yawing amplitude) greatly depends on the ratio of wave length (L_w) to the sailing length of the hull (L). The worst case seems to be when the wave length is approximately twice the hull length. Then, as indicated in Fig. 90, as the fore part of the hull reaches the trough, the aft part is buried in the crest. The destabilising effect of the orbital velocities is then strongest.*

endless confusion of waves, and associated surface currents, the helmsman must use continuous rudder action to neutralise strong broaching tendencies, aggravated by the rolling of the boat. This requires the utmost concentration and skill, not only in deciding what to do but in doing it *always* at the right moment. Sooner or later the concentration fails and mental fatigue may make the helmsman unable to respond adequately to the high frequency yaw deviation which occurs in short, steep waves. His delays in observing and responding to the threatening broach may then be of the same order as the period of yaw deviation.

The following quotation llustrates the point: 'We found that to sail *Munequita* to her best at all times required so much concentration that it was necessary to change helmsman every half hour'.

With large variation in speed and direction of the relative flow round the hull, fin-keel and rudder, the consequent hydrodynamic forces must also be subject to large fluctuations. If the boat is of heavy displacement type she will respond only slowly to these hydrodynamic forces, but a light displacement boat will respond more quickly.

This is one aspect of the boat's response to rough sea. The other is that, due to large variations in flow direction (caused by the orbital velocities when running in oblique waves (Fig. 150) and possibly augmented by rolling), the keel and the rudder may easily reach angles of incidence well beyond the stall. This imposes a source of energy exchange and may lead to instability similar to that produced by a sail in the downwind condition (Appendix 2). That is, the hull appendages as the lift-producing surfaces may, during at least a part of the full roll cycle, deliver negative damping, thus contributing to magnification of rolling instead of extinguishing it.

The directional stability of a boat rolling in waves is an exceedingly complex problem and one which it may never be possible to solve completely. If we can form some idea of the effects of the principal design factors involved and their importance in practical sailing, however, a mathematically complete solution can be dispensed with. The interest of yacht designers and sailing people is restricted mainly to whether some guide could be stablished which might help in differentiating an efficient hull/appendages configuration from an inefficient one. The crux of this matter is the radical difference between the action of any lift-producing device – be it sail, aircraft wing, keel or even suspension bridge – in *steady* as distinct from *unsteady* flow conditions. Clearly to understand the different mechanism by which the unsteady, destabilising forces may arise, consider first the foil action in steady flow conditions.

C. Foil action in steady flow conditions

The term foil is deliberately used to define any objcct (aerofoil, hydrofoil), which, while immersed in the air or water may be subjected to two kinds of forces, termed lift (L) and drag (D). Classic fluid dynamics has been mainly devoted to the study of forces developed on foils in steady state motion, and a tacit assumption is that the lift follows instantaneously any change in incidence angle. Thus, for example, it is customary to present the lift force developed on a fully immersed foil at given speed (be it spade rudder or keel) in the familiar manner shown in Fig. 152. When the incidence angle is 0 degrees no lift is generated simply because the flow on both sides of the symmetrical foil is symmetrical. Then, between incidence 0 degrees and the stall angle the graph is practically a straight line which means that as the angle of incidence increases steadily there is a proportional and steady increase in the lift.

The meaning of *steady flow* is that sufficient time is allowed for the flow around the foil to establish its final pattern for any given incidence angle as shown in photographs A and B in Fig. 152; and so the final magnitude of lift is reached for that angle. Implicitly, therefore, there is no random variation in either the flow velocity or its direction.

The stall angle is that angle of incidence at which maximum lift is reached; and beyond which it begins to decrease more or less rapidly depending on the

Fig. 152. *Lift force developed on a symmetrical foil at different incidence angles in steady state flow conditions. The meaning of* steady state *is that, for a given incidence angle, sufficient time is allowed for the flow around the foil to establish its final pattern, and so the final magnitude of lift is reached for that angle.*

(B) Flow past an aerofoil at zero angle of incidence (α) as shown by smoke streamlines.
(A) Stall of an aerofoil can be defined as an abrupt departure of the streamlines from the suction contour of the foil which is supposed to be guiding them.

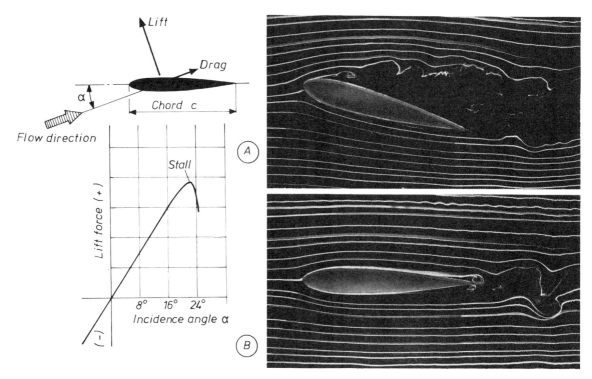

planform of the foil (aspect ratio), flow velocity (Reynolds Number), and the cross-section of the foil (thickness of the foil).

Planform effect

As shown in Fig. 153 the stall angle increases appreciably with decreasing aspect ratio (AR). There is a range of AR extending approximately from 0.75 to 1.5 wherein the flow round the foil tip, the so called tip vortex, causes a marked delay in the breakdown of longitudinal flow as the incidence angle is increased. The reason is that the boundary layer is considerably affected by the strong tip vortices and separation is delayed until higher incidence angles are reached. Figure 154 shows these tip vortices spinning round the keel of a Dragon type of boat. It is possible within the indicated range of low AR to obtain a maximum lift coefficient higher than can be obtained for a foil of the same section having say, an AR = 3.[59]

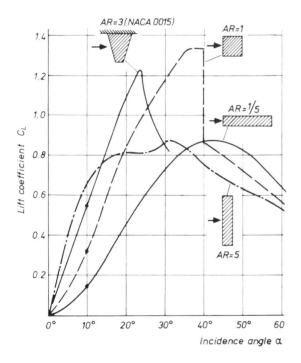

Fig. 153. *Dependence of angle of stall and maximum lift on aspect ratio (AR). The traditional long keel of low AR appears to be highly resistant to stall, within the range of periodically varying incidence angles which have been induced by the oscillating surface current in waves (possibly augmented by rolling). For this reason it is unlikely that low AR hull appendages may ever operate beyond the stall angle. This fact is of enormous practical significance from the viewpoint of course-keeping and handling in rough seas (see Fig. 84). Data for foil of AR = 5, 1 and 1/5 are relevant to flat plates.*

Fig. 154. *Tip vortex developing at the bottom of a Dragon keel. Every foil which produces lift dissipates energy into the stream of air or water, and this energy goes largely into generation of vortex motion at the foil tips, which in turn modifies the flow pattern around the hull adjacent to the foil.*

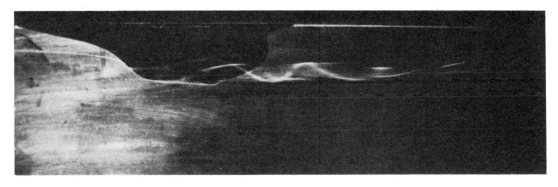

The most noticeable feature of the low AR foils is the development of marked three-dimensional flow, which continues without breakdown to high angles of incidence. As the AR decreases, the tip vortex motion (Fig. 154) and its effect on flow over the foil is increased to such a degree that the boundary layer tending to accumulate over the rear part of the foil (low pressure side) is swept away, and so the flow continues without separation to a much larger incidence angle. It has been found that, for AR ranging from about 0.75 to 1.5, the flow is decidedly more stable than for higher AR foils. This behaviour is characteristic regardless of planform or foil section, and was also evident in the results of tests made with flat plates.

As the AR increases, the effect of tip vortex on the flow over the foil gradually decreases, and so does the stall angle. It is noteworthy that the stall angle and the maximum lift for a foil of approximately square planform (AR = 1) are larger than that relevant to higher AR foils. The tip shape of the foil appears to be of some importance among the factors affecting the magnitudes of lift at large angle of incidence; foils with semi-circular tips were found to be much superior to those having rectangular or faired tips.[117] These characteristics should be taken into consideration when designing keels or rudders, if premature flow separation and stall are to be avoided.

The so-called geometric aspect ratio (AR_g) of a foil, as determined in accordance with conventional calculation (Fig. 153) is:

$$AR_g = \frac{\text{Span}^2}{\text{Lateral Area}}$$

But, if the root section of the keel or rudder attached to the hull is sealed, so that there is no flow over the root, the effective aspect ratio (AR_{ef}) may be roughly twice its geometric aspect ratio,

i.e.: $$AR_{ef} = 2\ AR_g$$

As shown in Fig. 84, a clear trend in yacht design is towards higher AR appendages, with AR_{ef} about 4 or even more, and for that reason it should be expected that they will stall at relatively low angles of incidence.

Flow velocity effect (Reynolds number)

Figure 155 illustrates, for example, four lift coefficients (C_L versus α), curves developed on the NACA 0015 symmetrical section at different Reynolds numbers (Re). These curves represent lift coefficients which would be produced at non-dynamic, fixed incidence modes, so that the flow velocity and α were maintained for such a sufficiently long period that the time-dependent lift was able to reach its final, steady state value.

The reader may recall that Reynolds number takes into account speed and length. Thus, considering the fin-keel action of a modern type of yacht sailing to windward at $V_s = 5$ knots, and assuming that the mean chord length of the

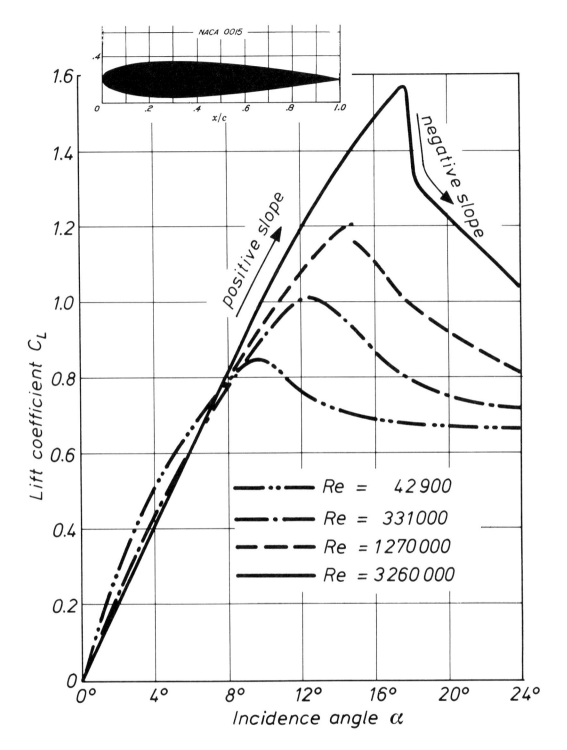

Fig. 155. *Dependence of angle of stall and maximum lift (C_{Lmax}) on flow velocity (Reynolds number) relative to foil (keel or rudder) with NACA 0015 section. Note the large decrease in both C_{Lmax} and angle of stall when Re decreases from, say, about 3,000,000 (sailing at speed) to about 40,000 (boat in irons after, say, an unsuccessful tack).*

keel (ℓ) = 4.0 ft (Fig. 84), we may find from the formula below[59]:

$$Re = 81.300 \times V_s \times \ell$$
where V_s is in ft/sec
ℓ is in ft

that the relevant $Re = 2.7 \times 10^6$.

If, however, the flow velocity in, say, the rudder's vicinity is reduced (possibly due to the action of an orbital current directed against the boat's motion (see Fig. 90)) then the Re will be reduced and so will the rudder power (lift).

Textbooks dealing with aero and hydrodynamic properties of foil sections usually present steady state lift characteristics in the form of a single $C_L - \alpha$ curve valid for one particular Reynolds number, and for a given aspect ratio. This kind of presentation has facilitated the spread of an erroneous belief, at least amongst some yacht designers, that hydrodynamic forces developed on the keel or rudder follow instantaneously any change in incidence angle or flow velocity; and that those data can with confidence be applied to unsteady flow conditions associated with rough weather. But this is not the case.

D. Unsteady flow conditions

As discussed earlier, in fresh and heavy weather conditions the hull appendages are subjected to a periodically varying incidence angle due to:

(a) changes in direction and velocity of the water flow caused by the orbital currents in waves.
(b) rolling caused by the action of waves.
(c) rolling inflicted by aerodynamic forces.
(d) rudder movement applied by the helmsman to control yaw.

The resulting variations in incidence angle, which will be particularly large if causes a–d operate in unison, can be of such magnitude that the high aspect ratio fin-keel and separated rudder may frequently operate beyond the steady state stall angle. As a result, lift generated on the foil is no longer a unique function of the incidence angle as it appears in Figs 153 and 155. Instead, the rate of change of incidence angle with respect to time becomes the controlling factor which largely modifies the forces developed on the foil:

$$\frac{\Delta\alpha}{\Delta t}$$

where $\Delta\alpha$ – amount of increase in incidence angle
Δt – time interval during which the incidence angle varies by $\Delta\alpha$

Although a great deal of air has flown through wind tunnels all over the world, there is lamentably still a requirement for reliable experimental determination of foil action and its damping effectiveness in the sort of unsteady conditions which are relevant to heavy weather sailing.

Since about 1925, however, it has been known that if the incidence angle of a hydrofoil (or aerofoil) changes suddenly by a given amount, say from zero to 15 degrees, the new lift force (proper for the new angle of incidence in steady flow condition) is not established instantaneously (Figs 156 and 157). Actually, about one half of the total change in lift occurs at once, and a time taken by the flow to travel six times the chord of the foil is needed to bring the change in lift to 9/10 of its final, steady state value.

The time lag in establishing steady flow at given angle of incidence is known as *Hysteresis*, or *Wagner's effect*, or *Memory effect*. A certain mass of water must be accelerated and a time lag is unavoidable. This is the reason why a high aspect ratio fin-keel or a spade rudder with short chord length gives quicker response in generating lift than a long, traditional keel with a flap-type rudder. Conversely, the steadiness conferred by length of keel is primarily due to the hysteresis which provides an averaging effect on the flow round the keel. This effect becomes more pronounced in short waves as the time interval (Δt) for each variation in angle of incidence ($\Delta \alpha$) of flow velocity diminishes, i.e. the rate of change $\dfrac{\Delta \alpha}{\Delta t}$ increases. The long keel of heavy displacement boats of

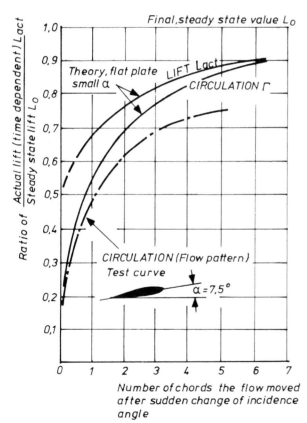

Fig. 156. *Development of circulation (flow pattern) and associated time dependent lift (L_{act}) after a sudden change of incidence angle. Because of the inertia forces involved, the flow pattern appropriate to a given incidence angle (α) cannot instantaneously be established (see Fig. 157). The flow must move a distance about six times the foil chord before 90 per cent of the steady state value of lift (L_0) is established. It takes time – the shorter the foil chord, the more quickly the lift is developed (and the stall too). As seen here, the test curve does not exactly follow theory, but the trend is similar in a qualitative sense. It should be stressed that lift must be considered as a time dependent quality in dynamic flow conditions.*

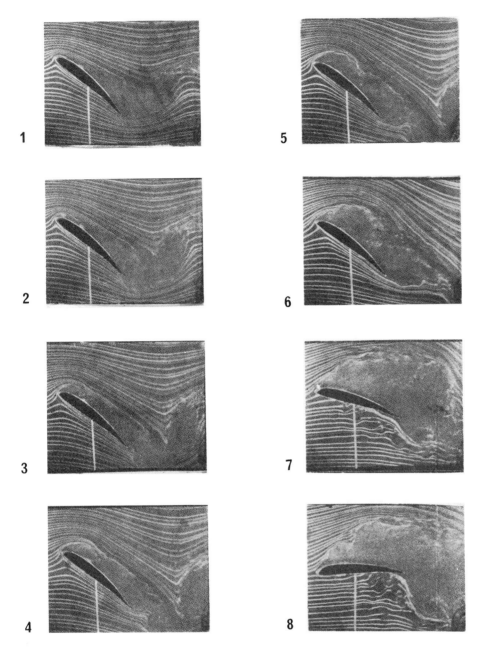

Fig. 157. *Hysteresis effect on the flow around a foil which is rapidly changing its angle of incidence. Actual flow does not follow the pattern which would develop in stationary conditions at a given angle of incidence. The practical meaning of this is that although, say, the keel attitude relative to the flow may be altered, the fluid* remembers *the initial flow pattern; in other words, in unsteady conditions, actual lift depends on the previous history of the flow. The flow pattern depicted in 1–8 may be similar to that developed over a high AR keel in unsteady conditions, when the boat is forced to roll. Once the stall (flow separation) has occurred, it takes time for the flow to re-attach, even if the incidence angle has been reduced to that at which, in steady flow conditions, stall would never occur. This why some boats make progress when beating to windward in drifting conditions, while their rivals remain stationary. The latter have allowed their keels to stall, and it takes a long time (and a course as much as 90° off the wind) to re-establish the attached flow enjoyed by the boats making progress. Photographs illustrate vividly large dynamic overshoot of the flow re-attachment. If such a situation occurs, keel efficiency as a damping device is greatly reduced, or it may even magnify the rolling motion (negative damping).*

type A in Fig. 7 may therefore rightly be called a yaw-damper. Its function is to average the effects of relatively high frequency variation of the orbital currents occurring in short waves; leaving only the low frequency effects which take place in long waves. These relatively slow deviations from the prescribed course give the helmsman a longer warning time to take preventive rudder action. The spread of this knowledge (acquired scientifically as far back as the early 1930s) has itself suffered from a certain amount of hysteresis (time lag) so it seems desirable to give it emphasis now when it seems most needed.

By contrast, contemporary light displacement shallow bodied craft of the type shown in Fig. 84 have no such built-in yaw damper. These boats react quickly to destabilising yawing moments exerted on separated appendages even in short waves. The higher the aspect ratio of the fin-keel and rudder, and the lower the displacement, the shorter is the time lag between the disturbing moment and a recognisable deviation from a straight course.

Such rapid variations in the flow around the keel when sailing in waves contrast strongly with the calm water situation. One may rightly expect that both the directional stability and steering, or the control of the boat, will be profoundly different. This is one of the reasons why suddenly, in deteriorating weather conditions, the modern type of boat with high AR hull appendages seems to go wrong and may become unmanageable. But there are other, more compelling, arguments against high AR keel or rudder.

E. Why long keel?

'A consistent theory should stand the test of non-mathematical statement. Truths as well as errors may be obscured or unperceived when stated in purely mathematical form.'

D.B. Steiman

When considering the damping action of hull appendages it is tacitly assumed that the keel will always do the work against rolling and that this corresponds to positive damping. In other words, the side force (lift) generated on the keel will always be directed against rolling motion and so will resist it. However, because of the hysteresis effect this is not always the case.

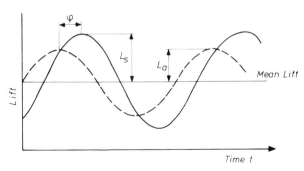

Fig. 158. *Variation of actual (momentary) lift (L_a) compared with static lift (L_s). The time marked along the horizontal axis should be understood as a variation of incidence angle with time.*

It has been found experimentally that in unsteady flow conditions the forces generated on any foil (and keel too) do not conform to our expectations, based on steady flow conditions, as depicted in Figs 153 or 155. Instead, as shown in Fig. 158, we note that:

(1) variation of actual (momentary) lift (L_a) may be either greater or less than that which would occur if the change of incidence angle (α) were infinitely slow, i.e. if at each angle of incidence the lift (L_s) were that corresponding to the steady state condition.

(2) variation of actual lift (L_a) may either lead or lag behind that of the incidence angle (α) relevant to steady flow conditions.

(3) the phase angle (γ), and the increment or decrement of actual lift (L_a) over the steady state lift values (L_s), depend upon the mode of foil oscillation relative to the oncoming flow direction as depicted in Fig. 159, where we can distinguish:

    (A) pure angular variations, i.e. direct variation in the incidence angle ($\pm \alpha$).

    (B) pure translational oscillation (sideways motion).

    (C) combination of A and B.

The dynamic reaction on a single foil whose angle of incidence is harmonically increasing and decreasing within the range of the positive slope of L versus α curve (Fig. 155) can be predicted within reasonable accuracy. Theories developed by Karman, Sears and others[118,169], and well supported by

Fig. 159. *Different modes of flow oscillation relative to the foil, resulting in periodic changes in the angle of incidence (α) and lift (side force).*

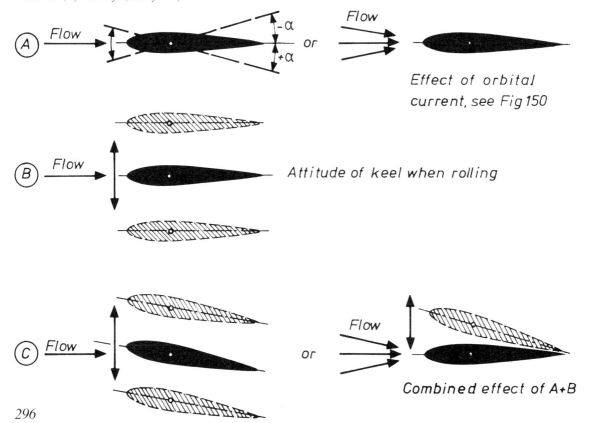

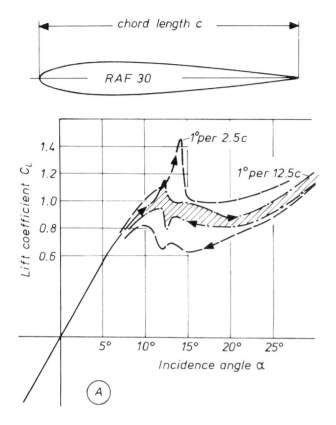

Fig. 160. *Hysteresis (memory) effect on lift produced by a foil whose angle of incidence is changing between 7.5–30 degrees. In this context, 'hysteresis' means a time lag in establishing the flow pattern, and thus the lift corresponding to the steady flow condition proper for any given angle of incidence (α).*

experimental evidence, can be used to calculate these reactions. For more complicated cases of foil motion, as indicated in sketch C of Fig. 159, particularly if the foil reaches an incidence angle beyond the stall angle, a quantitative estimate of what is going on must necessarily be based on experiment.

Test results on a symmetrical foil (RAF 30), whose angle of incidence (α) was first increasing and then decreasing rapidly within the range of 7.5 to 30 degrees (Fig. 160A) give some idea what response might be expected in the case of a fin-keel or rudder in a similar situation.[120] The lift curve for steady state incidence up to 7.5 degrees is given by a continuous line, and two broken line curves indicate lift variations for two different rates of incidence change; one when the incidence angle is changing 1 degree in the time the flow takes to travel 2.5 chords of the foil (fast change); the other for a change of incidence at the rate of 1 degree per 12.5 chords (slow change).

It is seen that a large hysteresis effect occurs above and beyond the stall angle. The lift on a foil whose angle is rising rapidly may appreciably exceed that measured at steady state incidence. Conversely, the lift associated with rapidly decreasing incidence is below that measured in steady state flow conditions. The area within the hysteresis loop, recorded before the attached flow is against established, depends on the rate of change in the incidence angle. A faster rate inflicts a larger hysteresis loop.

The general nature of this phenomenon and some damping implications are illustrated in Fig. 160B. When the angle of incidence ($\pm \alpha$) varies around a mean value close to zero, the lift-incidence curve would be extended below the horizontal α axis in roughly a mirror image fashion. Because of the time-lag necessary to re-establish attached flow, there is a phase lag (γ) between the incidence (α) corresponding to the actual, momentary lift (L_a), and the incidence relevant to the steady state lift (L_s). The lift will follow a different curve when α increases, and yet another one when α decreases. As long as the stall angle is not exceeded, the lift generated is directed against the motion, thus the foil does negative work ($-W$), thereby losing energy to the passing stream. The foil thus operates as a roll-damping device although, due to the phase lag (γ) the rolling boat receives an additional 'kick' in an unexpected direction which will in fact augment the roll. When the angle of stall is exceeded, that part of the foil which suffers stall abstracts energy from the stream, and the area within the hysteresis loop ($+W$) can be regarded as a measure of reduction in the damping efficiency of the foil.

Although it is rather unlikely that the whole area of the fin-keel will ever operate in the fully stalled condition (so that the keel might work as a rolling engine in a manner similar to that of sails), its damping efficiency may be greatly reduced. It may happen that in some unfavourable conditions the maximum aerodynamic input (negative damping) is far greater than the positive hydrodynamic damping delivered by the hull and its appendages. In such circumstances, the rolling amplitude will build up into one of those nightmarish affairs that contemporary racing crews know only too well.

It will be readily apparent from what has been said with reference to Fig. 160, that an increase in the angle of stall, leading to reduction of the hysteresis loop ($+W$), would result in better efficiency of the keel as a damping device. This goal can be achieved by decreasing the aspect ratio of appendages according to the implications of Fig. 153.

Hysteresis effect describes the physical phenomenon occuring in dynamic conditions that lies at the root of some unpredictable, sometimes mischievious, behaviour of man-made machines and structures – aircraft, boats, and even bridges. Numerous aircraft have crashed because of the so-called stall-flutter of the wings, in which hysteresis effect plays a prominent role. Suspension bridges have collapsed in relatively moderate winds just because, amongst other factors, unsteady aerodynamic forces were involved; and Fig. 161 shows the consequence of these unsteady forces which caused catastrophic divergent oscillations.

Unsteady and not always predictable forces appearing in a periodically stalled flow belong to the category of strange, nevertheless honest and legitimate phenomena which have to be reckoned with. High aspect ratio keels

Fig. 161. Above. *Divergent oscillations of the Tacoma Bridge building up.*
Below. *Final stages in the collapse of the bridge. This failure alerted designers to the severity of wind-induced oscillation caused by hysteresis effect, resulting in aerodynamic instability.*

and rudders, likewise sails, are not immune against all sorts of instability if they operate in these periodically stalled flow conditions.

Unsteady fin rudder interaction

One more phenomenon associated with unsteady sailing condition deserves to be briefly discussed. Apart from the effect of unsteady flow on damping efficiency of the keel, there is a sort unsteady interaction between a keel and separated rudder. Every change in angle of incidence of the foil is accompanied by a change in flow pattern about it, followed by a free vortex which is shed from the trailing edge at the moment of the angle change. Since vortices originate along the whole trailing edge of the foil, they form a vortex sheet. As a result, vertical velocities build up in the wake behind the foil as the vortices travel downstream. Photographs A, B, C, and D in Fig. 162 show such a vortex and the downwash caused by it, recorded after 0.9, 1.4, 2.4 and 3.0 chord length distance travelled by the foil. The horizontal line 0–0 indicates the direction of the foil motion, and the angle between the 0–0 line and the vortex sheet gives the downwash angle induced by the free vortex.

Figure 163A illustrates schematically a distribution of downwash velocities in the wake, normal to the basic motion of the fin-keel after sudden increase in

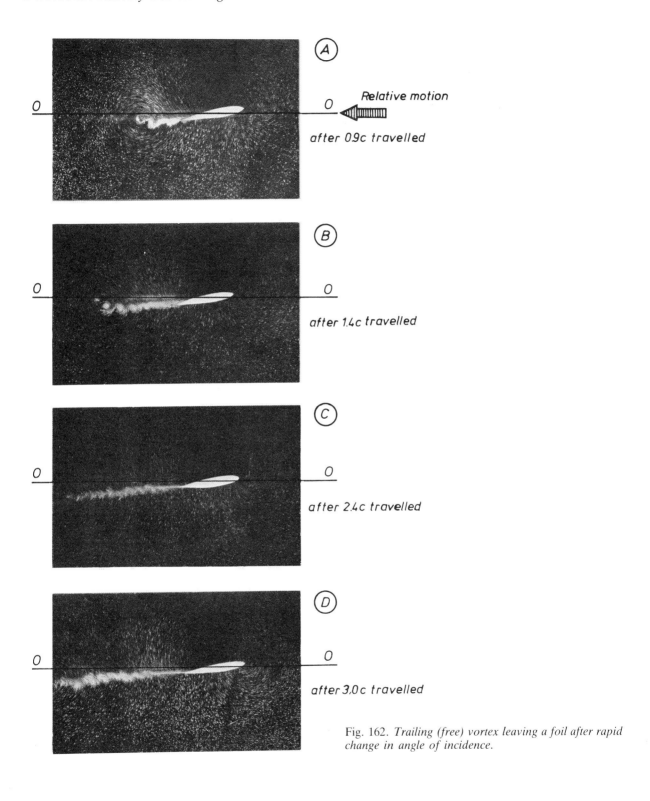

Fig. 162. *Trailing (free) vortex leaving a foil after rapid change in angle of incidence.*

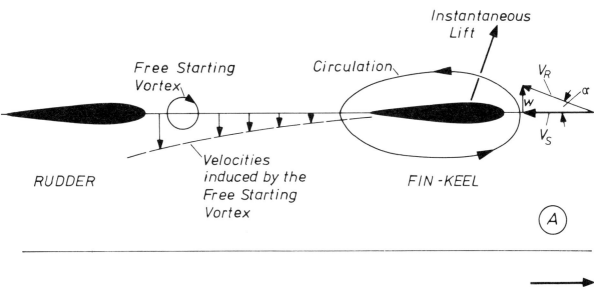

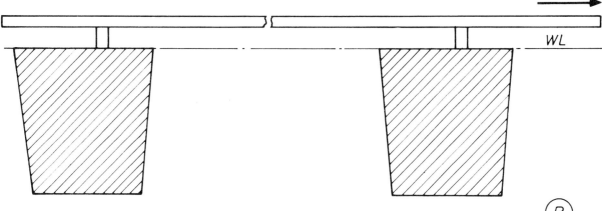

Fig. 163. *The effect of a free, starting vortex developed behind a keel on the flow affecting its separated rudder.*

For further details about these vortices, consult Aero-Hydrodynamics of Sailing *(Ref. 59).*

the incidence angle which might be induced either by rolling or orbital current in waves. The rudder blade entering the wake of the keel may experience a considerable impact when passing over the vortex trail released by the leading foil. Such a configuration of two fins shown in Fig. 163B was tested in a circulating water channel of the Admiralty Experiment Works at Gosport[121] in an attempt to establish quantitatively this interaction effect between foils. When the incidence angle of the leading foil was rapidly increased, there was a considerable degree of response on the second foil, amounting to about 40 per cent of the force recorded on the leading foil, but opposite in direction. The time delay (t_D) before the after-foil registered the yawing force generated on the first foil agrees with an estimate obtained from the flow speed (v) and the separation distance (S) so that:

$$t_D = \frac{S}{v}$$

This can be explained in physical terms by the time it would take the beginning of the trailing vortex to reach the after-foil and become effective as a mechanism of the yawing force transfer.

Thus, the large yawing force generated on a high AR fin-keel has rather strong influence on the rudder force; this works to the disadvantage of smaller boats in which case the destabilising yawing moment is much accentuated by their low inertia. Larger boats are subjected to relatively smaller directional disturbances.

Bearing in mind his unavoidable physiological delay in observation and appreciation of errors in applying corrective rudder action, the helmsman of small craft may not be able to respond quickly enough to high frequency yawing from the desired course.*

In the light of Figs 153 and 155 it can be expected that, within the range of Reynolds numbers encountered in sailing, both the maximum lift coefficient (C_{Lmax}) and the angle of stall of a high aspect ratio fin or separated rudder may decrease by about half, depending on boat speed. Actually, the Re number for the fin varies from almost zero when the boat begins to accelerate, to about 10 million (10^7) in the case of larger craft sailing fast. Of course in steady sailing conditions associated with fine weather, even high A R is unlikely to be near to stalling; but while manoeuvering at low speed or rolling in stronger winds, the stall can easily be reached. In such circumstances, deteriorating effectiveness both of the fin and the rudder may further be aggravated by a large drop in C_{Lmax}, followed by a simultaneous increase in drag. Reynolds number effect is just another factor which contributes to the often occurring erratic, sudden deterioration of steering efficiency suffered by boats equipped with high aspect ratio appendages of *small area*.

F. Coursekeeping

'As a quartermaster in corvettes once said during the war:
"These ships is all right. The only trouble with these ships is
that the bloke what invented 'em didn't invent the blokes that
should go with 'em"'

From an editorial in Ship
Building & Shipping Record,
November 1957

The process of steering a boat along a straight course in rough seas – defined as coursekeeping or dynamic route stability – involves rudder corrections to the

---

* Every human being has a definite time of reaction to any external stimulus, during which he does nothing whatever. This time varies from individual to individual. Besides, due to the delay in nervous signals reaching the brain, we always 'see' the event in its past state.

course, neutralising deviations that are caused by disturbances of one kind or another. Aspect ratio of the keel proper has much to do with the amount of rudder required to maintain the desired compass heading in a seaway.

It will be seen from Fig. 153 that, if the incidence angle of three different keels of aspect ratios: 1/5, 1.0 and 3.0 increases from 0 to 10 degrees (boat speed remaining the same) the respective lift coefficients (C_L) will be 0.14, 0.32 and 0.55. This means that the yaw inflicting side force (which is directly proportional to C_L) generated on the keel of AR = 3.0 will be almost 4 times greater than that on a longer keel of AR = 1/5. In order to compensate for rapid yawing from the desired compass course the helmsman must apply a rudder force appropriate to the keel side force tending to deviate the yacht from the desired path. Whether or not the rudder will be capable of delivering enough steering power to maintain the dynamic route stability in heavy seas depends on its configuration and, above all, on its aspect ratio.

The conclusion one can derive from Fig. 153 is evident: the higher the aspect ratio of the keel the more heavily loaded the rudder in a seaway. Moreover, Fig. 156 reveals that the instantaneous load (side force) on higher AR appendages will be larger because lift is a *time-dependent quality*. Therefore the side force developed in a given time interval on a high AR keel of short chord length, will reach a larger fraction of its final steady state magnitude (Figs 153 and 155) than that developed on a longer keel of low AR. In other words, the longer the keel the more efficient it is as a yaw-damper and, for that reason, the less heavily burdened the rudder (which is thus less likely to fail). To phrase it in yet another way: ability to maintain a given compass heading in a confused sea, with the least possible deviation and with the smallest possible movement of the rudder, is directly related to the length of the keel – the longer the keel the better the course-keeping ability.

Knowledge regarding the significance of the lateral planform of the hull underbody in relation to directional stability – acquired in the past through trial and error alone – was still alive amongst boat designers between the two World Wars. In the book *Naval Architecture of Planing Hulls*[122] we find the following remarks, much pertinent to the matter at hand:

'A distinguishing characteristic of the hull suited to blue-water cruising is the more generous lateral plane, distributed fore and aft throughout the underbody. The important function at sea of the lateral plane is twofold: first, is its tendency toward maintenance of directional stability under difficult conditions. Second, is its essential reaction in connection with steering.* Adequate realization of both functions is of primary importance . . . lateral plane and its distribution determine much of the hull's handling and sea-keeping qualities . . . the center of effective lateral plane area should coincide vertically with the boat's center of gravity and also that the whole area *should have maximum longitudinal distribution*.

'However if a theoretical lateral plane could be entirely localized in a single, concentrated area of fin directly below the center of gravity, steering, at least in smooth water, might be excellent. But because of the inadequate longitudinal spread of the effective lateral plane, the *hull would be practically helpless in*

---

* A large lateral skeg area in front of the rudder blade helps to maintain directional stability (course keeping ability). It works as an *averaging device* which makes the boat somewhat immune against rapid changes in her course and inflicted by the orbital motion in waves which causes periodic changes in the incidence angle at which keel and rudder operate.

Fig. 164. Trial, *Designed in 1946 by van de Stadt; LOA = 29 ft (8.9 m), Beam = 6.5 ft (2.0 m) and Draft = 4.6 ft (1.4 m). By virtue of its length, area and low aspect ratio, such a keel acts effectively in heavy weather as a yaw- and roll-damping device; this obviously makes steering easier. A high AR spade rudder may occasionally fail in rough seas (see also Fig. 139). Ease of steering, as well as an inherent propensity of the hull to run straight with rudder amidships – described in technical parlance as the* dynamic stability on course – *have long been valued by cruising people.*

heavy weather'. (The italics are mine.)

These precepts have usually been respected and incorporated in van de Stadt's boats such as *Zeevalk, Stormvogel* and *Trial* shown in Figs 139 and 164. Their relatively long keels of low AR certainly represent a design feature which secures better handling and coursekeeping qualities in rough water than comparable characteristics of more fashionable IOR boats shown in Fig. 84 which are notorious for their broaching tendencies.

It appears that most contemporary yacht designers defy the time-honoured precepts relevant to the influence of lateral planform of the hull underbody on coursekeeping and steering, and quoted above.[122] 'The ability to track,' said Bob Perry in an article in *Sail* magazine,[123] *'has little, if anything, to do with a full length keel.' (My italics.)* While talking to designer Ray Richards, Perry brought up the subject of directional stability. Richard's response was 'Have you ever seen an arrow with full-length feathers?' Such a creed is at variance with the accepted view prevailing half a century ago, aptly expressed by Commander E.G. Martin in his book *Deep Water Cruising*: 'All practical yachtsmen know that special advantages gained by designing a yacht with a straight keel and a good grip of water at the bow, are steadiness upon the helm under all conditions . . . the long-keeled ship with a good forefoot has an immense advantage over the other'. This view cannot be regarded as an Old Wives' Tale. There are good, scientifically verified reasons in this book which justify Commander Martin's opinion.

And one more point – yacht designers can learn nothing from either the dart or arrow analogy. The mechanics of yacht motion in waves are different altogether. It is the difference between steady and unsteady flow, and the peculiar effect of a confused air-water interface on yacht behaviour that must be understood. Analogies are notorious traps for the unwary. After all, appearances notwithstanding, the whale is not a fish!

From towing tank experiments on models in large waves, the following observations were made [98,101]: The light fin-keel form (model to the right in Fig. 165A) was compared with the traditional long keel hull (model to the left in Fig. 165A), and marked differences in behaviour were observed. 'The light fin-keel yacht appeared to be considerably more difficult to handle, particularly when running before the waves, when the *rudder seemed to have little influence*

Fig. 165. *Models tested in large breaking waves. In an attempt to evaluate the handling characteristics and to obtain some idea of the capsize vulnerability of different hull types, a number of powered models were fitted out with radio control. This was to enable them to be steered in the test tank, in breaking waves of scale heights from 13 to 18 ft.*

on the ultimate directional control of the model'. (The italics are mine.) 'More alarmingly, on many occasions the model remained floating upside-down and would not return to the upright position even when struck by further large waves (Fig. 165B). It appeared that it would require another breaking wave to right the yacht from this condition'.

On a number of occasions when a perfectly straight course across the waves was held by the model, the bow buried itself in the trough and the stern rose up over it. This led to a violent 'pitch pole' type of capsize that would clearly be catastrophic at full scale. *'This phenomenon was rarely observed with the traditional yacht. The traditional hull form seemed to be more easily controlled running before the waves and held its course, surfing ahead of the wave with no tendency to broach'*. (Yet again, the italics are mine.)

'When broadside to a breaking wave the traditional yacht was usually knocked down to near horizontal but returned quickly to the upright position'.[98]

When the models approached the crest of the wave from directly head on, it was possible to pass straight through the crest (Fig. 166), the model becoming almost airborne in the process. If, however, this was not executed perfectly and the hull was struck obliquely by the wave, then the model was knocked into a threatening beam-on attitude. On some occasions the model 'preferred' to surf backwards rather than pass through the crest. This demonstrated vividly the danger of the head-on approach with its potential for rudder damage.*

* This is applicable to any model shown in Fig. 165A, but the light displacement, wide, flat-bottomed hulls with fin-keels were more vulnerable to becoming airborne.

Fig. 166. '. . . *the perilous seas broke over the bows*
. . . like showers of silver chips, the foam flakes flew
over the bulwarks . . . day after day tore on through all
the swift madness and gladness of the demoniac waves.'
from Moby Dick *by Herman Melville*

Rudder efficiency

No waterborne craft, big or small, is immune from the danger of broaching. However, some boats of the same size and sailed by equally competent crews are less controllable than others, often because the principal danger to a boat running in following or overtaking seas is loss of rudder power which, as we have seen, largely depends on the size and AR of the keel. Ideally, rudder power should be enough to maintain a desired course under the most extreme conditions. However, as seen in Figs 164 and 167 the fashionable rudder of today's racers hung right at the stern – which is supposed to provide good steering control – becomes ineffective in waves. As the crest at the stern breaks in a high sweeping curve, the rudder is lifted up so high that a large part of it is actually in the air. The part remaining in the water is now in a region of high orbital current moving in the same direction as the boat, and the relative flow

Fig. 167. *A rudder should have its upper end well below the surface, or else have the upper end guarded by the hull from air leakage into the reduced pressure area. It appears that a rudder whose upper aft corner lies close to the edge of an immersed transom is particularly vulnerable in this respect. Loss of rudder power in a following sea can be caused by*
(1)   Part or all of the rudder may be lifted out of the water.
(2)   The rudder is working in a region where the resulting flow velocity is much reduced due to the effect of orbital flow.
(3)   A rudder operating close to the surface is prone to ventilation.

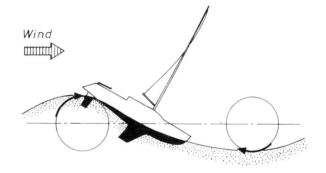

velocity (on which rudder power primarily depends) may become only a fraction of the boat speed. Under these conditions a rudder which is large enough for steering in calm water can become completely ineffective. Moreover, its effect can be further reduced by ventilation; the entrainment of aerated water. This may be particularly acute on a plain, high aspect-ratio spade rudder, which tends to develop a sharp suction peak at the leading edge, allowing air to flow down the suction side of the rudder blade. Steering control may then be almost completely lost.

Quite apart from wave effect, a modern beamy offshore racer, favoured under the current rating rule, may lose her steering power as a result of head-down trim; Fig. 39 illustrates the point. When the lee bow is pressed down by the sails, the weather quarter together with rudder can be raised entirely out of the water. In such a situation, even the best helmsman finds himself powerless to exercise control. On large breaking waves the effect is much worse and usually does incur acute danger. When the stern is lifted by an overtaking wave, the boat can easily be pivoted around her fin keel which is well forward, so that she goes into a rapid broach and is rolled over by the sea.*

Attention should perhaps be drawn to the fact that in the old type of cruising boats (Figs 10, 15 and 16A–D) the rudder, fitted to the after edge of a keep keel, was immune from ventilation. It could not easily be lifted out of the water and, being deeply immersed, was not so much affected by orbital currents in waves. For these reasons, that type of rudder was more reliable in rough seas and the probability of broaching was much lower than with contemporary boats, as corroborated by the towing tank tests to which reference has already been made.

One thing is certain, if a boat manifests broaching tendencies, it means that the steering power available in given weather conditions is not sufficiently large to compensate the yawing moment. This might happen when, for some reason, either the efficiency of the rudder is reduced or a disturbing yawing moment increases beyond control, or both. The problem is to recognise the reasons and conditions in which the directional instability in a yacht motion is most likely to occur to such an extent that the boat becomes unmanageable.

Of course, as already mentioned when discussing Fig. 153, a higher AR rudder is more liable to stall and, therefore, be more likely to fail than one with a lower AR. The smaller the area and the higher the aspect ratio of the rudder the more acute is the steering problem. Thus, one should expect that the sort of high AR rudder shown in Fig. 84 is unlikely to fulfil its duties in heavy weather.

For the sake of safety a skeg or dorsal fin extension in front of the rudder (Fig. 168A) appears to be justifiable, although in order to improve directional stability of the boat radically, one should reduce the AR of the keel in the first place. The effect of a skeg on rudder power, shown in Fig. 168B, demonstrates that such an anti-stall configuration makes the rudder much more reliable; it must be said, however, that it does not improve its effectiveness at small angles of incidence. Apart from improved hydrodynamic reliability, it is undoubtedly much safer to have the rudder attached to a skeg both for greater strength and protection.

---

* If the bow is depressed and the stern lifted up the centre of lateral resistance of the hull moves rapidly forward. This causes a stong weather helm tendency which increases with heel.

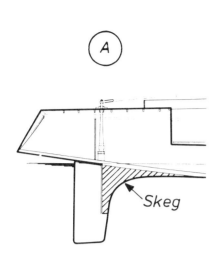

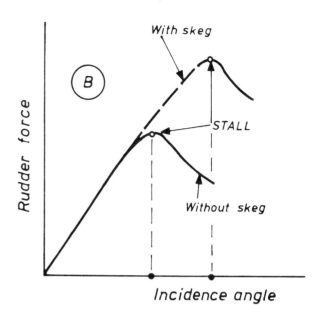

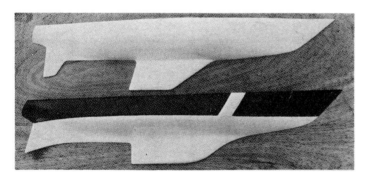

Fig. 168. *Force developed on the rudder against incidence of the rudder blade with and without skeg. The Photograph shows half-models of* Condor *(upper) and* Kriter II *(lower), with skegs. It will be seen in graph B that, with a skeg-attached rudder, the stall is delayed thus also delaying sudden separation of the flow and loss of rudder power.*

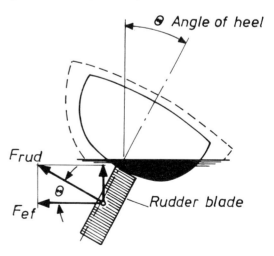

Fig. 169. *When the boat heels. the effective rudder force (F_{ef}) decreases proportionately to the cosine angle of heel (θ), i.e. $F_{ef} = F_{rud} \times \cos \theta$; so also does steering efficiency. Further limitations on the effective rudder force and directional control of the boat may be imposed when the rudder stalls or ventilation takes place.*

There is yet another reason for steering deficiency of the rudder in unfavourable conditions; Fig. 169, similarly to Fig. 105C, illustrates the point. A rolling boat demands more rudder power than one which is upright and stable; clearly, the destabilising yawing moment $F_T \times a$ (sketch B) in Fig. 105, when the boat heels to starboard, is greater than that when the boat is upright (sketch A). However, when the yacht heels, the effective rudder force (F_{ef} in Fig. 169) decreases proportionally to the cosine angle of heel, so also does steering efficiency. And when the heeling angle approaches 90 degrees steering power vanishes, even if the rudder remains fully immersed in the water.

*'No man will be a sailor who has contrivance
enough to get himself into a jail; for being in a
ship is being in a jail, with the chance of being
drowned. . . . A man in a jail has more room,
better food, and commonly better company'*

Samuel Johnson (1709–1784)

16 Survival Tactics

To consider even the basic physical aspects of survival tactics is beyond the scope of this book. However, there is one controversial issue which, to my mind, should not be left untouched. That is the problem of controllability and transverse stability when the skipper decides to run before a gale as a survival tactic. There seems to be some misconception about this technique, even amongst the best experts in heavy weather sailing, and this explains why one can quote controversial and contradictory advice from various books written on this subject.[124]

Referring again to Fig. 90 it will be seen that the influence of the surface current on the directional stability of a sailing craft will depend on:

(1)   course sailed relative to the wave crest
(2)   ratio of hull length to the wave length
(3)   position of the boat in relation to the crest
(4)   magnitude of the orbital current (Fig. 170)

The destabilising yawing moment on a boat running obliquely to the waves will be at its worst when the wave length is approximately twice the hull length, so that when the forepart reaches the trough the afterpart of the hull is on the crest. In this position, rudder efficiency is at its lowest because the orbital current at the rudder depth can considerably reduce the local flow velocity on which rudder effectiveness depends. Thus, for example, if that velocity is reduced by 40%, the force generated by the rudder will decrease by two thirds. So only one third of the normal steering power will be available. By 'normal' we mean one which would be developed by the rudder if the flow velocity in

Fig. 170. *Orbital current (u_{omax}) on the surface of regular waves of different length (L_w) and steepness ratio H_w/L_w. The higher the steepness ratio, the more intense the orbital current (see also Figs 148 and 150). The orbital current U_o marked along the vertical axis refers to its maximum value. U_o varies along the wave profile and its maximum is on the wave crest and in the wave trough but in opposite directions.*

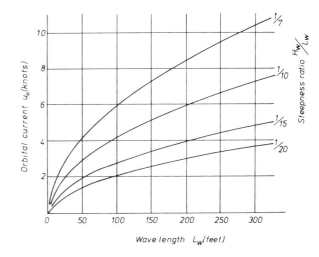

Fig. 171. *Three dimensional seas.*

the rudder depth were equal to the calm water speed of the boat, not affected by the orbital current.

It is believed that broaching or disconcerting behaviour cannot take place if the helmsman keeps a yacht running dead before the waves. This idea cannot, however, be trusted since the sea waves are not regular (Fig. 171), so destabilising yawing moments may always occur particularly when the boat is on the crest of a wave and both transverse and directional stability may greatly be diminished. In that condition the efficiency of the steering system and the helmsman's responses are deciding factors.

As already mentioned elsewhere in this book, the more rapid the deviation from course due to wave action, the more difficult is the helmsman's task to respond quickly enough against broaching. An unavoidable time delay in rudder action may be of three kinds: first, a psychological delay in observation of the yacht's tendency to broach and a decision to react adequately; secondly, a physical delay in making a correction when turning the wheel; and thirdly, hydrodynamic delay because generation of hydrodynamic rudder force, proper for a given angle of rudder incidence, also require time. Rightly or wrongly, all these factors are labelled as bad or good helmsmanship. Certainly, even the best helmsman can fail if the boat is inherently badly balanced.

A. Warps or no warps?

In his book, *Heavy Weather Sailing*, Adlard Coles[125], when referring to the two schools of thought, says: 'the subject of tactics in weathering gales and storms is one about which yachtsman like to argue . . . Moitessier describes yachtsmen believing in running at speed as belonging to the Dumas school. 'I am impressed by it myself,' says Coles, 'because I think the danger when running in gales is not due to speed alone, but to *loss of control, which may be attributable to lack of speed as much as to excessive speed.*' (The italics are mine.) 'However, I shrink from recommending the method of running at speed, because if it proves wrong it could lead to loss of life. For those who are in doubt, especially when caught out in ordinary gales, I recommend the well-tried expedient of streaming warps, following what Moitessier calls the Robinson school of thought' (i.e. reduced speed).

Robinson's tactics of survival would fit the idea of basic seamanship recommended in the *Yachting World Handbook*: 'Trailing warps in a heavy sea has an effect similar to that of a sea anchor, but is more often used as a method of reducing the boat's speed and minimising the risk of broaching-to'.

Let us illustrate both these tactics more dramatically by quoting the heroes who survived gales of supreme violence – 'Warps had been streaming astern and Moitessier found the vessel somewhat sluggish on the helm. He felt great anxiety that he might be pitch-poled by one of the enormous grey-beards, which carried the boat forward at great speed, the rush of water completely engulfing the hull so that only the masts were visible. Of a sudden, he wrote, he appreciated the wisdom of Dumas's technique of running free and taking the following seas at a slight angle. Immediately he cut his warps adrift and the vessel, becoming responsive to her helm, could be handled with safety. Moitessier *makes it clear that he owed the survival of his wife, himself and the yacht to his decision'.* (The italics are mine.) This ties up very closely with the experiences of W. Brown, who ran at speed in *Force Seven* before a hurricane, taking seas on the quarter.

Now, for a comparison, an opposing concept – from Robinson's experience when sailing *Varua* – 'The seas were so huge and concave at this point that the whole upper third seemed to collapse and roar vertically down on us. Our oil had little or no effect now . . .' Robinson unlashed the wheel and ran her off downwind dead before the storm, gathering speed under bare poles to 6 or 7 knots. As he considered this dangerous, he let go five 75 feet lengths of 2 in warps plus 100 fathoms of smaller lines. This reduced her speed to 3 or 4 knots and she steered under perfect control. 'Nevertheless at times she ran down a sea and buried her bowsprit in the trough before rising again . . . If *Varua* had not been trailing drags' says Robinson, 'she might have been run down'.

If one agrees with Adlard Coles that the men who actually survived exceptional storms or hurricanes probably did the right thing, and were the best judges of what could be done in particular conditions and seas, the question arises, why is there a discrepancy in recommending one technique rather than another? Certainly, they must refer to different conditions, but what is the clue? Before we attempt to answer this question, we should perhaps remind ourselves of some fundamental principles applicable to our case:

(a) safety depends upon giving to the seas and not standing up against them or, in other words, boat speed relative to wave train velocity should be at the possible minimum,

(b) it is essential to keep the yacht under directional control in order to avoid broaching-to. This can be done either by maintaining relatively high speed and relying upon the rudder, or by application of an additional stabilising moment by means of warps or a drogue to keep the yacht going straight, whereupon the rudder, as a steering device, becomes more or less of secondary or no importance.

Sometimes, the combined technique of maintaining a boat at speed and at the same time towing a drogue is used on lifeboats in very steep and confused seas. As described by an experienced member of the Dover Lifeboat crew[126] 'the faster you go, the steadier the boat sits in the water. As soon as you slow up to get the drogue in, the stern is all over the place again. The main thing which is keeping the lifeboat going straight is the terrific strain on that drogue'.

B. Strategy of sailing in storm conditions

In order to clarify our problem further, we need to resort to some experiments and statistical data concerning waves. From the series of experiments carried out in conditions simulating regular following seas on models of high speed hull

Fig. 172. *Picture taken from Dover lifeboat. As described by one of the crew members: 'The main thing which is keeping the lifeboat going straight is the terrific strain on that drogue'. The drogue is about three feet in diameter, with a really heavy warp (seen in the picture).*

form, one can deduce a general trend in the broaching tendencies of any sailing craft. The two factors of primary importance are incorporated in Fig. 173, namely the boat-speed wave-velocity ratio (V_s/c) and the wave steepness (H_w/L_w). The worst condition facilitating the tendency to excessive yaw or broaching occurs when the V_s/c ratio is about unity, i.e. where the relative velocity between boat and waves is around zero; but nevertheless persist beyond the condition $V_s/c = 1$. In this case, as we mentioned earlier, the rudder will be liable to lose a considerable amount of its effectiveness and, at the same time the destabilising yawing moment, due to orbital current being at its maximum, is much accentuated by a relatively long time during which the boat is exposed to its action.

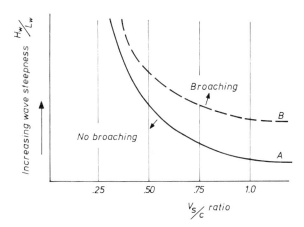

Fig. 173. *Broach or no-broach envelope curves for two types of boat sailing in non-breaking waves. The type marked B is less susceptible to broaching because of her better inherent directional stability, due to the larger more efficient yaw-damping planform of the hull underbody.*

The known liability to broach in conditions when boat speed/wave velocity ratio (V_s/c) = 1.0, is due to the fact that the relative velocity between the hull and waves oscillates around zero; therefore both yaw-damping efficiency and rudder power are greatly reduced.

For boats which are 30–60 feet long, the most dangerous waves would be of 50–100 feet in length respectively, including to some extent, surfing effect which increases the so-called 'displacement' or smooth water speed of the boat. Such relatively short but steep waves may appear:

(a)   at the beginning of a storm,
(b)   when the wind blows against the tide,
(c)   when a yacht running for shelter enters shallow waters and the waves become shorter and shorter, and finally break up.

In these conditions, even when the wave height is relatively small a broaching tendency may become threatening and may increase beyond control in steep waves. When surfing down the forward slope of the wave, due to the gravity force component (Fig. 38A) the boat's speed can increase to such an extent that the sea becomes effectively a head sea; then the forward part of the hull begins to penetrate the back slope of the wave in front. In such circumstances the yacht may bury herself in the rising slope of the next wave with further ultimate consequences of wild broaching or even pitch-poling. In short and steep waves it appears that the only sensible tactic left to the crew willing to sail actively is to stream warps, which stabilise the boat directionally and prevent dangerous surfing. If warps or a drogue produce a large drag and the resulting stabilising moment is also large, the boat can be sluggish on the helm, this means that she is steered automatically. Eventually, by adjusting sail area and the number or length of warps, the crew can find the most desirable balance between these two speed factors for given weather conditions and a particular hull. This tactic of survival, which corresponds to the Robinson school of thought, can be useless if, due to a long lasting gale, the waves become longer and longer. Why? In order to answer this question consider the implications of Fig. 174A which depicts some geometrical properties of storm waves; it is based on statistical observations. On the vertical axis the wave steepness ratio (H_w/L_w) is marked, on the horizontal axis there are numbers

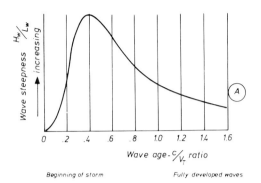

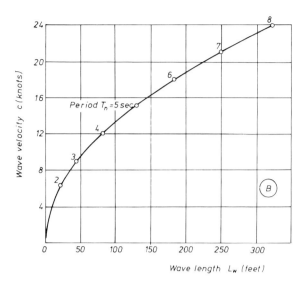

Fig. 174. *(A) Relationship between the wave steepness ratio (H_w/L_w), and wave age measured in terms of wave velocity/wind speed (c/V_T) ratio.*
(B) Relationship between the wave length (L_w), wave velocity (c) and natural wave period (T). Length of Atlantic waves is usually from 160–320 ft (50–100 m), with period from about 5–8 secs.

indicating the 'age of the wave system' in the form of wave velocity/wind velocity ratio (c/V_T). This term, which is perhaps not familiar to all sailing people, requires some explanation.

If strong winds begin to blow, the rate of growth of the wave height is much greater than the subsequent growth of the wave length. The c/V_T ratio is small, since corresponding wave velocity of short waves is relatively low (Fig. 174B). Consequently, the 'young waves' generated by the wind at the beginning of a gale are relatively steep, and their steepness grows until the c/V_T reaches a value of about 0.4; then, gradually, the waves become longer and longer and their steepness decreases (Fig. 174A). When the waves become 'older' their velocity (c) increases following the growth in wave length (L_w).

Looking again at Fig. 173, we can infer that when the waves become longer and faster, and the V_s/c ratio decreases, the tendency to broach is also reduced. Putting it another way, for a given wave length broaching is likely to occur when a certain wave steepness is surpassed. Assuming for example, that the average length of a well-developed wave system is 300 feet, then the wave velocity is about 23 knots. If in that condition a boat sailing under bare poles makes 5 knots, it means that the V_s/c ratio is $5/23 = 0.22$, i.e. well below a critical condition in which the destabilising yawing moment due to surface current might be dominant (Fig. 173). In such circumstances the problem of primary importance is to reduce the relative velocity between the boat and the overtaking seas. It can only be done by sailing faster. The slower the boat is sailed, the higher the probability of being pooped or being dangerously hit by a rapidly following breaking crest. Therefore, logical advice would be to sail fast in such circumstances. The longer the waves, the more justifiable is the tactic of sailing at speed.

Let us illustrate this by quoting once again W. Brown's experience when sailing *Force Seven* in a gale: 'The problem facing us was keeping the boat going fast enough in order to keep out of the way of huge breaking seas by sliding down their sides and keeping them on the quarter'.

Perhaps it sounds strange if we conclude that both techniques, slowing down by streaming warps astern or sailing at speed, can be used as a survival tactic by the same crew in the same storm, the first one at the beginning of a gale, the second one later, when the wave system has sufficiently been developed.

*'From the purely practical view point, it is
evident that however much one may strive after
absolute similarity, its attainment is not always
feasible'.*

H. Rouse
*Fluid Mechanics for
Hydraulic Engineers*

Appendix 1 Rating Rules versus the Similitude Law

The stability of a sailing vessel can be assessed by a ratio known as 'the power to carry sail'. The derivation of this ratio based on Fig. 1.1 is as follows:

A boat sailing to windward at a given apparent wind speed (V_A) will reach an angle of heel (Θ) when the heeling moment:

$$M_H = S_A \times C_H \times q \times h$$

becomes equal to the righting moment:

$$M_R = \Delta \times \text{righting lever}$$
$$= \Delta \times GM \times \sin \Theta$$

where: S_A – sail area in square feet

$\quad\quad\ C_H$ – heeling force coefficient, ranging from 1.2 to 1.8
depending on the type of rig

$\quad\quad\quad q$ – dynamic pressure [1] ($q = 0.00119 \times V_A^2$ lb/sq ft)

$\quad\quad\quad \Delta$ – displacement in pounds

$\quad\quad GM$ – metacentric height in feet

By equating the heeling moment (M_H) to the righting moment (M_R) we find that:

$$\sin \Theta = \frac{S_A \, C_H \, q \, h}{\Delta \times GM}$$

This equation, valid on condition that the angle of heel (Θ) does not exceed 6 degrees, is the base on which the so called Dellenbaugh Angle Method and the

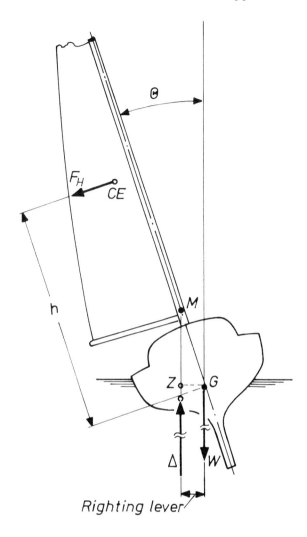

Fig. 1.1. *Equilibrium of moments at an angle of heel*
(θ).
 Heeling moment = righting moment
 $$F_H \times h = \Delta \times GM \times \sin\theta$$
 where F_H = heeling force $= S_A \times C_H \times q$
  h = heeling lever or distance between
   the centre of effort (CE) and the
   axis or rotation (assumed to pass
   through the centre of gravity, G,
   of the boat).

Wind Pressure Coefficient Method were derived [2].*

Consider the effect of stability or 'the power to carry sail' on a sailing yacht's performance in the light of the elementary similitude law [3]. As discussed in Chapter 3 measurement rules for racing have been built around some formulae whereby the potential speed of yachts of widely varying sizes and types, racing under widely varying weather conditions, could hopefully be assessed. There are many reasons why this laudable objective cannot truly be achieved, and the similitude of law (which links the size of boat, her power to carry sail and her speed performance) is one of the reasons – the importance of which is not properly recognised.

Usually, the measurement formula determines the rating of a boat in terms of her *rated* length (L), which subsequently is regarded as the *measure* of the boat's speed potential for handicap purposes. In fact rating rules and relevant handicap systems refer, although not explicitly, to Froude's famous 'Law of

* See references at the end of the Appendix.

Comparison' ennunciated in 1876. In a crude, initial form it states that the resistances of geometrically similar boats are in the ratio of the cubes of their linear dimensions (or displacements), when their speeds are in the ratio of square roots of those dimensions. Taking the water line length of the hull (L) as a representative dimension, it can be written that:

$$\text{Resistance } R \propto L^3$$
$$\text{or } R \propto \Delta$$
$$\text{when} \quad V_s \propto \sqrt{L}$$

where V_s is boat's speed
Δ is displacement
and $\propto$ as before designates 'is proportional to'

This is equivalent to saying that the resistances vary as the cube of the scale, when corresponding speeds vary as the square of the scale.

Disregarding the effect of displacement one might assume that, if the two boats have the same rated length (L) or rating, they should also have equal speed potentials, i.e.:

$$V_s \propto \sqrt{L}$$
$$V_s \propto \sqrt{\text{Rating}}$$

If all competing yachts were sailing downwind in a strong breeze at their so-called maximum *hull-speed*:

$$V_s \simeq 1.4\sqrt{L}$$

where V_s is the boat speed in knots
L is rated length in feet

a reasonably fair time allowance might be applied; if all of them were of the displacement type (no skimming dishes amongst them). In reality, the situation is much more complicated, thus making the rule-makers life difficult indeed.

Due to further advances made by Froude and others, it became evident that the friction resistance does not obey the 'Law of Comparison'; however, correction could be allowed for. When the frictional part of the resistance is deducted from the total resistance, the remaining part termed 'residual resistance', follows the Law of Comparison with reasonable accuracy.

Expressing Froude's idea in the simplest terms applicable to a boat sailing upright downwind, one might say that the total resistance (R) is made up of skin friction resistance (R_f), which is roughly proportional to the wetted surface of the hull and the residual resistance (R_r), which in turn is proportional to the displacement [1]. Thus:

$$R = R_f + R_r$$

The residual resistance (R_r) consists of two components – wave-making and form or eddy-making drag. The proportional contribution of basic components R_f and R_r towards the total resistance (R) depends, of course, on boat speed. This is shown in Fig. 1.2, and the resistance curve relates to the cruiser/racer type of boat sailing in an upright position.

In light weather conditions, when the yacht is sailing with relative speed in the order of $V_s = 0.8\sqrt{L}$, friction is dominating, rising to about 70% of the total resistance; the wave making resistance contribution is about 30%. In stronger winds, when the boat is sailing at the relative speed $V_s = 1.1\sqrt{L}$,

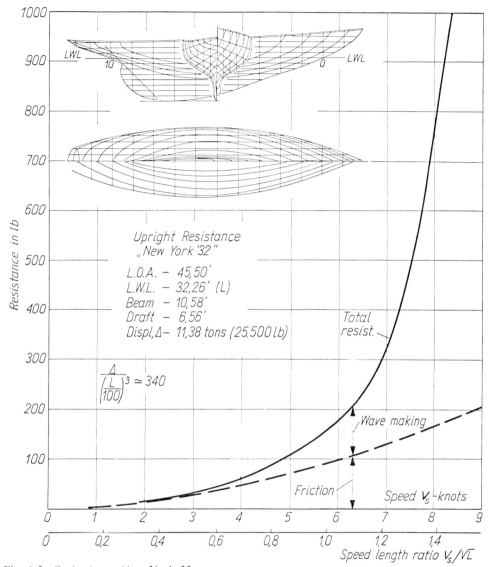

Fig. 1.2. *Cruiser/racer* New York 32

wavemaking drag contribution increases to 50% or even more. The average speeds of boats participating in the Bermuda Races are in the order of 0.8 to 1.1 $\sqrt{L}$.

Since, for steady sailing speed, hydrodynamic resistance must be balanced by aerodynamic driving force (which in any given wind speed is proportional to the sail area) two ratios immediately become of primary importance, namely: Sail Area/Wetted Surface and Sail Area/Displacement. The first ratio (S_A/A) governs yacht performance in light wind conditions; the second (S_A/Δ) prevails most of the time. As sail area represents the driving power, both ratios can be regarded as obvious indices of the sail power/resistance ratio.

It was recognised by Davidson some years ago [4] that the rock upon which rating and handicap systems have continually foundered is a disregard of the fact that changes in S_A/Δ (as yachts become bigger) cause corresponding changes of average relative speed $V_s/\sqrt{L}$.

Since rating rules and associated handicap systems deal with boats which are different in size, they cannot ignore serious complications implicitly imposed by what is called, in applied hydrodynamics, the 'Similitude Law'. Obvious conflict between simplifying assumptions on which rating rules are based and consequences of the similitude law, probably constitute the kernel of the whole problem of equitable handicap racing.

If, for example, a yacht has been geometrically expanded twofold so that: L (big boat) = 2 L (small boat), i.e. the scale ratio (SR) = 2, then the sail area will increase in proportion $(SR)^2$ i.e. fourfold, as also will the wetted area of the hull. The ratio S_A/A is therefore independent of size. However, displacement will increase in proportion $(SR)^3$, i.e. 8 times. If the relative speed of the big boat is to be maintained the same as that of the smaller boat, i.e.:

$$\frac{V_s \text{ (big boat)}}{\sqrt{L} \text{ (big boat)}} = \frac{V_s \text{ (small boat)}}{\sqrt{L} \text{ (small boat)}}$$

then V_s (big boat) = V_s (small boat) $\times \sqrt{SR}$ = 1.41 V_s (small boat).

The wave making resistance of the big boat will increase in the same ratio as her displacement, that is 8 times. But her sail area will increase 4 times only; this means that the S_A/Δ ratio will be drastically reduced by 2. In other words, the S_A/Δ ratio which governs yacht performance most of the time, varies inversely with size (or scale), on account of the square-cube relationship involved in the process of geometrical scaling.

Assuming that both yachts are sailing in the same wind conditions, stability of the larger boat, in terms of righting moment, will increase in proportion to the scale factor (SR) × (increase in displacement), which is proportional to $(SR)^3$, i.e. $2 \times (2)^3 = 16$ times. By the stability standard of the smaller boat, the big brother will be very much stiffer. However, by the standard of the smaller sister, the boat which is bigger on a simple geometric principle, will suffer deficit of sail power which becomes more marked as the size of the boat becomes greater.

This conclusion was elegantly proved by Barnaby [5]; the following is a short résumé of his findings. A typical tea-clipper of 200 ft in length and with other dimensions, such as sail area, etc., as shown in Table 1, was taken as the basic parent form for the family of sailing *'geosims'* plotted in Fig. 1.3. This term, which stands for *geometrically similar*, is used here to describe the family of resistance curves of gradually scaled down boats. Thus, if the resistance curve for the parent size was established by experiments in the towing tank, the resistance curve for any other size can be determined by computation.

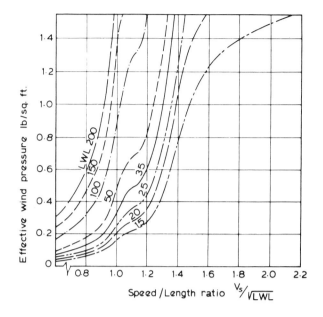

Fig. 1.3. *Family of resistance curves for a number of geometrically similar boats of different length.*

Table 1

Length on LWL in feet	—	200.0
Breadth in feet	—	34.6
Draught in feet	—	20.0
Displacement in tons	—	2000.0
Sail area in sq. ft	—	20000.0
$S_A/\Delta^{\frac{2}{3}}$ ratio	—	126.0
$\Delta/\left(\dfrac{L}{100}\right)^3$ ratio	—	250.0

In this particular case, the resistance curves of boats with lengths of 200, 150, 100, 50, 35, 25, 20, and 15 feet were calculated on the assumption that the boats were sailing in reaching conditions, therefore no correction for heeling or induced drag due to leeway was necessary. It was further assumed that their sail power was developed in the same wind.

On the horizontal axis in Fig. 1.3 there are marked values of the speed/length ratio, and on the vertical axis there is given the mean effective wind pressure in lb/sq ft which, when multiplied by the appropriate sail area, will just balance the resistance of a given hull. The results shown in Fig. 1.3 are only comparative and indicative of trends. Table 2 shows what can be termed the *natural maximum sailing speed* in reaching conditions, when the effective wind pressure is 1.4 lb/ft^2 (equivalent to wind force 5 on the Beaufort scale – a fresh breeze).

Table 2 (based on Fig. 1.3)

LWL in feet	Speed/Length ratio	Speed (V_s) in knots
200	0.97	13.7
150	1.07	13.1
100	1.16	11.6
50	1.30	9.2
35	1.36	8.0
25	1.43	7.1
20	1.50	6.7
15	1.80	7.0
10	planing	

It will be noted that as the size of boat increases, and she becomes undercanvassed by comparison to smaller boats, the maximum speed/length ratio for a given wind decreases; consequently the maximum speed V_s increases less than that one might expect from the length of the hull. It may also be seen that as the size decreases, and boats become overcanvassed in relation to larger ones, their relative speeds $V_s/\sqrt{L}$ increase at a faster rate. This trend becomes quite conspicuous in the case of the smallest boat of 10 ft LWL. Wind pressure then becomes sufficient for planing speeds, provided the geosim sail area can be carried, as in the case of overcanvassed boats of the dinghy type.

It can also be inferred from Table 2 that as the size of boat increases, the main problem every designer confronts is to provide enough sail area. The opposite is true when the size decreases – it is stability that is then the major difficulty.

With large sailing boats, every effort has to be made to carry as much sail area as possible and, if $V_s/\sqrt{L}$ were required to be constant as length varied, the sail area would have to vary as LWL^3. Thus a tremendous spread of canvas would have to be carried which would soon lead to structural and handling problems of the first magnitude.

Davidson once suggested [4] that this was another form of what is generally called the square-cube law. Only the invention of the steam engine saved the large sailing ship designers from battering their heads against the implications of this law.

This is an interesting point, because it seems to be true that wooden sailing ships could not have grown much larger than the Clipper ships of 1850. In this particular case, the square-cube law had a predominant effect in limiting the maximum size of the structure. In principle, there is no way of avoiding the implications of this law. Assuming geometrically similar hulls, with geometrically similar structural parts moving in geometrically similar seas, the weight of the structural parts of the hull and rig which must withstand the load stresses is bound to increase at a higher rate than the driving force offered by sails.

Modern yacht designers face the same implications of the square-cube law when considering a project for a large craft. Attempting to reduce displacement length ratio drastically in order to compensate for the lack of sail power, they are bound to sacrifice strength for lightness. If this is carried to extremes, a fast boat may be produced so dangerously light that after winning a race it may disintegrate. Such a tendency is already observed in some classes. Fortunately, perhaps, designers of big boats built to the existing rating rule may not need to worry about how to spread enormous sails to drive the large hull fast enough. The optimum sail area is not likely to be used, simply because the rule taxes sail area heavily. To phrase it in a different way, if the boat carries an adequate sail area for her size, the rating handicap increases out of proportion to the advantage which it confers as regard speed.

The rating rule (IOR) as it operates at the moment, like the RORC or CCA rules before, definitely encourages development of relatively small racers, overcanvassed by large boat standards, and frequently suffering deficiency of stability. At the same time, large boats deficient in sail power can hardly compete on equal terms with small rivals, except in heavier winds.

As the size of a boat increases and there is progressively less and less canvas in proportion to displacement, good engineering judgement prompts that there should be progressively less and less fullness in hull form in relation to the length. Beam, as a factor of stability, is partly losing its significance, since bigger boats have large reserve of inherent stability which is rarely used to advantage. Reduced hull fullness (which gives big boats a slim appearance) together with lower displacement/length ratio have a desirable effect on boat speed potential by virtue of decreasing the resistance. In fact, bigger and slimmer boats have a lower resistance per ton of displacement than smaller, fuller but overcanvassed rivals. This slimming treatment is not, however, a strong enough remedy to cure satisfactorily the consequences of sail power deficiency.

Comparative data on sailing performance of boats of different size, which are indicative of the effect of size on performance, can be found in the publication of the Stevens Institute, USA. [6] Figure 1.4 presents such a scatter graph of the variation of estimated performance of boats of different waterline lengths in close hauled conditions at three different wind speeds. In this case, performance is expressed in terms of speed made good to windward/length ratio ($V_{mg}/\sqrt{L}$). The general trend is fairly clear: in light winds, i.e. slow races, where sail area is the dominant speed factor, relatively small and well canvassed boats are superior performers. This is shown by the curve at the bottom of the graph and relevant to true wind velocity $V_T = 7.5$ knots.

In moderate weather conditions, when $V_T = 13$ knots, the differences in performance of small and large craft are less conspicuous, but still larger boats are handicapped uncomfortably. The only conditions in which 'big brothers' can compete effectively are heavy weather conditions when stability but not sail area is the primary factor affecting speed-made good. This is shown by the upper curve in the graph and relevant to wind speed $V_T = 19.5$ knots.

One may argue that the large yacht can win in a slow race. It is not uncommon in light weather (drifting conditions) to see large yachts sailing well, while their little sisters lie hopelessly becalmed. It happens simply because,

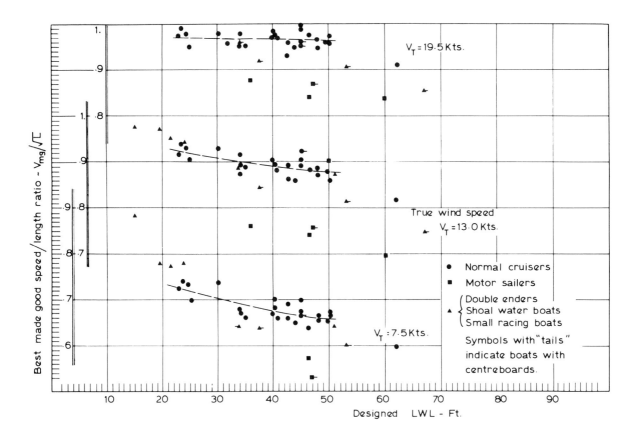

Fig. 1.4. *Best speed made good to windward/length ratio* $(V_{mg}/\sqrt{L})$ *for a variety of boats sailing in the same true wind conditions* (V_T), *and recorded in three wind régimes: light, medium and strong.*

occasionally, the tall rigs can reach the upper strata of the air and catch the wind aloft, which may not exist nearer the sea surface. Such rather exceptional circumstances, when relatively small deficiency in sail power (consider S_A/A effect) is offset by extraordinary wind velocity gradient, should not be used as a justifiable argument.

The fact remains that the sail power deficit, progressively increasing with the size of the yacht and its effect on relative speeds, invalidates the claims of the rule makers that the rating number, as calculated from, say, the IOR formula, reflects realistically the speed potential of a boat, namely that $V_s \propto \sqrt{\text{Rating}}$. Such a claim is no more than wishful thinking.

It has been argued that, if it were possible, any form of perfect rating rule would in the end be self-defeating. For if it measures all the speed parameters of the boat correctly it would not matter what we designed, the speed potential would be correctly measured and the only difference in the race would be the efforts of the crew. Just as it is in one-design classes. This is the built-in inconsistency of all forms of measurement rule and the inevitable limitations of any system will encourage one type of design or feature over another [7].

This inconsistency was revealed in two remarks recorded some 70 years ago by Francis Herreshoff which are still relevant today: 'The desire of some people to win a race not by virtue of their better sailing skill but by virtue of better boat design which, it is assumed, is equal in performance to that of other competitors.' And another one: 'One design classes may be all right for young democrats who are labouring under some inferiority complex or who are scared that someone with better mental equipment will take advantage of them, but as a matter of fact their only hope of winning is to race in an open class where, if they pick the right designer, they will have an advantage that will make up for their other deficiencies.'

References

[1] Marchaj, C.A. – *Sailing Theory and Practice* – Granada, Second Edit. 1981.

[2] Kinney, F.S. – *'Skenes' Elements of Yacht Design* – Dodd Mead Co, NY, 1962.

[3] Marchaj, C.A. – *A short Review of some Rating and Handicap Problems, The 1971 Lands' End Equipment Guide* also *Seahorse* September 1972.

[4] Davidson, K.S.M. – *Ships* – 9 Intern. Congress of Appl.Mechan. Brussels 1956.

[5] Barnaby, K.C. – *The Combination of Sail with an Alternative Source of Power*, RINA, 1961.

[6] Hamlin, C. – *Sailing Yacht Calculation Procedure*, Techn. Memor. No. 108, 1955.

[7] Hannay, I. (private communication).

Appendix 2 Theoretical and experimental background of rolling stability and instability

1 Rolling stability

A yacht's motion in waves made up of many components and coupling effects is such an exceedingly complex problem that some simplifications are necessary. Let us treat the rolling component of motion separately, assuming that the circumstances in which its maximum effect occurs are not, in principle, affected by the simultaneous existence of other components of motion such as yawing or heaving. The question to be considered is: why the boat sailing close-hauled is stable in the rolling plane?

The lack of rolling motion when going to windward has been shown by the author elsewhere to be due to simultaneously occurring heavy aerodynamic and hydrodynamic positive damping from sails and keel. [1] What follows is a résumé of the underlying theory of damping in these circumstances. This introduction will demonstrate the principle of the foil action in unsteady motion and its damping effectiveness applicable to any lift-producing device, including keel and rudder.

Classic fluid dynamics have mainly been used in the study of forces developed on foils in steady state motion; unsteady effects have often been ignored, and the tacit assumption is that lift instantaneously follows any change in incidence angle. Thus, for example, it is customary to present the lift force developed on a fully immersed foil at given speed (be it sail, spade rudder or keel) in the familiar manner shown in Fig. 2.1. When the incidence angle is 0 degrees, no lift is generated simply because the flow on both sides of the symmetrical foil is symmetrical. Then, between incidence 0 degrees and the stall angle, the graph is practically a straight line, which mens that, as the angle

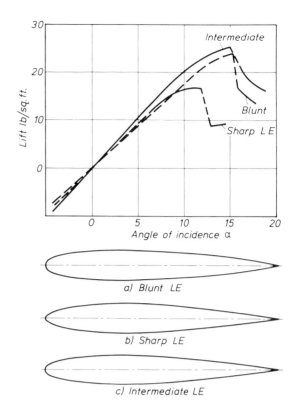

Fig. 2.1. *Lift curves of three aerofoil sections with different leading edge shapes (LE), but with the same thickness/chord ratio (12%). The section with a sharp LE is susceptible to early stall (see also Fig. 155).*

of incidence increases steadily there is a proportional and steady increase in lift. This implies that the strength of circulation Γ which is proportional to the flow velocity V_0, angle of incidence α and chord of the foil c, i.e.:

$$\Gamma = f\ (V_0 \alpha c) \qquad (2.1)$$

instantaneously assumes its proper value for every change in flow velocity and incidence angle. The relationship between the lift L per unit span and circulation is given by an equation which allows the calculation of lift if the strength of circulation Γ is known:

$$L = f\ (\varrho V_0 \Gamma) \qquad (2.2)$$

where ϱ is the fluid density
ϱ air = 0.00238 lb sec^2/ft^4
ϱ water (salt) = 1.99 lb sec^2/ft^4

Using the information provided by wind tunnel tests on the una-rig shown in Fig. 2.2, let us examine its stability in roll assuming that the so-called quasi-static approach is plausible as a first approximation; that is lift and drag assume instantaneously the magnitude prescribed by the instantaneous geometric angle of incidence. [2]

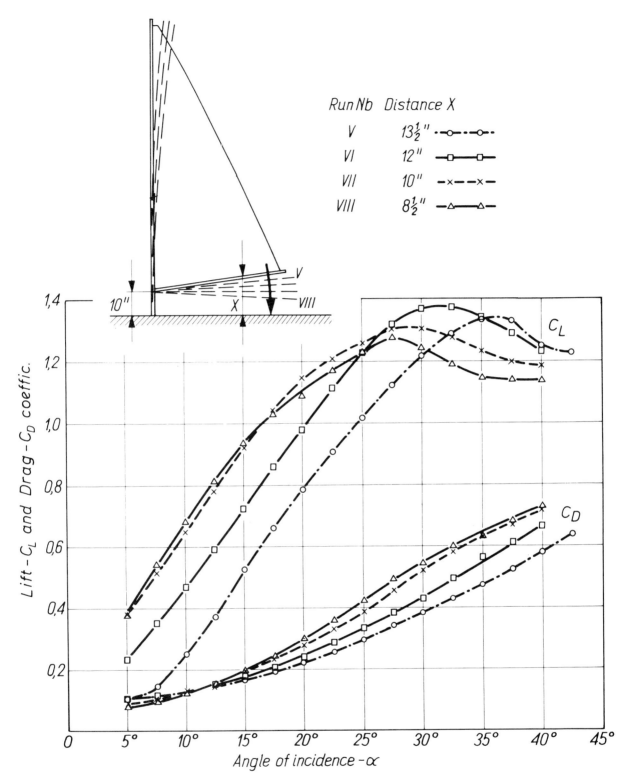

Fig. 2.2. *Lift and drag coefficients of a 2/5 scale model with $S_A = 18.1$ sq ft (1.7 m²), and of AR = 3:1 (AR is taken as luff²/S_A).*

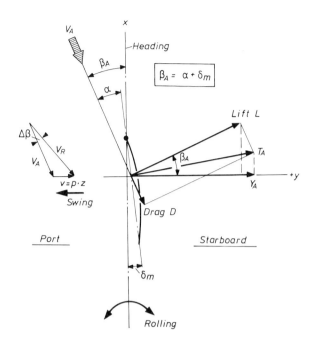

Fig. 2.3. *Diagram of forces and wind velocities when sailing close hauled.*

Figure 2.3 which refers to a narrow, horizontal strip of sail cut at a certain distance z from the axis of roll, depicts force and wind vectors as well as the geometric relations between them. When, due to a sudden gust or wave action, the sail swings to port (acquiring angular velocity p) the apparent wind (V_A) is modified by the component $v = p \times z$ induced by the swing. The instantaneous incidence angle (α) of the sail strip will be affected by the variation in direction of the resultant wind (V_R) which is the sum of V_A and v. If v is small relative to V_A, the aerodynamic force component (Y_A), which contributes to rolling, can be expressed at any instant as:

$$Y_A = L \cos (\beta_A \pm \Delta\beta) + D \sin (\beta_A \pm \Delta\beta)$$
$$Y_A = L \cos \beta'_A + D \sin \beta'_A \qquad (2.3)$$
$$\text{where } \beta'_A = \beta_A \pm \Delta\beta$$

Differentiation of Eq. 2.3 with respect to β_A will give the rate of change of Y_A due to rolling:

$$\frac{\delta Y_A}{\delta \beta_A} = \frac{\delta L}{\delta \beta_A} \cos \beta_A - L \sin \beta_A + \frac{\delta D}{\delta \beta_A} + D \cos \beta_A$$

$$= \cos \beta_A \left(\frac{\delta L}{\delta \beta_A} + D \right) - \sin \beta_A \left(L - \frac{\delta D}{\delta \beta_A} \right) \qquad (2.4)$$

Since the variation in L and D with β_A are equivalent to variation due to change in α (Fig. 2.3), the Eq. 2.4 can be rewritten in the form:

$$\frac{\delta CY_A}{\delta \alpha} = \cos \beta_A \left(\frac{\delta C_L}{\delta \alpha} + C_D \right) - \sin \beta_A \left(C_L - \frac{\delta C_D}{\delta \alpha} \right) \qquad (2.5)$$

This is more convenient to analyse, having already available the characteristics of the rig expressed in the standard form of C_L and C_D versus as shown in Fig. 2.2

Assume that for typical close-hauled sailing $\beta_A = 30°$ and $\alpha = 15°$. The slope of all C_L curves, i.e. the value of $\frac{\delta C_L}{\delta \alpha}$, is more or less constant within the practical limits of α from 5° to 20° and equals 2.86 (α expressed in radians). The average value of $\frac{\delta C_D}{\delta \alpha}$ for the drag curve VIII is 0.98. Substituting all remaining relevant numerical data from Fig. 2.2 to Eq. 2.5, we obtain:

$$\frac{\delta CY_A}{\delta \alpha} = 0.866 \ (2.86 + 0.2) - 0.5 \ (0.95 - 0.98)$$

The first term in the equation is positive and much greater than the second one, which for other values of α might be negative but negligible in comparison with the first one. Thus the first term in Eq. 2.5, i.e. $\cos \beta_A \left(\frac{\delta C_L}{\delta \alpha} + C_D \right)$ contributes most to the rolling response of the rig.

As long as $\frac{\delta C_L}{\delta \alpha}$ is positive, that is as long as the C_L coefficient at which the sail actually operates is related to the *rising slope* of the C_L versus α curve, the $\frac{\delta CY_A}{\delta \alpha}$ will be positive and directed against the rolling motion (Fig. 2.3). Thus the rig will do the work against the rolling motion, and this corresponds to positive damping. Therefore, in close-hauled conditions one should normally expect a stabilising or damping contribution from the aerodynamic forces whenever rolling is inflicted externally – by wave action or sudden gusts.

Wind tunnel experiments corroborated the above theoretical conclusions derived from Eq. 2.5, and Fig. 64 shown in Chapter 7 C – illustrates the test results. Equation 2.5 may also be applied to the keel regarded as a hydrofoil, and the same conclusion can be reached. Thus, a boat sailing to windward can be looked upon as a dynamic system with two in-built damping devices, one aerodynamic and the other hydrodynamic, working in unison. This explains why sailing boats are so stiff on the windward leg.

2. Rolling instability

From Eq. 2.5 (first term) one can infer that when $\dfrac{\delta C_L}{\delta \alpha}$ becomes negative and numerically greater than C_D, then $\dfrac{\delta CY_A}{\delta \alpha}$ will be negative, and the aerodynamic forces will be directed towards the rolling motion, so the rig will work as a *negative damper*. Consequently, one should expect that the rolling amplitude will increase with time.

Using the information provided by wind tunnel tests as presented in Fig. 2.4, let us examine, first theoretically, the condition in which rolling instability may occur. Figure 2.5A shows a una-rigged boat running downwind. The course sailed relative to apparent wind β is 180 degrees and the angle of sail incidence is about 90 degrees. The total aerodynamic force generated by the sail acts very

Fig. 2.4. *Lift and drag forces on the rig shown in Fig. 2.2, measured within the range of incidence angles (α) 15°-170°. There is also a plotted curve of $-\dfrac{dL}{d\alpha}$. In order to facilitate an immediate comparison of the magnitude of $-\dfrac{dL}{d\alpha}$ with that of D, the graph of the former is plotted above the abscissa.*

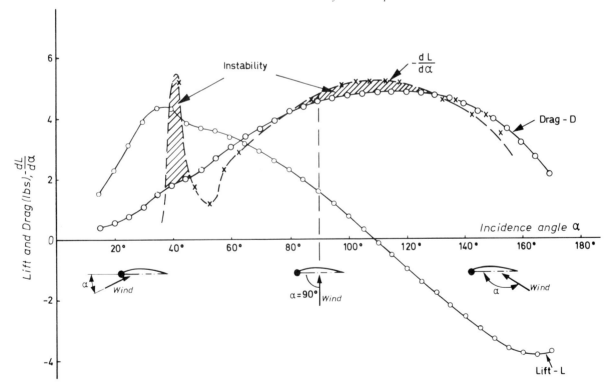

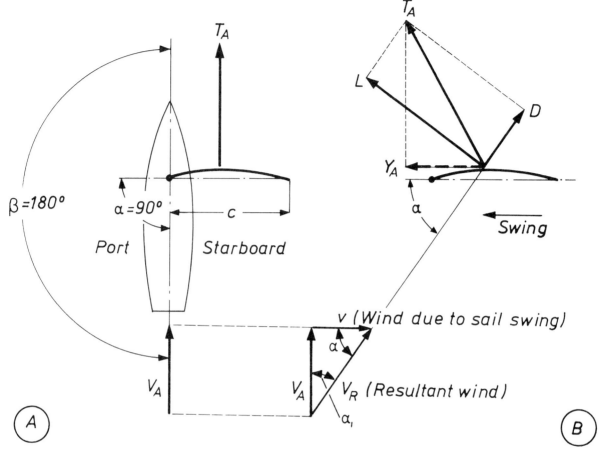

Fig. 2.5. *Diagram of forces and wind velocities when running before the wind, without and with rolling motion.*

nearly along the course sailed. If, for whatever reason, a small rolling motion is induced and the sail swings, say, to port, the resultant wind and aerodynamic force vectors L and D change both in magnitude and direction. This is shown in Fig. 2.5B, which refers to a narrow horizontal strip of sail, cut at some distance z from the axis of rolling. The resultant wind (V_R) which is, at any instant, the sum of the two vectors V_A and v, will increase in magnitude, and the instantaneous incidence angle (α) relative to the sail chord will be less than 90° by an amount $\dfrac{p \times z}{V_A}$. When the sail swings to starboard the whole situation is reversed and, as a result, the instantaneous incidence angle (α) will be greater than 90°. Under these conditions, the force component (Y_A) may act in the same direction as the rolling motion, i.e.:

$$-Y_A = -L \cos \alpha_1 + D \sin \alpha_1$$

since $\alpha_1 = 90 - \alpha$
then $Y_A = L \cos (90 - \alpha) - D \sin (90 - \alpha)$
$Y_A = L \sin \alpha - D \cos \alpha$ (2.6)

The actual magnitude and direction of the Y_A component will depend on the relative magnitudes of the L and D components at given instantaneous incidence α.

Differentiating Y_A with respect to α gives the rate of change of Y_A due to rolling:

$$\frac{\delta Y_A}{\delta \alpha} = \sin \alpha \left(\frac{\delta L}{\delta \alpha} + D \right) + \cos \alpha \left(L - \frac{\delta D}{\delta \alpha} \right)$$ (2.7)

When $\alpha \simeq 90°$ and the amplitude of rolling is small, then $\sin \alpha \to 1$ and $\cos \alpha \to 0$, therefore the second term of Eq. 2.7 becomes negligible and the motion is determined by the first term:

$$\frac{\delta Y_A}{\delta \alpha} = \frac{\delta L}{\delta \alpha} + D$$ (2.8)

Since the drag (D) is always positive there are three possibilities to consider namely:

(i) $\dfrac{\delta Y_A}{\delta \alpha} = 0$, $\left| -\dfrac{\delta L}{\delta \alpha} \right| = D$ rolling motion is not affected by the aerodynamic forces

(ii) $\dfrac{\delta Y_A}{\delta \alpha} < 0$, $\left| -\dfrac{\delta L}{\delta \alpha} \right| > D$ instability induced by aerodynamic forces (negative damping)

(iii) $\dfrac{\delta Y_A}{\delta \alpha} > 0$, $\left| -\dfrac{\delta L}{\delta \alpha} \right| < D$ rig produces positive damping

In Fig. 2.4 which presents the aerodynamic characteristics of the same una-rig as in Fig. 2.2, a graph of negative $\dfrac{\delta L}{\delta \alpha}$ is plotted together with L and D curves against incidence angle (α). Two shaded areas indicate the range of potential instability, where $\dfrac{\delta L}{\delta \alpha}$ is negative and at the same time its numerical value is greater than the drag component (D). The wind tunnel experiments demonstrated that the model rig responded dynamically according to the prediction based on an analysis of Eq. 2.8. Figure 63 in Chapter 7B depicts the typical behaviour of a una-rig model at different angles relative to the wind; with constant angle of trim of the sail (δ_m) = 85°, and constant damping due to hull action, corresponding to logarithmic decrement $\delta = 0.078$, i.e. the system was lightly damped.

Within the range of β from about 120° to 200° the recorded rolling oscillations shown below the curve are divergent, and the model clearly manifests *instability* due to the action of aerodynamic forces. It is apparent that the energy input to the system is not matched by the energy dissipated (limited by the amount of available damping). Therefore the amplitude of rolling grows.

These tests proved beyond any doubt that wild rolling may be induced by a sail for an aerodynamic reason. When running downwind, a sail can extract energy from the wind in a *self-excited manner* by its own periodic motion in such a way that the *sail can be regarded as a rolling engine*. Thus, the boat may capsize even in a completely flat sea if the energy inflow from the wind cannot, within a reasonable range of rolling angles, be dissipated into the water through hydrodynamic damping of the hull – mainly due to action of the keel.

Attention should be drawn to the *neutral stability* attained, for example, when the curve in Fig. 63 intersects the horizontal axis when β is about 120°. In this situation, the sail is subjected to periodically varying incidence angles below and beyond the stall angle, which is about 35° (Fig. 2.4). In the first case, the sail operating along the positive slope of the C_L curve $\left(\dfrac{\delta C_L}{\delta \alpha} > 0 \right)$ produces positive damping. In the second case, the sail operating along the negative slope of the C_L curve $\left(\dfrac{\delta C_L}{\delta \alpha} < 0 \right)$ produces negative damping. It is therefore conceivable that over a certain part of the full rolling cycle (from port to starboard and back to port) the energy extracted from the wind will be exactly balanced by the energy lost over another part of the same cycle; so the net work done by the sail is zero. This renders the zero stability index in Fig. 63, i.e. neutral stability.

References

[1] Marchaj, C.A. – *Unsteady Motion of Sailing Craft* Degree Thesis, Southampton University, 1976.

[2] Marchaj, C.A. – *The Aerodynamic Characteristics of a 2/5 Scale FINN Sail and its Efficiency when Sailing to Windward* – SUYR Report No. 13, January, 1964.

[3] Marchaj, C.A. – *Aero-Hydrodynamics of Sailing* Granada Publishing Ltd. 1979.

Appendix 3 Rolling Oscillations

It will be seen in Fig. 109 that a sailing boat rolling in waves can be looked upon as a dynamic, non-conservative system having two different forms of energy storage: kinetic energy and potential energy. It also has a damping capability, that is to say, dissipating energy coming from wind and waves back into the air and water.

The motion of such a system will always be made up of some combination of the two elementary patterns (Fig. 3.1):

(1) sinusoidal oscillation which represents cyclic transformation of potential energy (stored in the heeled attitude of the hull) into kinetic energy of rotation and back again.

(2) exponential growth (divergent oscillation in Fig. 3.1A) or decay (convergent oscillation in Fig. 3.1B). These indicate the rate of energy input or dissipation respectively, depending on whether the damping is negative or positive.

Negative damping implies that the system draws energy from either wind or waves, or both, and therefore the amplitude will build up with time as shown in Fig. 3.1A. Positive damping, on the other hand, implies that more energy is removed or dissipated back into the environment than is drawn from it, and therefore the amplitude will gradually diminish with time; this is shown in Fig. 3.1B. It may happen that once the amplitude of rolling reaches a certain magnitude (Fig. 3.1C) it becomes constant, thus indicating that there is energy balance coming in and going out of the system. Such a state of rolling motion can be called the limit cycle.

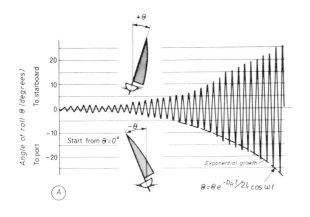

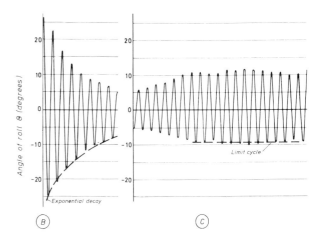

Fig. 3.1. *Three possible response records of a boat rolling due to combined action of exciting and damping forces.*
(A) Instability (divergent oscillation).

(B) Stability (convergent oscillation).
(C) Instability at first and then stability (limit-cycle oscillation).

The rolling motion as presented in Fig. 3.1 can be described mathematically in the form:

$$\Theta = \Theta_0 \ e^{\,-b_R t/2I_r} \cos \omega t \qquad (3.1)$$

where: Θ_0 initial amplitude
        b_R resultant damping coefficient: $b_R = b_H \pm b_A$
             (see Eq. 30A and B).
        I_r roll moment of inertia (see Eq. 38A).
        ω frequency of rolling oscillation:

$$\omega = \frac{2\pi}{T_n} \text{ (see Eq. 45).}$$

        t   time

The system will be dynamically stable if:

$$| \ b_R = (b_H - b_A) \ | > 0$$
where: b_H hydrodynamic damping coefficient
           b_A aerodynamic damping coefficient

With a positive resulting damping coefficient (b_R), which indicates that positive hydrodynamic damping (b_H) predominates, the net damping moment works against the rolling motion. Thus, each successive role has less amplitude (Θ) and less kinetic energy stored.

If $| \ b_R = (b_H - b_A) \ | < 0$; the system becomes dynamically unstable. Negative b_R indicates that aerodynamic excitation predominates, hence the amplitude of roll will grow with time. The net rolling moment does work on the system, extracting energy from the external source (wind) which will be stored in the form of increasing rolling energy of the boat, ultimately leading to capsize.

Referring to Eq. 3.1, it should be noted that the hydrostatic stability of the boat, as given by the metacentric height (GM), *does not* determine whether or not the boat will be dynamically stable. As shown earlier (see Eq. 20C), the metacentric height (GM) determines the natural period of rolling only ($T_n = 1.108 \dfrac{k}{\sqrt{GM}}$). In other words it indirectly tells us in what wavelength resonant rolling may occur and this hydrostatic contribution to rolling is reflected in the second term of Eq. 3.1 above (cos ωt). Thus, dynamic stability of sailing boats depends entirely on the first term of Eq. 3.1, that is $e^{-b_R t/2I_R}$; more specifically it depends on the resulting damping coefficient (b_R). The fact that the roll moment of inertia (I_r) is in the denominator of this expression ($b_R/2I_r$), indicates that the build-up of rolling will be slower with increased I_r, as will the rate of roll decay.

It follows from formula 3.1 that, in order to improve the seagoing characteristics of a vessel, be it a sailing yacht or a fishing boat, one must strive to increase the damping efficiency of the hull. And this has little in common with hydrostatic stability.

Appendix 4 Centrifugal Force Controversy

Some textbooks on physics warn, not infrequently dogmatically, against the fallacy of thinking that there is centrifugal force in a rotating system. Objections are voiced against the recognition of centrifugal force as a real force; instead it is alleged to be merely a fictitious, imaginary force which does not in fact exist. 'The fictitious centrifugal force' – we read in a textbook – 'is indeed a mysterious one for it has no obvious source, no strings no magnet, no spring.'

One might argue that for these reasons the force of gravity might also well be regarded as sufficiently mysterious to be discarded as unreal; nevertheless it keeps us unmistakably and firmly attached to Mother Earth.

It has been demonstrated, and not only in physics, that the interpretation of certain phenomena may depend upon an assumed frame of reference. Admittedly, that things depend upon one's point of view is so simple an idea that it is not even necessary to go to all the trouble of the theory of relativity in order to discover it.

Which particular frame of reference we may use to describe events is a matter of convenience. Consider a stone attached to a piece of string whirling around in a circle of radius (r) with a constant speed (v) (Fig. 4.1). As distinct from the term speed, the velocity contains two bits of information: the speed as well as the direction in which a body (in our case the stone), is moving. According to the implication of Newton's second law of motion, a change in either speed or direction, or both, will result in inward radial acceleration. Although, as viewed by a stationary observer not participating in the circular

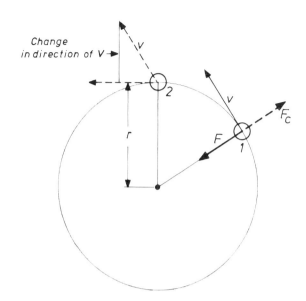

Fig. 4.1. *Forces operating in circular motion. F is centripetal force, recognised by an external observer (inertial frame of reference). F_c is centrifugal force, experienced by an observer rotating round the circle (non-inertial frame of reference).*

motion, i.e. from a stationary frame of reference called also the inertial frame of reference, the speed (v) does not change, the direction of motion changes continually. Hence, the stone is accelerated towards the centre of the circle by the force called *centripetal force* applied to it through the string.

It should be stressed that from the viewpoint of an external observer this force alone can be recognised to be acting on the stone. Since the centripetal acceleration exerted by this force is v^2/r, therefore the force is given by:

$$F = \text{mass of the stone} \times \text{acceleration}$$
$$F = m \times \frac{v^2}{r}$$

It is instructive to look at the same problem from the rotating, accelerating frame of reference fixed to the whirling stone. An observer attached to such so called non-inertial frame of reference would feel a different kind of force acting on him. He would feel an *inertia reaction* or *inertia force* (F_c) acting outward from the centre of rotation – the faster the speed of rotation the stronger the inertia force (Fig. 4.1).*

To illustrate the point let us quote an example given in a splendid book *Phenomenal Physics* [1] – the case of a passenger in a car that is turning sharply. 'The car door flies open, the passenger flies out. From your sublime and inertial vantage point, you can explain that the car door no longer provided sufficient centripetal force to keep the passenger going in a circle. From the passenger's point of view, of course, the door flew open and he *shot out*. You would have a hard time convincing the coroner that the death was caused by a fictitious force.'

How far from fictitious the centrifugal force is, can be judged by the loadings

---

* This reaction is named the centrifugal or centre fleeing force F_c. Forces F and F_c do not act on the same body, but on two different ones – on the string and on the stone respectively, as indicated in Fig. 4.1. Both forces disappear simultaneously when the string breaks.

on aircraft (and pilot) when he pulls out rapidly from a high-speed dive. The centrifugal stresses in rotating machinery are another example. The centrifugal force arising from the spin of the Earth, rather small because of the angular speed of rotation (one rotation in 24 hours), is nevertheless responsible for a certain flattening of our globe (a larger diameter at the Equator than the distance measured between North and South poles); hence the 'oblate spheroid' of which many of us have heard at school.

Some additional information on centrifugal forces operating within wave systems can be found in the *Theory of Naval Architecture*. [2] It may be added that 'there is never any conflict between descriptions from different reference frames *as long as we don't mix them up*. We must not, for example, equate a centrifugal force in one reference frame to a centripetal force in another. If we are stationed in an inertial reference frame, observing events in an accelerating frame, then we have no need to use inertial forces such as the centrifugal force. On the other hand, if we are *in* an accelerating system, such as a merry-go-round, it may be more convenient to describe effects using the net local field produced by gravitation and by any inertial forces.' [1]

And one more point. In some textbooks on physics referring to the so called d'Alembert free body diagram, in which centrifugal forces are taken into account, we read: 'The logic of this procedure is obscure since, although it involves the negation of Newton's laws, these laws are nevertheless implicit in certain stages of the argument'. Such a wording suggests that Newton himself was either against the concept of centrifugal force or perhaps was unaware of its significance. Therefore let Sir Isaac himself speak: 'The effects which distinguish absolute from relative motion are centrifugal forces, or those forces in circular motion which produce a tendency of recession from the axis. For in a circular motion which is purely relative no such forces exist, but in a true and absolute circular motion they do exist, and are greater or less according to the quantity of the absolute motion'. [3]*

He then described the rotating-bucket-of-water experiment in which he indicated that centrifugal force is the result of absolute motion, and not relative motion.

References

[1] Swartz, C.E. – *Phenomenal Physics* – John Wiley & Son, New York, 1981.
[2] Robb, A.M. – *Theory of Naval Architecture* – Griffin, London, 1953.
[3] Newton, Sir Isaac – *Mathematical Principles of Natural Philosophy* (Originally written in Latin and published in 1687).

---

* Presumably, what Newton had in mind when talking about the absolute as distinct from the relative motion is the feeling of an observer. If he is participating in the absolute, true motion (merry-go-round) he is subjected to the centrifugal force – he *feels* the action of that force. But when an observer is outside and considers relative motion, say, looking from above, he can only see the action of the centrepetal force which keeps an object in rotation relative to a given centre. In such a situation, an outside observer may not understand what sort of force the *rotating* human being really experiences.

Appendix 5 Pendulum Analogy of Rolling-heaving Coupling

Let us assume that at the beginning of oscillation the centre of gravity of a bob is at G_0 in Fig. 5.1. When the pendulum is at G_1, i.e. at the lowest point in the motion, the centre of gravity is suddenly transferred to G_2 by the distance ΔR. This position is kept until G_3 is reached, when it is suddenly dropped to G_4 by the same amount ΔR. It keeps that position until G_5 and then moves to G_6, remains there until G_7 and then is suddenly dropped to G_8, and so forth.

The work required in order to change the position of the centre of gravity from G_1 to G_2 or G_5 to G_6 can be expressed as follows:

$$\text{Work done} = (|W + F_c) \times \Delta R \tag{5.1}$$

where W – weight of the bob.

             F_c – the centrifugal force always directed outwards from the centre of the swing 0. Its magnitude changes depending on the angular velocity ω of the bob:

             $F_c = \text{mass} \times \text{acceleration}$

$$F_c = \frac{W}{g} (R \times \omega_{max}^2) \tag{5.2}$$

In turn the magnitude of angular velocity (ω_{max}) depends on the angle Θ from which the swing begins, i.e.:

$$\omega_{max} = \omega \times \Theta \; (\Theta \text{ in radians}) \tag{5.3}$$

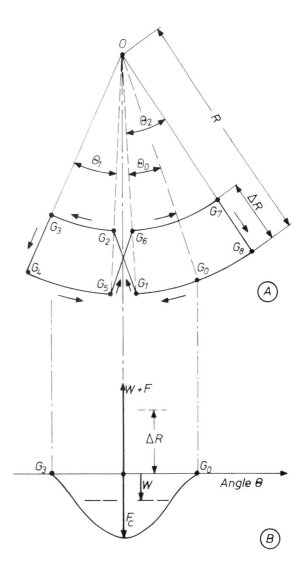

Fig. 5.1. *Forces operating on a pendulum (in which the centre of gravity moves periodically up and down); an example of parametric excitation. Forces marked W and F (weight of the bob and centripetal force respectively) in sketch (B) directed upwards, represent reaction on the pendulum arm, and ultimately the supporting pivot of the pendulum. Forces marked W and F_c (weight of the bob and centrifugal force respectively) directed downwards are balanced by W and F. Forces F and F_c have been magnified for the sake of clarity.*

where $\omega = \dfrac{2\pi}{T}$

and   T is the period of swing.

Accordingly, as shown in Fig. 5.1, the maximum value of the centrifugal force (F_c) is attained at the lowest point of the pendulum motion, where angular velocity is greatest and so is centrifugal acceleration.

The work returned at the extreme positions of the pendulum, i.e. at $G_3 - G_4$ and $G_7 - G_8$ is:

$$W \times \Delta R \times \cos \Theta$$

Thus the gain in energy (ΔE) during one complete swing of the pendulum can with good approximation, be given by the equation:

$$\Delta E = 2\{(W + F_c) \times \Delta R - \frac{W}{g} \times \Delta R \times \cos \Theta\}$$

or by putting:

$F_c = \frac{W}{g}\Delta R \ \omega_{max}^2$ into the above equation we have:

$$\Delta E = 2\{(W + \frac{W}{g} \times R \times \omega_{max}^2) \times \Delta R - W \times \Delta R \cos \Theta\} \qquad (5.4)$$

Of course this surplus of energy (ΔE), introduced as an input to the oscillating system, will inevitably increase the amplitude of subsequent swings and in this way a large oscillation can be built up.

It is seen from Eqs 5.2 and 5.4 that the rate at which the amplitude of motion increases is proportional to the movement of the centre of gravity (ΔR) and to the *square* of the angular velocity (ω_{max}) or, in other words, square of the angle of swing (Θ). The greater the initial angle of swing and the greater the amplitude of the up-and-down movement of the centre of gravity, the more rapidly will the angle of swing increase.

Translating this finding into rolling boat behaviour and wave characteristics, the term ΔR is equivalent to the wave height and Θ to the boat's rolling angle. Thus, if the initial angle of roll and the wave height are large, substantial amounts of energy can be transferred from the wave into the rolling boat, even in half a roll. If, in addition, the swing-rolling boat analogy is extended, and R from Eq. 5.4 is assumed to be equivalent to the metacentric height, one may infer that a large metacentric height appears to be detrimental to the boat's motion in waves. This reinforces the previously quoted observation from Barnaby: 'that the more stable the vessel really is, the more unstable she appears in waves'.

In our example a variation of the length (R) of the pendulum was considered. But a similar effect of parametric excitation can be obtained if, instead of variable length, a variable acceleration is introduced, as happens when a boat is heaving and rolling in waves. Physical analogy can be accomplished, as discussed earlier (page 195), if the pivot point of support (about which the pendulum swings) is given up-and-down harmonic motion (accelerations) say, by hand. In order to build large oscillations the support point O has to be pulled up in the middle of the swing and let down at the extreme positions, the bob describing a sort of figure of eight, as indicated in Fig. 5.1 i.e. swinging from G_1 to G_8 and back to G_1, as shown by the small arrows drawn along the bob trajectory.

Postscript

In order to ensure a better chance of survival in adverse weather conditions various worldwide organizations and sailing clubs* have recently attempted to develop and legally impose certain seaworthiness criteria and requirements for ballasted monohull sailing craft. So far no guarantee exists against the production and placing on the market of potentially dangerous boats.

As a result of increasing awareness of the deteriorating nature of the world's offshore racing fleet with respect to the range of positive static stability, certain requirements were suggested as to the minimum angle of vanishing stability Θ. In the light of statistical analysis of recorded casualties discussed earlier in this book, this minimum required value of Θ is dependent on the size of the vessel. Thus, it has been argued, that for craft of overall length LOA in excess of 22 metres (72 ft) the minimum value of Θ seems to be in the order of 100 degrees. While for boats of LOA below 10 metres (33 ft) the minimum would seem to be about 130 degrees.

It should be noted that the requirement of a lower value of Θ for larger craft is not suggested because these vessels recover from an inversion more easily, but rather because a larger capsizing force is necessary to cause a knockdown in the first place.

It is also proposed that sailing vessels are divided in three types:

1　Sailing vessels (mono and multihull) reliant on the use of the crew weight for capsize recovery.

* Such as, for example, the International Standards Organization (ISO), Royal Ocean Racing Council (RORC), Royal Yachting Association (RYA), Australia Yachting Federation (AYF), Cruising Club of America (CCA) and the Offshore Racing Council (ORC) responsible for the International Measurement System (IMS).

2 Sailing vessels (mono and multihull) reliant mainly on hull form for stability.

3 Monohull sailing vessels reliant mainly on both hull form and ballast for stability.

The above subdivision recognizes the different mechanisms involved in capsize recovery and safety against capsize. That is, crew weight as in the case of sailing dinghies and the like; the use of form stability only as in the case of multihulls; and the use of ballast in combination with form stability, as in the case of monohull sailing yachts.

Since the *static stability* is one of a number of factors which determine seaworthiness, several other factors describing certain aspects of *dynamic stability* in monohull sailing craft have been identified, namely:

Base Size Factor (FBS) accounts for the effect of the size of sailing craft in relation to the wind strength and wave forces. It is considered to be of primary importance since the dynamic response of a boat in adverse wind and wave conditions is related to her size and inertia (see Tables 2 and 3 pages 81–83).

Displacement Length Factor (FDL) accounts for the fact that a light displacement craft for its length experiences a greater motion response to wind and wave forces. This factor is necessary in addition to the FBS since the latter is defined in terms of length scale only.

Beam Displacement Factor (FBD) accounts for the fact that a craft with wide beam in relation to displacement manifests a greater motion response to wave induced forces, particularly at some initial angle of heel. Accordingly, FBD is defined in such a way that a high beam displacement ratio is identified as a risk, while a low ratio should not give undue credit.

Sail Area Displacement Beam Length Factor (FSDBL) accounts for the size of the rig in relation to the ability of the hull to carry sails. Accordingly, FSDBL gives credit to craft with small rigs in relation to the displacement and the beam length ratio.

Self Righting Factor (FSR). The area under the static righting moment or righting lever curve (see Figs 55 and 56) between the heel angle of 90 degrees and the angle of vanishing stability is related to the ability of the craft to recover from capsize. The larger this area, the sooner the craft recovers from an upside-down attitude.

Relative Area Factor (FRA) The propensity of a craft, after capsize, to remain in a dangerous inverted position in waves is related to the 'negative' area (danger zone) above the righting moment (or righting lever) curve (see Figs 55, 56 and 134) from the angle of vanishing stability to 180 degrees of heel. It is well known that the ratio of the 'positive' area (safe zone) to the 'negative' area (danger zone) is indicative of the degree of stability in the inverted position; in other words, the time during which the craft may remain in the inverted position.

Stability Speed Loss Factor (FSSL). At higher speed the wave formation along the hull is such that the inertia of the waterplane is significantly reduced. The associated decrease in transverse stability for round-bilge hull forms is well documented. The beam-draft ratio of the canoe body (of the hull) is the main parameter involved.

Roll Moment of Inertia Factor (FRMI) Capsize studies have indicated that a high roll moment of inertia decreases the likelihood of a capsize due to wave induced forces broadside to the hull (see page 218 and also 153).

Downflooding Angle Factor (FDA) Significant downflooding during a knock-down or capsize will influence the probability of recovery from capsize. Accordingly, the heel angle at which downflooding occurs and the amount of water which may enter the hull interior during the capsize needs to be taken into account.

What factors and in what form they will eventually be incorporated into the internationally recognized regulations or requirements, and when, remains to be seen.

References

[1] 'Stability Revisited' – Tech notes, *Sail*, October 1989.
[2] 'Stability of Sailing Craft' – Dr. Peter van Ossanen, *Schip en Werf de Zee*, Rotterdam, December 1994.

References and Notes

1. Herreshoff, F. 'The Common Sense of Yacht Design' – 1946.
2. View expressed by Warrick 'Commodore' Tompkins, published in *Sail* magazine – 'Survivors Ocean Racing Conference' – 1978.
3. Rule Management Policy – *Seahorse* No. 53, July, 1979.
4. (A) Jeffery, A. T. 'Holland's Fastnet' – *Yachting World* February 1980.
   (B) *The Fastnet Race Inquiry*, published December 1979 by the Royal Yachting Association and Royal Ocean Racing Club, England.
5. (A) The *Odyssey* of Homer, translated by Sir William Marris, Oxford University Press, 1925.
   (B) Humphreys, R. – *Yachts and Yachting*, March 1973.
6. Foley, R.K. – *Oregon Law Review*, June 1967.
7. Leather, J. – *Colin Archer and Seaworthy Double-Ender*, Stanford Maritime Publication 1979.
8. *Ships in Rough Seas* – Occasional Publication RINA – Proceedings of the Seminar on the Norwegian SIS Project.
9. Phillips-Birt, D. – *An Eye for a Yacht* – Faber & Faber Ltd, London, 1965.
10. Phillips-Birt, D. – *Sailing Yacht Design* – Adlard Coles, London, 1966.
11. Humphreys, R. – 'Rating rules have little bearing on the basic design geometry of an offshore boat' – *Sail* magazine, 1974.
12. Phillips-Birt, D. – *British Ocean Racing* – Adlard Coles Ltd, 1960.
13. Laurent Giles, J. – 'Some Consideration on the Design of the Cruising Sailing Yacht' – Paper read before the Association of Northern Universities Sailing Clubs.
14. Baker, M. – *Fragments of Ancient English Shipwrightry* (about 1572), Pepysian Library at Magdalene College, Cambridge.
15. Chapman, F.H. – *Architectura Navalis Mercatoria* (1768), Adlard Coles Ltd, London.

16.   INA Transactions, 1863, page 226.

17.   Transactions of the Royal Society of Edinburgh, 1839, Volume XIV, Part I.

18.   INA Transactions, 1878, 'The Wave Principle Applied to the Longitudinal Disposition of Immersed Volume'.

19.   Reynolds-Brown, A.E. – '*America*: did she really win?' *Yachting World*, April 1977. In *The Lawson History of the* America's *Cup* – published in Boston in 1902 – there is a note on page 26 which reads: 'Royal Yacht Squadron cup' was the original name of the *America*'s trophy. It was not in any sense a Queen's cup.'

20.   Turner, A. – 'A Law of Hydrostatics and its Influence on the Shapes of Sailing Yachts' – INA Transactions, 1937.

21.   In the early days of merchant ships it was necessary for practical reason to measure the vessel's size – its capacity for carrying cargo. When ordering a ship it became important to know what her 'tunnage' would be. The notion 'tunnage' had been derived from the word 'tun' – a wine cask containing 252 gallons. The size of a ship was described by the number of tuns she could carry. As time went on it became even more important to know this figure, because tunnage formed a basis for harbour dues for imported goods to England. Thus, for instance, King Edward III was empowered in 1347 to levy a tax of three shillings on every 'tun' of imported wine.

Shipwrights were supplying certificates of tonnage and the measurements were based upon length (L), breadth (B) and depth of hold (D) of the hull. When multiplied together these measurements gave some idea of the vessel's capacity in cubic feet. Divided by 100 this gave the tonnage with reasonable accuracy. The formula was:

$$\frac{L \times B \times D}{100} = \text{tonnage} \tag{1}$$

Over the years the formula was varied in a number of ways. For practical reason, the length was taken as the 'tread of the keel' or 'as much as lay on the ground'; the breadth was measured from ceiling to ceiling inside amidships; and owing to the difficulty of measuring the depth when the vessel was loaded, it was assumed to be half the breadth, as it actually was in the average vessel of this era. (Ref. 22) By substituting 1/2 B for D only L and B appeared in the formula:

$$\frac{L \times B \times 1/2\ B}{94} = \text{tonnage}$$

In 1773 the formula was modified again. To allow for the forward rake of the stem a deduction of 3/5 the breadth was taken from the length; and the length was measured along the rabbet of the keel; from a perpendicular dropped from the fore side of the stem under the bowsprit to the after part of the main sternpost. The beam was taken outside of planking. This new formula was known as Builders' Old Measurement (BOM):

$$\frac{(L - 3/5\ B) \times B \times 1/2\ B}{94} = \text{tonnage} \tag{2}$$

was in use when the schooner *America* visited Britain in 1851.* An almost identical formula was at that time adopted in the United States under the name of Carpenters'

* At the beginning of yacht measurements for racing purposes the existing rules for measuring the size of merchant vessels were applied, such as rule 1 or 2. The reason was quite simple, these rules were at hand and contemporary yachtsmen and designers had no experience of dealing with

Measurement. But true depth of hold (D) was used instead of 1/2 B and length (L) was taken on the deck. The formula was:

$$\frac{(L - 3/5\ B) \times B \times D}{95} = \text{tonnage}$$

The yacht *America* was measured under this formula at 170 tons, but under the British BOM formula at 208 tons.

22.   Stephens, W.P. – 'Yacht Measurement' – SNAME Transactions, Volume 43, 1935.
23.   *Yachting World* – May, 1982 issue.
24.   The Thames Measurement formula, TM, had been modified further in 1874:

$$\frac{L \times B \times D}{200} = \text{tonnage (New Thames Yacht Club)},$$

D measured from upper side of planksheer to lower side of keel; and again in 1882:

$$\frac{(L + B)^2 \times B}{1730} = \text{tonnage (Yacht Racing Association – 1730 Rule)}$$

But the basic measurement factors were still the same – length and beam. i.e. the cubic content of the hull was regarded as the measure of speed potential. The divisor 1730 being chosen to bring the final result approximately the same as under the old tonnage rule. That the '1730 Rule' failed so rapidly and so completely – says W.P. Stephens (Ref. 22) – 'was due largely to the passing of the old generation through death and business troubles and the surrender of the entire field of yacht design to the young men . . . only too keenly appreciative of the possibilities still left them for further increasing length, draft, displacement and lead at the expense of beam'.

25.   *Yachting* – The Badmington Library, 1894.
26.   Dixon Kemp – 'Fifty Years of Yacht Building' – INA Transactions, 1887.
27.   Thompson, W.M. and Lawson, T.W. – *The Lawson History of the America's Cup*, Boston 1902. Privately printed in a limited edition of 3000 copies.
28.   Gardner Cox, F. – 'Kinetic Sailing comes of age' – *Sail* May, 1980.
29.   At about that time, i.e. from 1890 onwards, when the Length/Sail Area Rule (Eq. 6) was in force, it became evident that for each class of racing boats of given rating there is a 'best' length for given wind conditions which wins the prizes. This best length depends far more upon the prevailing wind strength during the racing season than on any assumed connection between L and S_A. It will vary, of course, on different days and for different seasons and different localities, the water being rougher and the wind harder or comparatively, water being smooth and the wind light. Thus, for example, R. E. Froude (son of the famous William Froude) built a small yacht which, as reported, 'won every race in any heavy weather but in light weather she lost every race, and was nearly always the last home.'
30.   *The Times* – May 25, 1937.
31.   The quotation given is an extract from Austen Chamberlain's reply to the French delegate M. Painlevé in an attempt to arrive at a clearer understanding of a certain amount of tension between the English and the French at the Assembly of the League of Nations in September, 1925.

yachts. As the knowledge of yacht design increased better rules, specifically orientated towards measuring speed rather than size, were developed, and so older tonnage rules were abandoned.

32. Churchill, Randolph S. – *Winston Churchill the Young Statesman* page 5 – Boston, 1967.
33. Froude, R.E. – 'Yacht Racing Measurement Rules and the International Conference' – INA Transactions, 1906.
34. The evolution of the Royal Ocean Racing Club rule, which in its latest form reads:

$$0.15 \left(\frac{L \times \sqrt{S_A}}{\sqrt{B \times D}} + 0.2\,L + 2\,\sqrt{S_A} \right) \pm \text{Stability allowance}$$

$\pm$ Prop. allowance + Draft penalty = Rating (in ft) began in 1912 when the British Boat Racing Association (BRA) adopted, in principle, the American rule called the Universal Rule. The rule proposed by N.Herreshoff in 1902 was framed initially as follows:

$$0.2 \frac{L \times \sqrt{S_A}}{\sqrt[3]{\text{Displ.}}} = \text{Rating*}$$

where displacement (Displ.) in the denominator was intended to encourage better accommodation. Unlike the Universal Rule the RORC rule used Beam × Depth (B × D) instead of direct displacement. Since B measurement is in the denominator of the formula, a larger B gave more favourable rating. At that time, however, the beam was not appreciated as a loophole for the psychological reason already mentioned, namely: discouraging experiences with skimming dishes were still alive in the memory of the majority of sailing people. The Cruising Club of America (CCA) decided in 1934 on a quite different rule for ocean racing in the form:

$$0.6\,\sqrt{S_A} \times \text{Rig Allowance} + 0.4L \pm B \pm D \pm \text{Displ} \pm F + A + C = \text{Rating}$$

where
- A = length penalty for excessive rake of the stem
- B = beam
- C = correction for length
- D = Draft
- F = Freeboard

This rule was a result of a design contest organised by the CCA in an attempt to detect what kind of freaks, if any, would be inspired by a tentative rule proposed earlier. In its latest form in 1967 the rule was expressed as:

$$0.95\,(L \pm B_m \pm \text{Draft} \pm \text{Displ.} \pm S_A \pm \text{Freeboard} \pm \text{Iron keel factor}) \times$$
$$\text{Ballast ratio} \times \text{Prop. Factor} = \text{Rating (in ft)}$$

All of the plus or minus corrections in the rule were calculated depending on how the actual design had departed from a 'baseboat' – an envisaged ideal yacht. Thus the factors for beam, sail area, draft and so on, related to given length of the boat, when added or subtracted to measured length L gave a theoretical sailing length or rating, and so the speed potential of the boat (see Appendix 1). The philosophy behind the IOR is the same as that of the RORC rule, that is, the IOR should be a development rule, attempting to evaluate the relative speed of boats of diverse hulls and sailplans with reasonable fairness.

* Constant 0.2 as a multiplier for the entire formula was reduced to 0.18 in 1909. Famous J class yachts competing for the America's Cup were measured according to this formula. The correct

In the CCA rule the approach was significantly different in the sense that only minor deviations from the 'ideal' base boat were tolerated. Relatively heavy displacement was encouraged. Midship sections featured an easy turn of the bilge, full garboards and a slow transition of the hull into keel like that shown in Figs 30C or 31.

As we can see in the Fig. 1 opposite, the measurement system of the International Offshore Rule looks rather complicated. To obtain rating for handicap purpose there are about 140 sail and hull measurements to be taken – some of them, such as stability test, on board. Ordinary yachtsmen, who race occasionally, have found the complexity, expense and frequent changes of the IOR a considerable burden. A letter received by the editor of one of the leading British yachting magazines, from a distinguished ex-Flag Officer of the New York Yacht Club is a delightful example of a reaction against these complexities. He says:

'Many yachtsmen are confused as to effect that the new International Rating Rule may have on their present boat, it is hoped that this simplified explanation will be of assistance.

If the waterline of your boat exceeds the overall length by more than the difference between the headstay and the head, if the latter is located below deck and forward of the cockpit, it will be necessary for you to make changes. Measure the luff of your largest jib, then check the distance from where the headstay meets the deck to the point midway between where the sheet should legally lead and where it actually does; multiply by the square root of the monthly overdraft from your bank and deduct your monthly boatyard bills; if the former is greater than the latter but not less than your present rating, divide the figure into fifths and move the mast aft three feet. If for any reason it is impractical to move the mast leave it where it is and move the boat forward an equal distance. This change will make it possible for you to compete on an international basis without fear or favour or hope.'

35.   The Royal Offshore Racing Club (RORC) was founded in 1925 upon the Ocean Racing Club, which in turn transformed itself from the Ocean Race Committee which, in 1925, organised the first Ocean Race later to become the Fastnet Race, the most prestigious race in European waters.

The Cruising Club of America (CCA) has similar objectives to those of RORC 'to make it possible for yachtsmen to race seaworthy cruising boats of various design, types and construction on a fair and equitable basis'. In a report on the aims of the CCA the following views have been expressed and which are much alive today: 'The Cruising Club of America, as its name proclaims and its constitution declares, is organised to promote cruising . . . The cruiser chooses his rig, the type of hull and fixes upon all the details with an eye single to the comforts, convenience and safety of cruising. After all these ends have been accomplished he will add all features contributing to speed that are not inconsistent with the demand of his ideal cruiser. The real fact must always remain that the cruising boat cannot be a racer.'

36.   *Fishing Boats of the World*, Volume 2, Publ. Fishing News (Books) Ltd, London, 1960.
37.   Barnaby, K.C. – *Basic Naval Architecture*, Hutchinson Publ. London, 1967.
38.   Hadler, J.B. and Sarchin, T.H. – 'Seakeeping Criteria and Specifications', article in *Seakeeping*, SNAME, 1976.
39.   Tyler, D.B. and Bard, P. 'Motion Sickness' – *Physiological Review*, October, 1949.

and legal title of this class was 76 foot Rating Class. The letter J was merely a symbol carried on sails as a convenience for identifying the class.

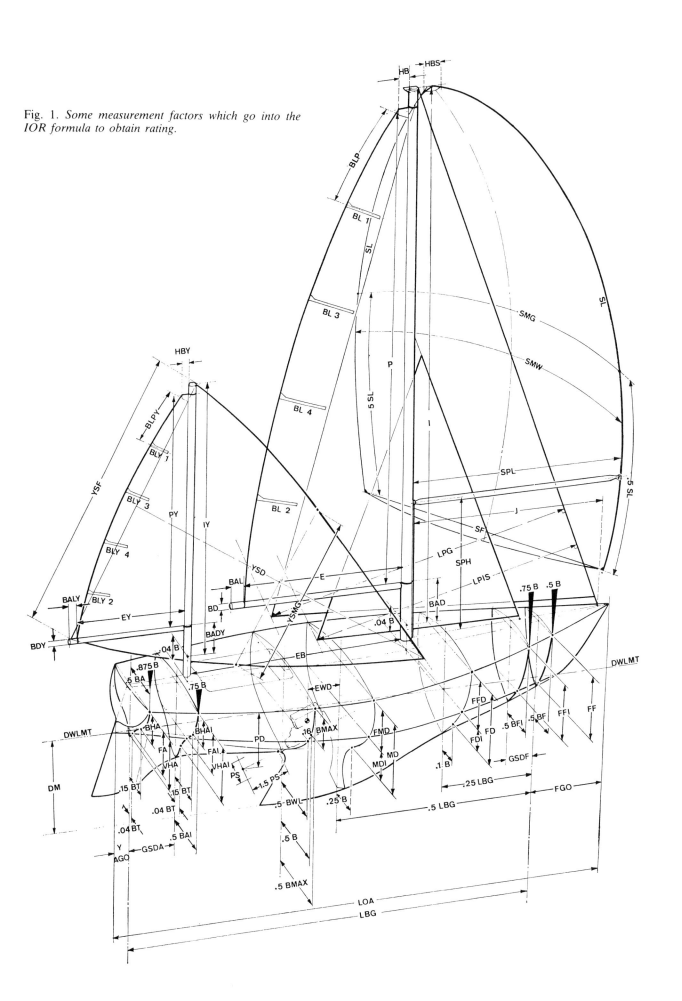

Fig. 1. *Some measurement factors which go into the IOR formula to obtain rating.*

40.   'Fastnet Report – too few answers', *Sail*, February, 1980.

41.   Popper, Sir Karl R. – *Objective Knowledge*, Oxford University Press, 1974.

42.   Knight, Jack – 'Fastnet Inquiry Report', *Yachts and Yachting*, January 4, 1980.

43.   'A Presentation of Yacht Stability' – WUMTIA Report, February 1980.

44.   Johnson, P., Fayle, D., Glover, R., Hall, J., Henderson, M., Hood Sailmakers, Mackworth, Sir David, *Yachtsman's Guide to the Rating Rule* – Nautical Publ. Co. 1971.

45.   Stephens, O. – 'Measurement Parameters of the IOR' The Chesapeake Symposium, January, 1974.

46.   Modification of the Tenderness Ratio, TR, formula.

$$TR = \frac{0.97 \, L \, BWL^3}{RM, \, 1°} \text{ as defined by the rule.}$$

$$RM, \, 1° = GM \times \triangle \times \sin 1°$$
$$= GM \times (\triangledown \times 64) \times 0.0175$$
$$= 1.12 \, GM \times \triangledown$$

where $\triangle$ – displacement in lb

$\triangledown$ – displacement in cubic feet

(weight density of 1 cubic foot of salt water = 64 lb)

Assuming further that LWL = 0.97 rated length L we have:

$$TR = \frac{LWL \times (BWL)^3}{1.12 \, GM \times \triangledown} \qquad (1)$$

The distance BM of centre of buoyancy (B) from the metacentre can be determined from the formula:

$$BM = \frac{IT}{\triangledown} = \frac{k \times LWL \times (BWL)^3}{\triangledown} \qquad (2)$$

where – IT transverse moment of inertia = k × LWL × (BWL)³ (k coefficient ranges from 0.037 for fine and 0.043 for full waterplane – see 'Skenes' Elements of Yacht Design' Kinney, F.S., Dodd, Mead and Co., 1973).

Assuming that k = 0.04 we have:

$$BM = \frac{0.04 \times LWL \times BWL^3}{\triangledown}$$

Hence LWL × (BWL)³ – the numerator in formula 1 $= \dfrac{BM \times \triangledown}{0.04}$

Taking some simple arithmetical steps further we have:

$$TR = \frac{BM \times \triangledown}{0.04 \times 1.12 \times GM \times \triangledown} = 22.3 \frac{BM}{GM} \qquad (3)$$

It is interesting to note that TR is, in fact, proportional to the ratio $\dfrac{BM}{GM}$.

47.   Kenning, J.A. – 'On Stability of Sailing Yachts at Large Angle of Heel' – Delft University Rep N 499, April, 1980.

48. Bouzaid, Christopher – 'Dangerous Design Trends' – Letter to *Sail*, April, 1980. The missing One-Tonners are: *Smackwater Jack*, owned by New Zealand yacht designer Whiting, P. and *Charleston*, owned by Davies, C. of Tasmania.

49. Stephens, O., Kirkman, K., Peterson, R. 'Sailing Yacht Capsizing', SNAME, 1981.

50. Kelley, C.B. – 'IOR Analysis: Another Look at CGF' – *Sail* – 1976.

51. Barkla, H. – 'An Equal-Tempered Scale for Yachts' AIAA/SNAME Symposium, Los Angeles, January, 1975.

52. Norlin, P. – 'Designed for Boat Speed' – *Sail*, January, 1978.

53. Valentijn, J. – 'CGF and Stability' – *Seahorse*, April, 1976.

54. Van de Stadt, E.G. – 'A design lesson' letter to *Yachting World*, February, 1980.

55. The IMO (International Maritime Organisation) originally called International Maritime Consultative Organisation (IMCO) criteria – endorsed in 1977 at the International Convention for the Safety of Fishing Vessels – are expressed in terms of minimum values for certain key features of hydrostatic stability such as: the metacentric height (GM), the righting lever (GZ) at specified heel angle, and the area under the stability curve (GZ vs Θ), which indicates the reserve of stability in static conditions only. The IMO is the body which holds responsibility for developing marine safety criteria satisfactory for all nations.

56. Humphreys, R. – 'Ultimate Stability', *Yachts and Yachting*, February 15, 1980.

57. Hind, J.A. – *Stability and Trim of Fishing Vessels*, Fishing News Books Ltd, 1982.

58. *Yachting World* Forum on Design of Offshore Racing Boats' 1964. Angus Primrose was a partner of the famous Illingworth Primrose team which, among other successful offshore racers, designed *Outlaw* in class 1.

59. Marchaj, C.A. – *Aero-Hydrodynamics of Sailing*, Adlard Coles Ltd, 1979.

60. The Papers of William Froude, published by the RINA, London, 1955, original paper publ. INA 1861. Froude, W., an English engineer, can be regarded as the first man to persevere in a scientific approach to the problems of hull design, ship motion in waves and more rigorous methods of predicting ship performance by means of towing tank testing.

61. Serat, M.E. – 'Effect of Form on Roll' – SNAME, 1933.

62. Robb, A.M. – *Theory of Naval Architecture* – Griffin, London, 1953.

63. Saunders, H.E. – 'Hydrodynamics in Ship Design' – SNAME Publ. 1965.

64. Symposium on Ship Operation – SNAME Vol. 63, p. 611 – 1955.

65. Holt, C.F. – 'Stability and Seaworthiness' – INA, 1925.

66. Froude, W. – 'On the practical Limits of the Rolling of Ships in a heavy Sea' – INA, 1865.

67. Yagamata, M. – 'Standard of Stability adopted in Japan', RINA, 1959.

68. Mull, G. – 'Evolution of the Modern Cruising Boat' – *Yacht Racing and Cruising*, January, 1983.

69. Mudie, C. – 'An overview of Safety Regulation affecting Design of small Commercial or Pleasure Craft' – International Conference on Design Considerations for Small Craft – RINA, London, 1984.

70. The logarithm of the ratio of succeeding amplitudes is given (in the mechanics of oscillation) the symbol δ as shown in Eq. 25. The decrement coefficient δ can approximately be estimated from the curve of declining angles (Fig. 82B) as follows:

$$\delta = \log\frac{\Theta_1}{\Theta_2} = \log\left(\frac{\Theta_2 + \Delta\Theta}{\Theta_2}\right) = \log\left(1 + \frac{\Delta\Theta}{\Theta_2}\right)$$
$$= \frac{\Delta\Theta}{\Theta_2} + \frac{1}{2}\left(\frac{\Delta\Theta}{\Theta_2}\right)^2 + \frac{1}{3}\left(\frac{\Delta\Theta}{\Theta_2}\right)^3 + \ldots$$

If $\frac{\Delta\Theta}{\Theta_2}$ is relatively small the higher order terms 2 and 3 may be dropped and

$$\delta = \frac{\Delta\Theta}{\Theta_2} \tag{1}$$

Thus, the logarithmic decrement is approximately equal to the fractional decrease in angle of heel during one cycle of oscillation. In the case of a boat which is dynamically unstable (Fig. 63A–D) the increment δ can be estimated in a similar manner from the curve of increasing angles of heel. It can be shown (Fig. 82) that energy dissipated ΔE during the roll from Θ_0 to Θ_1, i.e. the energy drained away by the work done against the water resistance, is:

$$\Delta E = \frac{1}{2}\Delta GM\,(\Theta_0^2 - \Theta_1^2) \tag{2}$$

It should be remembered that in this kind of calculation the radian unit of circular measure is to be used for Θ angles instead of degrees, i.e.:

$$1 \text{ radian} = 360°/2\pi = 57.3°$$

To convert an angle given in degrees into radians it must be divided by 57.3; for example:

$$\Theta = 32 \text{ degrees} = \frac{32}{57.3} = 0.558 \text{ radians}$$

It can also be shown that the energy lost ΔE during the swing from Θ_0 to Θ_1, expressed as a fraction of the total potential energy stored in heeled position at Θ_0 is twice the logarithmic decrement, i.e.:

$$\frac{\Delta E}{E_{tot}} \simeq 2\delta \tag{3}$$

71. Marchaj, C.A. – 'Instability of Sailing Craft – Rolling' The Ancient Interface Conference, California, November, 1971.
72. Morrall, A. – 'Capsizing of Small Trawlers' – RINA paper, 1979.
73. Froude, W. – 'On the Influence of Resistance upon the Rolling of Ships' – *Naval Science*, October, 1872 (with additional matter contributed later by the author after original publication). vide *Naval Science* p. 504, 1874.
74. The reader should perhaps be reminded that in conditions of synchronism without damping – or even in condition when the differences in the co-periodicity between the wave period and the vessel period of rolling are in the order of 10% – the angle of rolling would increase up to 90 degrees in the transit of three waves; if we assume that the maximum slope of the waves were 9 degrees only!
75. 'Stability of Trawlers' – the *Naval Architect*, January, 1982.

76.   Suyehiro, K. – 'Yawing of Ships caused by Oscillation amongst Waves' – INA, 1920.

77.   White, W.H. – 'On the Rolling of Ships' – INA, 1881.

78.   Kjeldsen, S.P., Myrhaug, D. and Brevig, P. – 'Kinematics of deep water breaking waves' – Offshore Technology Conference, 1980.

79.   Baker, G.S., Miss Keary, E.M. – 'The Effect of the longitudinal motion of a Ship on its statical transverse Stability'. INA, 1918.

80.   Paulling, J.R. – 'Transverse Stability of Tuna Clippers' – Paper published in *Fishing Boats of the World* Vol. 2. (Ref. 36)

81.   Turner, A. Engineer Rear Admiral – 'A Law of Hydrostatics and its Influence on the Shapes of sailing Yachts' – INA, 1937.

82.   Paulling, J.R., Oakley, O.H., Wood, P.D. – 'Ship capsizing in heavy seas. The correlation of theory and experiments'. Int.Conf. on Stab; of Ship and Ocean Vehicles, Univ. of Strathclyde, 1975.

83.   Oakley, O.H., Paulling, J.R., Wood, P.D. – 'Ship motions and capsizing in astern seas', 10th Naval Hydr. Symp. MIT, June, 1974.

84.   Vossers, G. – 'New Perspectives in sea behaviour'. Paper in *Fishing Boats of the World*. (Ref. 36)

85.   Barkla, H. – Private communication and also his paper – 'The Morphology of the Yacht' – HISWA Symposium, 1981.

86.   Kure, K. and Bang, C.J. – Proceedings of the International Conference on Stability of Ships and Ocean Vehicles – University of Strathclyde, Glasgow 1975.

87.   Desoutter, D. – 'Light or Heavy' *Practical Boat Owner*, April, 1984. See also Witt, R. – 'Guide to British Sailing Cruisers'.

88.   Amount of potential energy stored in the heeled position of a hull can be estimated as follows: when a boat heels due to action of an external moment the centre of gravity is

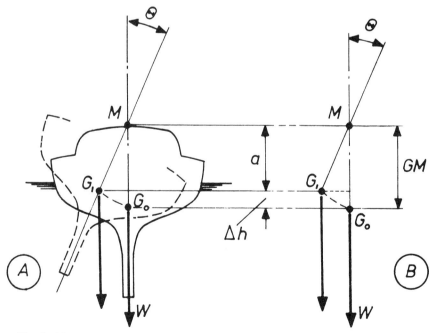

Fig. 2. *Movement of the centre of gravity G of a boat which heels.*

shifted upward from G_0 to G_1 by a distance Δh shown in Fig. 2. Consider the oscillating centre of gravity G of the hull as a pendulum with its point of suspension at metacentre M and the centre of gravity G acting as the bob (see Fig. 3, Note 89). The moving bob G rises up swinging to the left to a maximum height Δh. There, at an angle Θ it is momentarily brought to rest and all its energy is potential E_p = maximum, remembering that the potential energy is always measured with respect to some reference level. Thus the bob in its vertical position is at the reference level 0 – similar to the upright position of the rolling yacht. As the bob falls from position 1 its angular velocity gradually increases and the height Δh above the reference level 0 decreases. In other words, its potential energy E_p is gradually converted into the kinetic energy of motion. At the instant when the pendulum is going through the vertical (i.e. it is at the lowest point of its motion $\Theta = 0$) all its energy is kinetic and the bob is moving with maximum angular velocity ω_{max}. If there were no friction, the pendulum once set in motion would swing for ever between positions 1 and 2.

Referring to a rolling yacht, the maximum rolling velocity reached in the upright position can be calculated if we know the natural period of rolling T_n of the boat, i.e. the time taken to roll from, say, port to starboard and back to port. Thus, the rolling velocity for a boat rolling with period $T_n = 3$ sec from, say, angle of heel $\Theta = 30$ degrees would be:

$$\omega = \frac{2\pi}{T_n} = \frac{2 \times 3.14}{3} = 2.1 \text{ radians/sec}$$

But the maximum angular velocity reached when upright:

$$\omega_{max} = \omega \times \Theta$$

where ω given in radians $= \dfrac{30}{57.3} = 0.52$ radians

so:

$$\omega_{max} = 2.1 \times 0.52 = 1.1 \text{ radians/sec}$$

Maximum kinetic energy E_k of a rolling boat can be calculated according to formula:
$\Delta h \quad GM - a$ (see Fig. 2)
But $\quad a = GM \cos \Theta$
Hence $\quad \Delta h = GM - GM \cos \Theta$
$\Delta h = GM (1 - \cos \Theta)$

Increase in potential energy (ΔE_p) in heeled position equals the work required to lift the centre of gravity of the hull of weight W by distance Δh:

$$\Delta E_p = W \times \Delta h$$
$$\Delta E_p = W \times GM (1 - \cos \Theta)$$

Strictly speaking the above formula is valid for a centroid hull which has a fixed GM position, i.e. independent of the heeling angle. Round-bottomed hull is close in shape to centroid.

89. Leonhard Euler – famous Swiss scientist who developed a theory of ship motion in still

water (published in the fundamental work 'Ship Science' in 1749) – approached the rolling motion from the viewpoint of the pendulum interpretation. This is illustrated in Fig. 3 below. Although a hull does not behave exactly like a pendulum, with its point suspension at metacentre M and the centre of gravity G acting as the bob, such an interpretation is helpful. It is a good example of the conversion of energy – from potential energy E_p to kinetic energy E_k and back again.

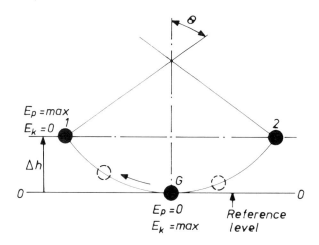

Fig. 3. *Rolling boat – pendulum analogy.*

Maximum kinetic energy E_k of a rolling boat can be calculated according to formula:

$$E_k = 1/2\ I_r \omega_{max}^2$$

which explicitly indicates that apart from ω_{max} we must also know the roll moment of inertia (I_r) of the boat in question. (See Note 90.) It should perhaps be added that the maximum kinetic energy (friction effect being ignored) equals maximum potential energy (Note 88), i.e. $1/2\ I_r \omega_{max}^2 = W \times GM\ (1 - \cos \Theta)$.

90. In order to calculate the roll moment of inertia (I_r) the designer must know the weight of all the components of the yacht and the distance of each of them from the fore-and-aft axis of rolling. This axis usually lies somewhere between the centre of gravity and the waterline of the hull. The distance of each component from the rolling axis (k) is squared and the result multiplied by the weight (W) of each component divided by the acceleration due to gravity (g). Thus, the inertia contribution of each component can be written:

$$I_r \text{ (component)} = \frac{W}{g} \times k^2$$

where k is the approximate distance of the centre of gravity of the weight component from the axis of rolling.

The total roll moment of inertia of the whole boat is the sum of all these components. Such an accurate piece-by-piece calculation is laborious and for that reason is rather seldom used by yacht designers. There exists an approximate method of estimating the roll moment of inertia of boats which have the MHS certificate. A relevant computer program is reproduced as an appendix to: 'Interim report, Safety from Capsizing' USYRU, June, 1984.

91.   Stephens, O., Kirkman, K., Peterson, R. – 'Sailing Yacht Capsizing' – SNAME, 1981.
92.   Kirkman, K., Nagle, T.J., Salsich, J.O. – 'Sailing Yacht Capsizing' – SNAME, 1983.
93.   Salsich, J., Zseleczky, J. – 'Experimental Studies of Capsizing in Breaking Waves' – The 13th AAIA Symposium, Vol. 29, 1983. The model used for the single wave impact capsize experiments was a 'two dimensional' representation of a sailing yacht hull. This consisted of a midship section extended length-wise, thus having no form change along its length and also having a rectangular waterplane area. A scaled midship section of the yacht 'Standfast 40' was used – the yacht which was the parent hull form for a systematic series of hull forms used in the development of the Measurement Handicap System (MHS) rule. (See Kerwin, J. and Newman, J.N. 'A summary of the H. Irving Pratt Ocean Race Handicapping Project' CSYS, 1979.) The principal dimensions of the two-dimensional model tested and its photograph (Fig. 4) are given below.

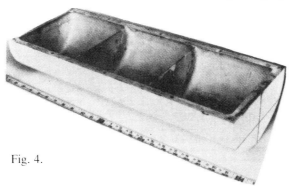

Dimensions of the model
Length   – 22 in
Beam   – 8 in
Draft   – 4.75 in
Δ – 6.93 lb
Freeboard – 2.5 in
Keel area – 14.2 in^2
AR (keel) – 0.66

Fig. 4.

94.   McCurdy, USYRU Safety-at-Sea Committee, 'Safety from Capsizing' (Interim Report) June, 1984.
95.   Kirkman, K.L. – 'On the avoidance of inverted stable equilibrium', Ancient Interface Symposium XIII, October, 1983.
96.   Cokelet, E.D. – 'Breaking Waves' – *Nature*, June, 1977.
97.   Peregrine, D., Cokelet, E., McIver, P. – 'The fluid mechanics of waves approaching breaking' – Proc. Conf; Coastal Eng. 17th 1980.
98.   Claughton, A., Handley, P. – 'An Investigation into the Stability of Sailing Yachts in Large Breaking Waves'. Southampton University Report, January, 1984. Handley, P. – 'Capsizing Yachts' – *Yachting Monthly*, July, 1984.
99.   Dahle, E.A., Kjearland, O. – 'Capsizing of M/S Helland – Hansen RINA paper, April, 1979.
100.   Darion, Joe., 'The Quest' from Man of La Mancha.
101.   Claughton, A. – 'Capsizing in Waves' – *Seahorse*, May/June, 1984.
102.   Amy, J.R., Johnson, R.E., Miller, E.R. – 'Development of Intact Stability criteria for Towing and Fishing Vessels' SNAME, 1966.

103.   Jordan, D.J.
      (1) 'What causes a boat capsize' – *Sail*, February, 1982.
      (2) 'Small Boats and Breaking Waves' – *Sail*, December, 1982.
      (3) 'Preventing capsize in breaking waves' – *Sail*, September 1984.

104.   Popper, K. R. (Sir) – *Objective Knowledge* – Oxford University Press, 1974.

105.   Motora, S., Shimamoto, S., Fujino, M., – 'Capsizing Experiment on a Totally Enclosed Lifeboat' – Sec.Int.Conf. on Stability of Ships – Tokyo, October, 1982.

106.   Payne, B. – 'Surviving Hurricane Assault' – *Sail*, February, 1981.
      The crew of four spent forty-two hours in the raft – part of that time within the very eye of the hurricane – before they were picked up by a Norwegian tanker.

107.   van de Stadt, E.G. – 'Seaworthy Yachts' – *Practical Boat Owner*, February, 1984.

108.   Mandel, P. – 'Some Hydrodynamic Aspects of Appendage Design', SNAME, 1953.

109.   South, B., Viewpoint, *Sail*, June, 1984.

110.   Discussion on the author's paper 'Vulnerability of Modern Sailing Boat to Capsize in Rough Weather', Intern. Confer. on Design Considerations for Small Craft, London, February, 1984.

111.   Gerritsma, J., Moeyes, G. – 'Steering Performance' – *Sail*, May, 1973; also: 'Fin v Long Keel' – Letter by Berry, C.D. – *Sail*, December, 1975.

112.   Gerritsma, J., Moeyes, G. – 'The Seakeeping Performance and Steering Properties of Sailing Yachts', HISWA Symposium, Amsterdam, 1973.

113.   Kerwin, J.E. – 'Yacht Hull Research' – Symposium on Sailing Yacht Research, MIT, November, 1966.

114.   Spens, P.G., de Saix, P., Brown, P.W. – 'Some Further Experimental Studies of the Sailing Yacht', SNAME paper, November, 1967.

115.   De Saix, P. – 'Experiments with End Plate and Keel Profile Shape Variations on a 5.5 Metre Yacht'. D.L. Note 589, May, 1960.

116.   Young, Chey – 'Experimental Determination of Wave-Excited Forces and Moments Acting on Ship Model Running in Oblique Regular Waves' – D.L. Rep. 1046, 1964.

117.   Zimmerman, C.H. – 'Characteristics of Clark Y Airfoils of Small AR', NACA Rep. 431, 1932.

118.   von Karman, T., Sears, W.R. – 'Aerofoil Theory for Non-Uniform Motion' – *Journal of Aeron. Science*, Vol. 5, 1938.

119.   Fung, Y.C. – *An Introduction to the Theory of Aeroelasticity* – Dover, 1945.

120.   Farren, W.S. – 'The Reaction on a Wing whose Angle of Incidence is changing rapidly' – Rep. and Mem. N. 1648, 1935.

121.   Bishop, R.E., Burcher, R.K., Price, W.G. – 'The Determination of Ship Manoeuvering Characteristics from Model Tests' – RINA paper 1974.

122.   Lindsay, Lord – *Naval Architecture of Planing Hulls*, Cornell Maritime Press, 1946.

123.   Perry, B. – 'Renaissance in Cruising Design', *Sail*, June, 1978.

124   Marchaj, C.A. – 'Heavy Weather Techniques' – An Analysis of the causes of broaching. *Yachting World*, June, 1972.

125.   Coles, A. – *Heavy Weather Sailing* – Granada Publ. 1980.

126.   Yaching World Forum – 'Heavy Weather' – *Yachting World*, January, 1968. The opinion quoted was expressed by Dick Davidson, a man who has cruised and raced extensively and who is also a member of Dover Lifeboat crew.

127.   Du Cane, P., Goodrich, G.J. – 'The following Sea, Broaching and Surging' – RINA paper, April, 1962.

Index